Handbook of
Safety Management

Handbook of
Safety Management

Roger Saunders
Timothy Wheeler

Pitman

Pitman Publishing
128 Long Acre, London WC2E 9AN
A Division of Longman Group UK Limited
First published in 1991

British Library Cataloguing in Publication Data

Saunders, Roger
  Managing safety.
  1. Great Britain.   Industrial health & industrial safety.
  Management aspects
  I. Title   II. Wheeler, Timothy
  658.3820941

ISBN 0 273 03202 X

Printed in Great Britain by The Bath Press, Avon

Contents

Preface

There is a dearth of literature outlining the procedures and practices which should be undertaken by those employed in the field of accident prevention and reduction. These publications explain what should be done, but there are few books which adequately prepare the safety practitioner for his management role within an organisation. The object of this book, therefore, is to discuss the management principles required to undertake an efficient and effective operational safety strategy.

This book is not intended to teach chemical engineers, nuclear scientists, electrical engineers or anyone else, those tasks required to carry out safe operation of equipment and/or procedures within a specific specialisation. On the contrary, this book assumes a professional level of competence and experience which will already have been gained within the reader's industry or area of employment.

Safety should be an integral part of an organisational management plan and not treated in isolation. To do this it is necessary to have a good understanding of some basic safety sensitive management procedures and practices and time should be spent understanding the role of the safety practitioner within the organisation. Although the Health and Safety at Work Act 1974 placed a statutory obligation upon industry to ensure safe procedures and practices in the work place, some companies reacted more enthusiastically than others to the legislation.

Some organisations implement a highly intelligent safety strategy whilst others carry out the minimum requirements permitted by law or from pressure exerted by insurance companies. Those carrying out the less intelligent safety strategies do so not necessarily by choice. More often than not We have found that the most serious problem has been with inadequate provision of safety management training. As early as 1956, Rollin Simonds and John Grimaldi in their book *Safety Management* emphasised the need for adequate training and stressed the importance of using basic accounting principles to justify a safety policy.

A number of current occupational safety and health courses consider 'safety and health' management but not all provide adequate coverage of the operational requirements needed to implement a strategy efficiently and effectively within an organisation. To do this it is necessary to understand the importance of accident investigation in the work place and to use this information as part of the decision making process. Financial management, the planning, implementation, monitoring and evaluation of remedial measures are also important considerations which develop from legal responsibilities.

This book examines these issues and it is hoped will provide the reader with an opportunity to develop further some safety management skills in practice.

9th January 1990
R A Saunders
T J Wheeler

Acknowledgements

We are grateful to all those safety practitioners in the private and public sectors who have made various comments and for their valuable contributions to the contents of this book. In particular we would like to thank Bournemouth Polytechnic, Dorset County Council, St. John's College, Oxford and to Dr D Sheppard for reading the whole manuscript and for his valuable comments. We would also like to thank Professor B Brown and Mr P Swainson for providing valuable material from the Resources Unit at the Centre for Safety Studies and to the library staff at the Royal Society for the Prevention of Accidents for helping with the research needed to undertake this work. We would like to thank our colleagues and friends at the Centre for Safety Studies for their encouragement and support whilst the manuscript was being written, and our wives and children for their patience and understanding whilst the houses were filled with research material.

Safety and the law

Part 1: Civil liability

Introduction

Managers with a safety responsibility have a key role in their organisation for ensuring that appropriate safety systems are in force and that they thus comply with the law and obey statutory regulations. Their role is to see that both the general policy and strategic decisions relating to safety are in place. Further that these are translated on a day to day basis into detailed plans and procedures for staff to follow. Finally that these systems operate effectively without any lapses. Generally the law requires the manager to ensure the following:

1. That safe systems exist within the organisation;
2. That there is effective maintenance of both buildings and equipment;
3. That staff have received appropriate and adequate:
    (a) training regarding safety,
    (b) information about health and safety,
    (c) instruction about safe practices,
    (d) the correct supervision when undertaking hazardous activities;
4. The safety of others including the general public who may be affected by operations of the organisation;
5. That third parties such as contractors or consultants hired by the organisation do not endanger staff nor are endangered by them.

Failure to comply will almost certainly result in the prosecution of your organisation and in certain circumstances you can be held personally liable for both criminal and civil proceedings.

There are a number of good publications already in existence which deal with safety and the law in precise detail. In this chapter it is intended only to trace the developments in certain legal areas which are of interest to managers. For more serious students of the law a reading list is given at the end of the chapter.

Developed countries have provided for the safety of their employees for hundreds of years within their respective legal frameworks. Either via the English or Roman legal systems an employer has had to avoid practices which are considered or found to be dangerous or harmful by certain courts of law. During this century, legislation has been formulated by various governments which reinforce the old established rules or have been introduced to define clearly certain safe procedures or practices. In the United Kingdom for example, safety and health are identified separately whereas in other countries anything considered harmful or dangerous is simply referred to as safety in a much broader context. Within this book, safety will naturally refer to all health issues and any other areas which are hazardous or dangerous.

Enforcement strategies operating within the legal framework do, however, impinge on safety managers, particularly when things go wrong. It has been said by some that ideally, safety practitioners should not be personnel or industrial relations officers 'filling in', nor should they be medical or legal practitioners found within 'occupational safety and health' units. These specialists play a part in the overall corporate safety plan but may not have a wide enough understanding of the broad issues affecting the daily operational plan of the organisation. It is the safety manager's role to know when plans under discussion need expert advice and to seek it from qualified legal staff.

When examining safety related case law, one can conclude that it has been established as the result of the safety management system failing to meet the aims and objectives of the organisation. It is axiomatic that companies do not maliciously set out to injure their workforce, but there are many examples where 'other factors', usually of a financial nature, have compromised the need for an effective safety policy. In such cases it would seem that safety is regarded as a worthwhile priority by an organisation until a conflict arises between safety and the balance sheet. To illustrate these points it is necessary to acquaint the reader with some of the relevant issues regarding safety and the law from a management standpoint.

Common law

Common law is that part of our legal system which is said to be traditional and is effective in areas not covered by Act of Parliament. The principles and rules of common law are contained in those decisions taken previously in English courts. They are recorded in the law reports and go back to the Middle Ages. Health and safety issues began to appear in case law during the industrial revolution when casualties began to sue for compensation following injuries received at work. Common law is based on what has been decided before by judges and is referred to as precedent. Although there are a few technical exceptions, a court is bound to follow those decisions made earlier in courts of equal or higher status, unless statute law dictates to the contrary. Common law governs the rights and duties of individuals towards one another.

Generally there are four remedies that are available to an individual:

1. *Compensation.* A monetary value is placed upon the injury suffered or the loss experienced where an employer is found to be liable through failure to comply with the law.
2. *Reparation.* Where an employer could be required to restore conditions so that they are the same as before the breach of the law.
3. *Performance.* Where an employer can be compelled to perform his obligations.
4. *Injunction.* Where an employer can be required to desist from an activity where it interferes with the common law rights of another.

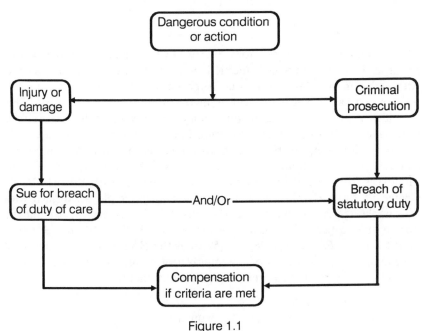

Figure 1.1

Courses of action in a claim for compensation

Civil actions can be initiated in a variety of courts. In order of increasing seniority:

County Court

Inexpensive, relatively fast. Single circuit judge can award damages up to £5,000.

High Court (Queen's Bench Division)

Expensive, relatively slow. Single judge can award unlimited damages.

Court of Appeal

Very expensive, can be relatively quick. Typically three senior judges have the power to hear appeals from the High Court, County Courts, Tribunals and can uphold, amend or reverse the decision of a lower court.

House of Lords

Extremely expensive and slow. Three most senior judges constitute the final court of appeal within the United Kingdom.

European Court

It can potentially cause a case to be reviewed where interpretation is needed about an EEC directive on domestic law in the field of health and safety. Although common law can be said to go back a thousand years, matters referring to safety began to appear in the mid-nineteenth century. This coincided with the industrial revolution and the advent of the factory type of workplace. Workers, under common law, could sue their employers in the courts for compensation for injuries received at work. Common law requires that an employer must take reasonable care to protect his employees from risk of foreseeable injury, disease or death at work. In the nineteenth and early part of the twentieth century, employers argued with reasonable degrees of success against this duty in respect of proving the 'foreseeable' aspect of the law. It was not until 1938 in *Wilsons & Clyde Coal Co Ltd* v *English* ([1938] AC 57) that the House of Lords identified in general terms, the duties of an employer at common law. They judged that all employers are required to provide and maintain:

1. A safe place of work
2. A competent staff of men (or women)
3. A safe system of work; and
4. Safe plant and appliances.

In addition, employers were made liable for injury causing accidents to their employees as a consequence of the negligence of other of their employees, with the following proviso: that the act of negligence arises out of and in the course of employment. This principle is the effect of the application of vicarious liability at common law. This is a similar standard to which an employer must conform under the Health and Safety at Work Act which came into being in 1974, and is discussed later.

Duty of care

Lord Atkin established two related principles:

'You must take reasonable care to avoid acts or omissions which you can reasonably foresee would be likely to injure your neighbour. Who then in law is my neighbour? The answer seems to be persons who are so closely and directly affected by my act that I ought reasonably to have them in contemplation as being so affected when I am directing my mind to the acts or omissions which are called in question'.

Leading case 1.1

An important and influential case which occurred this century within the soft drinks industry was that of *Donoghue* v *Stevenson* ([1932] AC 562). The judges' findings would apply to all industries in the future. Stevenson, the defendant, manufactured ginger beer which was put into opaque bottles before selling. R, a retailer, sold the ginger beer to C and he gave a bottle to a friend Donoghue, the plaintiff. Donoghue complained that the bottle contained the decomposed remains of a snail. As a result, Donoghue was ill from drinking the contents of the bottle. Donoghue had no contract with Stevenson on which liability could be based. The legal question was whether there was any other basis of liability. The House of Lords found by a three to two majority that there was. How this can be, can only be found by reading the judgments of the three judges who found for Donoghue. It is possible for different judges to arrive at the same conclusion but for different reasons. In this particular case, the reasons were similar and the principle can be found in the words of Lord Atkin:

'A manufacturer of products, which he sells in such a form as to show that he intends them to reach the ultimate consumer in the form in which they left him with no reasonable possibility of intermediate examination, and with the knowledge that the absence of reasonable care in the preparation or putting up of the products will result in an injury to the consumer's life or property, owes a duty to the consumer to take that reasonable care.'

This principle was to influence judges in other cases as will be seen below. Although here it was specifically health that was at issue, it is both safety and health matters which are the responsibility of the safety manager. In this particular case, the principle can be seen to influence both health and safety aspects within an organisation.

Leading case 1.2

The neighbour principle has been defined in a number of legal case precedents, for example, in *Bourhill (or Hay)* v *Young* ([1943] AC 92), Young was a motorcyclist who, because of his careless driving, was killed in a collision with a car. Bourhill, who was pregnant, heard the collision from a distance and on approaching saw blood in the road. This caused her nervous shock and as a consequence she subsequently gave birth to a stillborn child. Bourhill sued Young's representatives. She failed in her case because it was held that Young could not reasonably be expected to foresee injury to a person so far from the accident as the plaintiff had been at the time of the collision. Thus Bourhill was not Young's neighbour and was owed no duty of care.

Leading case 1.3

In *King* v *Phillips* ([1953] 1 QB 429), a careless taxi-driver reversed over a child's tricycle in the road occasioning the child to scream. The child's mother, thinking that her child had been killed, suffered nervous shock and became ill. King sued the taxi-driver. It was held that Phillips owed only a duty of care to such persons as he could reasonably foresee might be injured by his actions in the immediate vicinity of his vehicle. As King had been in a house nearby, she was not Phillips' neighbour and was again owed no duty of care.

Leading case 1.4

When assessing reasonably foreseeable risks at work, the employer's actual or imputed knowledge of the risks is most important. As a safety manager you will be held liable for your own actions and those of your subordinates with regard to communicating or otherwise acting on complaints from employees or other sources of information.

In *Doughty* v *Turner Manufacturing Co Ltd* ([1964] 1 QB 518), a fellow worker of Doughty let an asbestos cement cover fall into a cauldron of molten metal which resulted in an explosion causing an injury to Doughty. No similar accidents of this kind had occurred previously and it was not known that explosions were caused by asbestos cement mixing with molten metal. Although the action of the defendant's servant was the direct cause of the accident, it could not be shown that the defendant had failed to exercise reasonable foresight. Thus the defendant was not liable.

Leading case 1.5

In *Smith* v *Leech Braine & Co Ltd* ([1962] 2 QB 405), molten zinc flew out of a galvanising tank causing a burn to the lip of Smith, an employee. Subsequently cancer developed on the site of the burn which resulted in the man's death. The widow sued her husband's former employer. It was held that the defendants were liable, even though the death could not have been foreseeable as a result of the accident.

The main difference between the last two cases is that there was an unforeseeable cause in the former and an unforeseeable consequence in the latter. Leech Braine were negligent in that the cause of the accident was foreseeable.

Leading case 1.6

It has been said that an employer has a duty to take reasonable care for the safety of his employees acting in the course of their employment. Under common law, there is no liability without proof of negligence. The duty is to take reasonable care, not guarantee the employees' safety. If the employer can show that he has taken reasonable care then the employee's claim under this head will fail despite the seriousness of any injuries which may have been received. The general duty to take reasonable care is well illustrated in *Stokes* v *Guest, Keen & Nettlefold (Bolts & Nuts) Ltd* ([1968] 1 WLR 1776).

Stokes had been employed by GKN for 15 years as a toolsetter. He died of scrotal cancer in 1966. His work involved leaning over machines in such a way as to bring the lower part of his body and upper thighs into contact with cutting oil. As a result his clothes became saturated with the oil which resulted in the skin of the groin being frequently smothered in lubricant. This undoubtedly caused the cancer and his subsequent death.

The standard to apply here and in all matters of 'negligence' is that of a reasonable and prudent employer who adopts a positive attitude towards safety in the light of what is known and what should be known. It is right to assume that an employer will keep abreast of new developments and knowledge and must be ready to use and apply them. However, the duty of care does not necessarily require a person to have done everything possible to prevent an injury producing accident. On the contrary, risk must be assessed and one has to consider the likelihood of an accident happening and be aware of the consequences. From this, a person may balance the effectiveness of precautions or preventative methods against the expense and any inconvenience of taking them. In the case discussed above, the court found that the work could not reasonably have been organised or indeed the machines modified to obviate the regular contact with the oil. Also, the plaintiff did not argue that any less potentially carcinogenic oil was commercially available (though failure to investigate that possibility could, in other circumstances, constitute negligence). In addition, the plaintiff did not argue that it was unreasonable to carry on this work in the circumstances described. But, did the defendants act reasonably in respect of protective clothing?

The court found that the only clothing available at the time was un-popular, hot and very cumbersome. The important point here is Stokes's reluctance to wear the clothing. If an employee claims that the employer was negligent in failing to provide protective clothing, but the employer can demonstrate that if he had, it would not have been worn anyway, then the action will fail because the injury could not have been caused by the employer's but the employee's omission. This raises a valid point in questioning how far an employer should go in making his workforce wear protective clothing.

There is no clear answer and circumstances will decide the issue. For example, if the employee is highly experienced at his job and is fully aware of the dangers presented to him whilst carrying out his work, it might be considered satisfactory to advertise the availability of protective clothing and no more. However, if he was young and inexperienced then the employer would need to do much more.

In the case described above, the judge was satisfied with safety standards within GKN. There was a full-time medical officer employed with qualified assistants and a well equipped surgery. Washing facilities were available and a scheme for cleaning overalls was provided. A safety officer was on the staff. Despite all this, the main weight against GKN was in its failure to warn and/or instruct the deceased about the dangers to which he was exposed. Information about the precautions he should take were lacking and regular medical examinations of high risk toolsetters were not carried out. When questioned on this, the medical officer, who was well aware of the risks, advised management to the contrary. This was because the doctor felt that the time spent examining employees far outweighed the risks involved. The court felt that the medical officer exaggerated this claim. The problem could have been rectified with the employment of additional staff but the doctor was reluctant to do this because management were not sup-portive of such suggestions. The court heard of a similar case in 1963 involving another toolsetter dying from scrotal cancer yet still the doctor did not consider regular medical examinations as important. As is usual with fatalities, details of the case became known via a variety of ways to other workers in the factory. The judge commented harshly on the unsatis-factory way in which staff were to learn of this type of danger. At the same time he was critical of management in that they had not obtained and circulated a leaflet produced by the factory inspectorate on this subject.

The court applied the 'test of the prudent employer' and found that there was negligence on the part of GKN in the following:

1. Not instituting periodical medical examinations after the first death in 1963,
2. Not issuing the factory inspectorate leaflet on this matter.

It was deemed that these steps could have saved the life of Stokes and damages of £10,000 were awarded.

This particular case illustrates a break-down in the safety management processes within the workplace and it is important that safety managers have authority within an organisation in order to maximise the efficiency and effectiveness of safety policies and programmes. It is wrong, on the one hand to employ a safety expert, and on the other to override his advice. Being aware of how the law views certain matters is important. A case which might appear before a judge concerning a particular industry may have far reaching implications for all industries and not just the one under discussion in court.

Leading case 1.7

In 1959, a case was heard between *Davie* v *New Merton Board Mills Ltd*, ([1959] AC 604) where New Merton Board Mills, the employer, bought a number of drifts (a tool made up of a bar of tapered steel measuring approximately one foot long) from a reputable supplier, B. When Davie, an employee, was using one of the drifts in the correct manner, a splinter shot off and caught him in the eye. This resulted in Davie losing the sight in this eye. From an examination of the tool, the steel used was excessively hard caused by the negligence of G during manufacture. G was liable to Davie on the *Donoghue* v *Stevenson* principle discussed above. It was found that New Merton Board Mills had purchased from a reputable supplier, that the drift was in good condition and that New Merton Board Mills's system of maintenance was not negligent. It was deemed unreasonable to expect an employer to test a drift for hardness before issuing it to an employee. This problem could not reasonably have been noticed without submitting the drift to such a test. New Merton Board Mills was deemed to have taken reasonable care and was found not liable.

This highlights a weakness not in New Merton Board Mills's system but in that of B. In this case B should have examined its quality control methods to identify how this problem occurred and to take all reasonable steps to prevent it happening again. These would be regarded as environmental investigations and should be supervised by the safety manager.

However, an employer's negligence may lie in failure to take reasonable care to ensure that a place of work is safe. There are several simple cases to illustrate this aspect of the law and one such example is quoted below.

Leading case 1.8

In *Morris* v *West Hartlepool Steam Navigation Co* ([1956] AC 552), a seaman fell into the hold of a ship. The hold was unfenced. The ship was following the accepted practice in this particular industry of not fencing the hold in the circumstances. Because of this, it was held to constitute negligence. The House of Lords said that the risk was obvious, and that there was great danger and risk of injury which was simple to guard against. Although accepted practice can normally be used in defence, the duty of care extends to the employer considering whether the practice is adequate and the need to change it if necessary. This case highlights a reactive management strategy whereby no action is taken until the law provides for it. Such management strategies are open to action of this nature, particularly if an organisation chooses to allow courts of law to make their safety management decisions. An over enthusiastic safety policy can close most factories by making them too safe. In this instance, it can be said that a workplace can only be deemed to be safe when it is shut! Risks have to be accepted, therefore it is essential that safety management is proactive by nature. Risk analysis and a historical accident and dangerous occurrence database are prerequisites. A court is influenced if safety management decisions are made for sound reasons. Management strategies that are incompetent are easily shown to be negligent by courts as can be seen here.

Whilst the requirements of the law have been discussed here there is one aspect of the enforcement strategy which is important. This is in the area of discipline. Many safety practitioners need to appreciate that the enforcement strategy includes the safety rules which operate within an organisation. Breaches of discipline must be dealt with quickly and fairly. If an employee is in breach of a rule or rules then a fair system for dealing with this must be established. The ultimate disciplinary action here would be dismissal.

In law, the duty of care may require an employer to discipline or even dismiss an employee who is a source of danger to his work mates. This was proven in *Hudson* v *Ridge Manufacturing* ([1957] 2 QB 348) where an employee continually took part in dangerous horseplay against his work mates. Despite several reprimands from his foreman to desist a worker was eventually injured as a result of the skylarking. The company was held liable as reprimands are not enough. Another implication of this case is discussed subsequently.

Reasonable care and the breach of duty

The test of reasonable care is determined by a court on the basis of what a reasonable man would do in the same circumstances as a defendant. If the existence of the duty of care is established as a matter of law then the breach of this duty is decided by the judge.

Leading case 1.9

In *Latimer* v *AEC Ltd* ([1953] AC 643), a very heavy rain flooded the defendant's workshops and caused oil to spread over the floors where it remained in patches. The defendant immediately sent men to clean the floor and cover any oil patches with sawdust. There was insufficient sawdust and some oily patches were left uncovered. Latimer slipped on one of these patches, broke his leg and sued his employers. Where an employer fails in his duty and an employee is injured the employer will be held to be negligent. The employer must just take reasonable care not to subject his employees to unnecessary risk. Despite Latimer showing cause and effect, directness, foresight and a duty of care, the defendants were held not to be liable because their only alternative was to close the factory which would have been unreasonable. The degree of care, the amount of effort required and the cost to the employer will depend chiefly on the magnitude of the risk.

Leading case 1.10

In *Edwards* v *NCB* ([1949] 1 KB 704), Asquith L J stated 'a computation must be made in which the quantum of risk is placed on one scale, and the sacrifice involved in the measures necessary for averting the risk is placed on the other'. The more probable an accident is, the greater the duty to guard against it. Even if the probability is quite small, but the magnitude of risk in terms of serious potential injury is great, stringent precautions will be necessary.

There are five factors in determining reasonable care:

1. **Cost**. The amount of money that it is necessary to spend against a slight possibility of risk is limited.
2. **Obviousness of risk**. The more obvious the danger the more liable the employer will be held for failing to prevent an accident. A partial defence to this is that the employee may have been aware of the risk in which case, there is held to be contributory negligence.
3. **Inherent risk**. All work carries with it some possibility of risk which is irreducible or irremovable for which the employer cannot be held responsible.
4. **Likelihood of injury**. 'The greater the risk, the greater the liability'.
5. **Seriousness of injury**. 'The more serious the consequences, the more precautions should have been taken'.

Burden of proof

'He who asserts must prove'. Generally the plaintiff must prove that the action or omission of the defendant actually caused the injury. However the rule of *res ipsa loquitur* (the thing speaks for itself) assumes that the only possible explanation for the injury was the defendant's negligence. In this case the onus is on the defendant to prove that this was not the case.

The plaintiff is required to demonstrate:

Cause and effect. The plaintiff must show the defendant's negligent act or omission caused the injury or loss.

Leading case 1.11

In *McWilliams (or Cummings)* v *Sir William Arrol & Co* ([1962] 1 WLR 295), a steel erector fell 70 feet and was killed. Evidence showed that a safety belt would have prevented the fall, but that even if it had been provided it would not have been worn. It was held by the House of Lords that the failure to provide equipment was not the cause of the damage.

Leading case 1.12

However in *Paris* v *Stepney Council* ([1951] AC 367), it was held that goggles were thought necessary for an employee known by his employers to have only one eye, though not for other employees doing the same work. Although the likelihood of injury to his remaining good eye was slight, the consequences for Paris were clearly serious since it resulted in total blindness. Where an employer knows that an employee is disabled or is particularly at risk, a greater duty of care is owed to these employees compared to that afforded to normal, healthy employees with no disability.

Alternative. The plaintiff must show that there was a reasonable alternative open to the defendant which, if taken, would have prevented the injury or loss.

Foresight. As mentioned earlier, the plaintiff has to demonstrate that the defendant should have known of the risk.

Directness. The Leech Braine case defines the principle that the defendant is liable for all damage, whether foreseeable or not, which is a direct consequence of his act or omission.

Leading case 1.13

This principle was upheld in *Re Polemis* v *Furness Withy & Co* ([1921] 3 KB 560). Stevedores, employed by charterers of a ship, negligently caused a plank to fall into a hold of a ship containing flammable vapour. The resulting spark caused a fire which destroyed the ship. Although some damage to the ship could be seen, the sparks could not have been foreseen. The charterers were held liable for the ship's loss as this was a direct, although not foreseeable consequence of the negligence of the stevedores. Thus the reasonable person should foresee that his act would cause the plaintiff some harm. The defendant would thus be liable for all direct consequences of his act even though they were not foreseen.

Directness v Remoteness. The consequences of a defendant's act can be endless and the law cannot take into account everything that follows from a wrongful act. A plaintiff who has established loss caused by the defendant's wrong may therefore be unable to recover damages because the loss is too remote from the wrongful act, i.e. the damage is not sufficiently connected with the defendant's act.

Leading case 1.14

In *Overseas Tankship (UK) Ltd* v *Morts Docks & Engineering Co Ltd* ([1961] AC 388), the defendants discharged oil from their ship into Sydney Harbour and left port six hours later. The oil, carried by wind and tide, came beneath the plaintiff's wharf some 200 yards away from where welding operations were in progress. A piece of molten metal fell from the wharf and ignited a piece of floating rag on the oil. In a resulting fire the wharf was severely damaged. The defendant neither knew nor ought to have known that the oil was capable of being set alight when spread on water. The damage was held to be too remote from the original act. Two principles emerge from this case:

1. A defendant is only liable for the damage which a reasonable person would have foreseen as a likely consequence of an act;
2. A defendant is only liable to compensate for damage that was foreseeable and not all the direct consequences of the act.

Where the consequences of an act are direct, where one consequence flows automatically from another and cannot be avoided then the *Re Polemis* rules will apply. However, if there is an interruption, diversion or an intervening and new physical event, the chain of causation is broken and the result will be held to be too remote.

Employers have a common law duty of care

Leading case 1.15

The leading case in this regard is *Wilson's and Clyde Coal Co* v *English* ([1938] AC 57). The employer tried to argue that he had discharged his duty by employing a mine manager whose responsibilities included safety. A miner was leaving the pit when the haulage system was put into operation. He was crushed against a wall before he had time to reach a refuge hole. It was held that it was an unsafe practice for the haulage system to be operated while the morning shift was leaving work.

The House of Lords held that it was the personal duty of the employer to take reasonable care for the safety of his workforce and this duty was threefold:

1. To provide safe plant and machinery;
2. To ensure he employs competent staff;
3. To provide safe systems of work.

It is a personal duty because the employer is the person in control of the work and any dangers. He cannot relinquish his responsibility for the provision of any of the three things mentioned above and must take reasonable care in all circumstances.

The duty to provide competent staff

An employer should not employ or continue to employ a person at a particular task for which he is not qualified or insufficiently experienced where to do so would possibly endanger his fellow employees. The employer can be held liable for the negligence of his staff. This is known as vicarious liability.

Leading case 1.16

In *Hudson v Ridge Manufacturing Co Ltd* ([1957] 2 QB 348), Hudson broke his wrist because of the action of a fellow employee who was known for playing practical jokes. It was held that it was the employer's duty to reprimand, discipline or dismiss a fellow employee of Hudson so as to remove this danger.

The duty to provide adequate material, premises and plant

Where an employee is injured because of some defect in the materials, equipment or plant in circumstances where the employer did not take reasonable care to make them safe, the employee can pursue an action for negligence. If the employer showed that he had taken reasonable care in buying equipment from a reputable supplier this was held to be an adequate defence. However, where common law seems to be unfair, statute law is often introduced to rectify this, for example, the Employers' Liability (Defective Equipment) Act 1969 stipulates that the employee can make a direct claim against the employer, who can in turn sue the supplier or manufacturer of the equipment. An employer now has to provide tools of the right quality, and sufficient tools and equipment for the job.

The duty to provide a proper system and effective supervision

A system of work is a practice which is permanent and continuous and not merely a method which is casual and emerging in a day's work. It can cover the physical layout of a job, the sequence in which the work is undertaken, the provisions of warnings and notices and the issue of special instructions.

Leading case 1.17

In *Rushton* v *Turner Bros Asbestos Co Ltd* ([1959] 3 AER 517), it was stated that 'an experienced workman must know the ordinary risks of the work which he is employed to do. In doing that work he is expected to take the ordinary routine precautions which are common to it, and should not expect to be told by his employer of every danger which might arise and every step that should be taken to counteract that danger'. Thus an employer's duty is to initiate and maintain a safe system of working where there is a real risk of injury, some degree of complexity or unfamiliarity in the work and where some practicable precaution can be taken.

Vicarious liability

This is defined as where one person is held to be liable for the behaviour of people acting on his behalf. It would be unfair to make an employer a target for a common law claim as a result of all negligent behaviour so a set of rules has been established by which to judge the extent of this liability. An employer may be liable for the torts of his employees and those of independent contractors.

Liability for the torts of employees exists where:

1. A wrongful act or omission has been expressly or impliedly authorised by the employer;
2. A wrongful act or omission is committed by doing something authorised by the employer in an unauthorised manner;
3. A wrongful act or omission is committed and ratified by the employer.

Before liability can be proved it has to be shown that:

1. The employee is a true employee (is paid and is subject to normal procedures of hiring and dismissal);
2. The employee has committed a tort or crime;

3. The tort was committed in the course and scope of his/her employment, for example doing what he/she was employed to do.

Specific defences

There are several defences available to an employer which either rebut
the allegation of negligence, or attribute the damage or accident to a
circumstance which is beyond his control. He can plead that as he took
reasonable care there was no negligence or that no duty of care was owed.
There are also some specific defences:

Novus actus interveniens

'A new act has intervened'. This covers the actions of a third party between
the negligent act and the subsequent damage to the injured person. It is the
function of the court to decide if the intervening act could have been
reasonably foreseen by the defendant.

Leading case 1.18

In *Scott* v *Shepherd* ([1773] 2 Wm BL 892), the defendant threw a lighted
squib onto a market stall whose owner quickly threw it to another stall. The
next stall owner did the same eventually injuring the plaintiff. The
defendant was held liable because a chain of causation had not been broken
by a new act.

Volenti non fit injuria

'No harm can be done to a willing person'. This defence is used to show
that an injured person was aware of the risk involved and consents to it.

Leading case 1.19

In the case of *Bowater* v *Rowley Regis Corporation* ([1944] KB 476), the
plaintiff, an employee of the defendant, was asked to take out an unruly
horse and cart. He protested at this, but the foreman insisted that he should
do as he was told. The horse bolted and Bowater was injured. The defendants were held to be negligent. The defence of *non volenti fit injuria* failed
because it was held that 'a man cannot be said to be truly willing unless he
is in a position to choose freely. Free choice requires (a) knowledge of the
danger, and (b) the absence in his mind of any feeling of constraint'. Thus
compliance with an employer's request is not normally consent.

Leading case 1.20

A second type of case where this defence will fail is where a person has been under a moral or legal duty to act. In the case of *Haynes* v *Harwood* ([1935] 1 KB 146), a policeman was injured when he tried to control Harwood's horse which had bolted in a crowded street. Haynes seized the horse to stop it injuring innocent bystanders. The court held that the defence of *volenti* failed because the police officer assumed the risk involved in tackling a horse and cart which was out of control.

Leading case 1.21

In a parallel case, *Cutler* v *United Dairies* ([1933] 2 KB 297), Cutler assisted a dairyman in catching a runaway horse. In the course of this Cutler was injured. United Dairies were successful in their defence of *non volenti fit injuria* because Cutler was not intervening to rescue people from injury and he had time to consider the risk and was deemed to have implicitly consented to this.

Contributory negligence

This is used to describe the behaviour of an injured person whose actions contributed to the occurrence giving rise to his injuries. Until the Law Reform (Contributory Negligence) Act 1945 this was held to be a complete defence. Now damages shall be reduced for the plaintiff in proportion to the proportion to which their own negligence contributed to their injury.

Leading case 1.22

In *Sawyers* v *Harlow UDC* ([1958] 2 All ER 342), the plaintiff entered a public lavatory owned by Harlow UDC. Owing to a defective lock that jammed, she could not get out and whilst attempting to climb out, she fell and injured herself. It was held that the defendants were negligent, but that the award should be reduced by 25% because she tried to balance on a revolving toilet-roll holder.

Leading case 1.23

In *Oliver* v *Birmingham Bus Co* ([1932] 1 KB 35), it was held that a young child cannot be guilty of contributory negligence even if accompanied by an adult. A four year old in the company of his grandfather was run over by a bus when the grandfather let go of his hand while crossing the road. The damages were not reduced.

Agony of the moment

This is a defence against contributory negligence.

Leading case 1.24

In *Jones* v *Boyce* ([1816] 1 Starkie 493), a coach passenger believed the coach he was riding in was about to crash due to the drivers' negligence and jumped off breaking a leg. The coach did not crash. It was held that there was no contributory negligence and he could recover from the defendant as he had acted reasonably in the 'agony of the moment'. Contributory negligence cannot be applied where the principle of alternative danger exists. If the negligence of the defendant puts the plaintiff in a position of imminent personal danger, the plaintiff's conduct, even if it results in personal harm, does not amount to contributory negligence if his conduct is reasonable in the 'agony of the moment'.

Implications of common law for the management of an effective safety campaign

An employer's duty consists of the provision of safe plant and materials, competent staff and safe systems.

Leading case 1.25

In *Woods* v *Durable Suites* ([1953] 1 WLR 857), a common problem was ruled on. This concerned the misuse or non use of personal protective equipment. The employer was a furniture manufacturer. Woods was an experienced glue spreader. Durable Suites knew that there was a real risk of dermatitis in Woods' work and to counteract this risk they provided barrier cream and washing facilities. They also ran an extensive poster campaign about the danger of contracting dermatitis and the use and importance of precautions. They also told Mr Woods personally about the risk which, as an experienced man, he already fully understood. The level of supervision was such that the employers did not know that Mr Woods was not taking the proper precautions and as a result he contracted dermatitis. It was ruled that the defendants had discharged their responsibilities running an appropriate safety campaign. Further, that the amount of energy expended had been appropriate to the risk to which employees were exposed.

Therefore as a safety manager you must make sure that:

1. The employee is aware of any dangers associated with the job;
2. The employee knows what precautions must be taken in view of those dangers;
3. The precautions that are necessary are always available for use; and
4. The employee knows that the precautions are available for use.

To achieve these aims an energetic safety campaign has to be undertaken to get the message over to employees. You will not have discharged your common law duty of care simply by issuing safety equipment or protective clothing if you do not educate your employees as to why these are necessary. You should be able to demonstrate that you have undertaken group and/or individual training exercises. Further, that you ensure so far as it is reasonably practicable, that employees take these precautions. Supervision must ensure that precautions made available by the employer are used, otherwise the employer can be held liable in the event of an accident.

Common law duties to non-employees

In essence the degree of responsibility will be proportional to the amount of control the occupier has over the visitor. Sometimes the occupier may have so much control over the activities of the visitor or user that his duty is as high as if they were employer and employee. This is particularly true where the visitor is a contractor's workman working under the instruction of the occupier. The civil liability of an occupier of land or buildings or fixed or movable structures such as vehicles and scaffolding towards persons coming lawfully on to those premises is laid down in the Occupiers' Liability Act 1957.

The extent of an organisation's responsibility will depend on the type of work being carried out. If one employment is more dangerous than another, a greater degree of care must be taken by the employer. If employers are not able to eliminate the risk, they must at least take reasonable care to reduce it as far as possible. Employers must take reasonable care to ensure the safety of their employees' workplace even when it involves work at another occupier's premises. However, in the latter case, the employer can only be expected to take limited precautions. He must ensure, however, that proper safety equipment and instruction is given.

Under section 2 of the Occupiers' Liability Act 1957, the occupier must take reasonable care to see that their visitors are reasonably safe in using the premises for the agreed purposes of the visit. The same duty is owed to all lawful visitors, including people with a legal right of entry such as HSE inspectors, utility engineers, etc. The Act makes provision for the circumstances of the visitor, for example, children will be less careful than adults.

Leading case 1.26

In the case of *Glasgow Corporation* v *Taylor* ([1922] 1 AC 44), a seven year old child died after eating some poisonous berries from a shrub in a public park which was under the control of the Corporation. The Corporation were found liable as they knew the berries were poisonous and that children used the park, but did nothing to give effective warning of the danger to children.

Leading case 1.27

In *Moloney* v *Lambeth LBC* ([1966] 64 LGR 440), the local authority was liable to a four year old who fell through a gap in a balustrade in a block of corporation flats. Under the Occupier's Liability Act 1984, the organisation has a statutory duty of care to trespassers and other uninvited persons. This duty can normally be discharged by giving warning and discouraging people from incurring the risk. There is no duty to persons who willingly accept the risks once they are aware of and understand them. Warning signs must be clear, unambiguous and use standard pictorial representations as specified under BS5378 Part 1.

The organisation has a twofold duty of care with regard to contractors, both a responsibility to them and for them. Liability rests with the person in control (the occupier). Control, however, may be divided between different occupiers.

Leading case 1.28

In the case of *Wheat* v *Lacon* ([1966] AC 552), control was divided between the brewery in charge of the public house and the manager who lived in part of it. The division of blame in such a case will depend on how the accident occurred and whose particular responsibility it was to avoid it. It is possible for visiting contractors or subcontractors to become occupiers of the whole or part of the premises if they are the only people involved in working there. This can be achieved by handing over control of the worksite to the contractor within a physical boundary for a specified time period.

However, there are two circumstances which are likely to put liability back on to your organisation. The first is where your own employees have recourse to the area occupied by the contractor (you are still, in effect, occupying that part of the premises and have a personal duty to your employees). The second is where your organisation has been negligent in the choice of contractor and has selected someone who is not competent to do the job safely.

Checklist:

1. Have they done this kind of work before?
2. How much experience do they have?
3. Can anyone furnish references as to the quality of their workmanship?
4. What provisions will they make for the safety of your employees?
5. What guarantees do they give for completion and performance of contract?
6. Have you specified safe working practices?
7. Have you checked compliance on a regular basis so far as it is reasonably practicable?

If the dangers are caused by contractors working on the occupiers' premises, the Act states that the occupier is not liable if he has taken reasonable care to see that the premises are safe.

There are however, four circumstances where the manager and the organisation cannot escape liability.

Where the employer asks the contractor to break the law

Leading case 1.29

In *Ellis* v *Sheffield Gas Consumers Co* ([1853] 2 E & B 767), the company employed a contractor to dig up streets in Sheffield even though they had no legal right to authorise this. The contractor's workmen left a pile of stones in the street over which the plaintiff fell and was injured. The defendants were held liable for the consequences of their unlawful act.

Where the operation is on or adjoining a public highway other than for the normal use of the highway

Leading case 1.30

In the case of *Tarry* v *Ashton* ([1876] 1 QBD 314), Ashton (the occupier) hired a contractor to repair a heavy lamp attached to the front of his house and overhanging the street. The repair was carried out negligently and the lamp collapsed injuring Tarry. It was held that the occupier was liable in

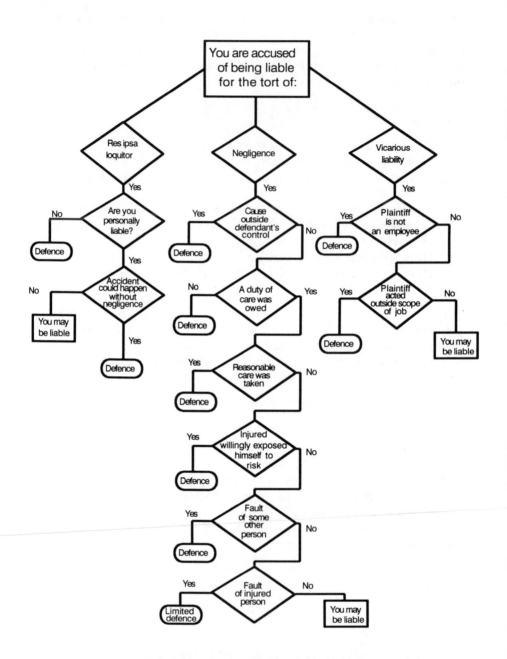

Figure 1.2   Some examples of defences

that he failed to discharge his duty by not ensuring that the lamp was maintained. That this was due to the negligence of a third party was no defence.

Where the contractor is employed to undertake extra-hazardous activities

Leading case 1.31

In the case of *Honeywill & Stein* v *Larkin Bros* ([1934] 1 KB 191), the plaintiffs instructed Larkin to photograph the interior of a cinema and in the process the cinema was set on fire due to the magnesium flash being used. The cinema owner successfully claimed damages from Honeywill & Stein, who in turn sought indemnity from Larkin Bros.

> 'Any person who brings onto his lands anything likely to do mischief and it escapes, must keep it at his peril, or be answerable for the consequences should it escape'

Leading case 1.32

In *Rylands* v *Fletcher* ([1868] LR 3 HL 330), this precedent was established when contractors constructing a reservoir on Fletcher's land negligently plugged a disused mineshaft which connected with Rylands' mine. When the reservoir was filled with water, it escaped through the mineshaft, flooding Rylands' mine.

Liability to visiting contractors

Essentially occupiers are liable to other people's workers for risks which are not occupational hazards, but which are peculiar to premises and of which they themselves know or ought to know.

Leading case 1.33

In *Woollins* v *British Celanese* ([1966] 110 SJ 686), the occupier was held to blame for an unusually fragile roof which was held not to be a normal hazard for a post office engineer who injured himself when he fell through the roof.

Legislation affecting employers' liability at common law

Legislation has consolidated the common law rules of employers' liability and has given rise to a civil liability to pay compensation.

Employers' Liability (Defective Equipment) Act 1969

This Act made the employer liable for the fault of the manufacture of defective equipment. The employer will have to pay the employee compensation. He will then be able to claim his money back from the manufacturer. This is known as the principle of loss distribution.

Employers' Liability (Compulsory Insurance) Act, 1969

This Act makes it obligatory for most employers (except nationalised industries, local authorities and the police) to insure against liability for injury to employees. Failure to buy such insurance or display a certificate of insurance can lead to fines on a daily basis of up to £500 and £200 respectively under the Criminal Law Act 1977.

Occupiers' Liability Act 1959

This imposes duties on occupiers of premises. Where an employee goes to work on third party premises, his employer is liable if the employee is injured through the employer having failed to set up a safe system of work. However, if the employee is injured by a structural defect in the premises which is not incidental to the work, the employer is not liable. The injured person must sue the occupier of the premises. This will only succeed if there are unusual dangers which the occupier knew or should have known about. Until the Unfair Contract Terms Act 1977, it was possible for the occupier to contract out of their liability by posting a warning notice and condition.

Congenital Disabilities (Civil Liability) Act 1976

This Act makes it possible for a child, who is born disabled as a result of a breach of common law or statutory duty to a parent, to sue the parent's employer.

Fatal Accidents Act 1976

This allows dependents of employees killed at work through the employer's negligence, to sue the employer for damages. Compensation is assessed on the actual or prospective earnings of the deceased breadwinner.

Law Reform (Miscellaneous Provisions) Act 1934

This allows the person entitled to the property of a deceased employee killed at work, to inherit any right of action against the employer which the deceased person might have had.

Limitation Act 1975

This controls the time period within which actions must be brought against the employer. The period is normally three years from the date when the cause of the action began. The cause of action begins when the injured employee had the necessary legal and medical knowledge to realise that he had a probable right to sue his employer.

Part 2: Criminal liability

Law of statute

Acts of Parliament impose duties upon all of us. For example, we must insure our vehicles if we drive one on the public highway, sell goods fit for the purpose, not allow certain rooms to fall below a certain temperature, etc. These duties are enforceable by punishments which are usually decided by a court unless a fixed penalty has already been agreed and established. Statute law governs matters that affect the state as a community. In safety management terms, certain statutory laws allow for a person injured as a result of a breach of this law to bring civil proceedings against the other for the injuries received. However, most, if not all statutes, place general standards of conduct upon people and these are usually not very specific. It is then up to judges to interpret the law in order to test whether such action was meant and covered by the statutory act.

This may also mean that an employee injured as the result of a breach of statutory duty may also claim as a result of negligence. It is equally feasible to win on one point and lose on the other as it is to lose both or win both. It must be said that an employee winning on both does not necessarily get double damages.

Failure to comply with a statutory duty is a crime and prosecutions can be initiated in a variety of courts.

Magistrates' Court

The proceedings are relatively inexpensive and quick. The vast majority of criminal cases in England and Wales are dealt with here. Typically, three magistrates will try summary offences specified by statutes, for example, most of the offences listed in section 30 of the Health and Safety at Work Act 1974 (HASAWA) are these and carry a punishment of a fine up to £2,000.

The HASAWA makes provision for some offences that are triable either summarily or on indictment. Magistrates can offer the defendant the choice of trial for a hybrid offence either in the magistrates' court or, after preliminary consideration, by a Crown Court.

Crown Court

More expensive and usually slower. The Crown Court deals with indictable offences. The court can impose a sentence of an unlimited fine and/or a maximum of two years' imprisonment.

Court of Appeal

Very expensive but can be relatively quick. It can:

1. Dismiss or allow an appeal;
2. Order that a conviction recorded in a lower Court be quashed; and
3. Order a retrial.

House of Lords

Extremely expensive and relatively slow. The Law Lords only become involved with cases which have an important point of law of general precedent or interest.

An important statutory duty is placed on the occupier of a factory under the Factories Act 1961. Generally the issues contained in the Act are:

1. Health;
2. Safety;
3. Welfare.

The first covers such things as cleanliness, ventilation, toilet facilities, lighting, working temperatures, drainage and overcrowding. The second concerns machinery fencing, hoists, chains, obstructions, fire escapes etc., whilst the third provides for first-aid facilities, washing and rest facilities, provision of drinking water, etc. These points are quite specific and action for damages can be brought for loss suffered through a breach of these duties and responsibilities. The Factories Act 1961 applies to all factories of whatever size, irrespective of the number of employees and the type of trade or business being carried out. The definition of a factory is very long and appears based upon the employment of manual labour. An example to illustrate this is in respect of the canteen. A canteen within the physical bounds of the factory used for feeding and entertaining the workers is deemed to be part of the factory yet a restaurant used solely by management is not. This is based upon the distinction that feeding and entertaining the workers is not incidental to the normal processes of the factory, but feeding the management is. A person injured whilst cleaning the workers' canteen would get damages whilst a person injured whilst cleaning the managers' restaurant would not!

Whilst the factory is covered by the Factories Act 1961, the Offices, Shops and Railway Premises Act 1963, covers the occupiers of offices, shops and railway premises. The Act deals with the same issues covered by the Factories Act and includes advice on health, safety and welfare issues. Workers in agriculture and forestry were similarly provided for in the Agriculture (Safety, Health and Welfare Provisions) Act 1956, whilst the Mines and Quarries Act 1954 provided rules for the control and management of mines and safety including roof supports, ventilation, protection against dust, winding apparatus, construction and fencing of machinery and the use of explosives. Under all three Acts, an action for breach of statutory duty lies on the same principles as apply to the Factories Act.

At this time, there were still some employees who did not enjoy statutory protection. It was not until the introduction of the HASAWA that full protection was provided. It gives protection to all at work (except those in private domestic employment) including those workers on oil rigs and other offshore installations. Earlier laws were unaffected by this piece of legislation and the HASAWA enables regulations and codes of practice to be altered with relative ease. This is a particularly important feature since technology in some industries is known to move faster than the law. An example of this occurred following the Flixborough Nypro Chemical explosion in 1974. The Health and Safety Commission established an advisory committee on major hazards and it published new guidelines in 1976.

The main thrust of the HASAWA comes in Section 2. Here an employer's duties to his employees are discussed. Briefly these are:

1. The provision and maintenance of plant and systems of work that are, so far as is reasonably practicable, safe and without risk to health;
2. Arrangements for ensuring, so far as is reasonably practicable, safety and absence of risks to health in connection with the use, handling, storage and transport of articles and substances;
3. The provision of such information, instruction, training and supervision as is necessary to ensure, so far as is reasonably practicable, the health and safety at work of his employees;
4. So far as is reasonably practicable as regards any place of work under the employer's control, the maintenance of it in a condition that is safe and without risks to health and the provision and maintenance of means of access to and egress from it that are safe and without such risks; and
5. The provision and maintenance of a working environment for his employees that is, so far as is reasonably practicable, safe, without risks to health and adequate as regards facilities and arrangements for their welfare at work.

Safety practitioners find the legislation of immense value but are frustrated as to the vagueness of the repeated statement 'where reasonably

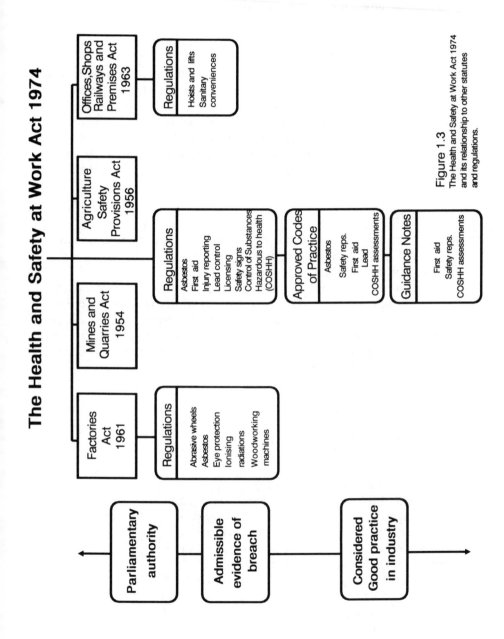

Figure 1.3
The Health and Safety at Work Act 1974 and its relationship to other statutes and regulations.

practicable'. What might be deemed by one to be reasonably practicable, may not be deemed so by another. This confusion can only be made clearer by examining how judges have interpreted this matter in court.

General duties of employers

'Reasonably practicable' is a narrower term than 'physically possible' and seems to me to imply that a computation must be made by the (employer) in which the quantum of risk is placed on one scale and the sacrifice involved in the measures necessary for averting the risk (whether in money, time or trouble) is placed on the other; and that, if it is shown that there is gross disproportion between them — the risk being insignificant in relation to the sacrifice — the defendants discharge the onus on them.

Onus of proof

Unlike the common law which places the burden of proof on the plaintiff, the HASAWA places the onus of proving the limits of what was reasonably practicable with the accused.

It is important to show the court under these circumstances that this assessment was made before the charges were laid, for example before the alleged offence had taken place. Lack of money or resources is no defence.

Section 2 of the HASAWA goes on to outline the general areas to be considered by the employer when complying with the general duty previously described.

General duties of employers (A)

1. (a) fire precautions taken;
   (b) sufficient lighting;
   (c) sufficient working space;
   (d) clear unobstructed gangways;
   (e) tidy workplace, floors in good condition;
   (f) steps, stairs, ladders, scaffolding etc in good condition.
2. (a) dangerous machinery to be guarded;
   (b) regular inspection and maintenance procedures;
   (c) emergency stop buttons;
   (d) sufficient equipment of the right quality.
3. (a) correct procedures laid down;
   (b) safety equipment;
   (c) clear instructions;
   (d) permits to work in extra-hazardous areas.
4. (a) adequate ventilation;

    (b) reasonable temperature;
    (c) accidents promptly investigated;
    (d) first aid facilities;
    (e) washing facilities;
    (f) sanitary conveniences;
    (g) cleanliness of workplace;
    (h) waste disposal, etc.

5. (a) instructions, training, etc;
    (b) protective clothing and equipment, mechanical handling equipment;
    (c) forklift trucks, conveyors, trolleys, etc;
    (d) storage areas defined.

Factors to be considered when discharging your duty towards contractors' employees include:

- The competence or specialist skills possessed by the contractors and their workforce.
- The amount of control you have over their activities.
- Whether or not you are providing plant and equipment for their use.
- What dangers exist in the workplace of which the contractor ought to be warned.
- Are there any areas which may contain potential hazards of which you are not aware.

General duties of employers (B)

Five duties are concerned with physical aspects of work and environment:

1. Safe place of work with a safe means of access and exit;
2. Safe plant and equipment – including maintenance;
3. Safe systems of work;
4. Safe working environment and adequate facilities and arrangements for employees' welfare;
5. Safe methods for handling storing and transporting goods.

Duties concerning the physical aspects of the work environment and of the people who are employed:

1. Provision of information, instruction, training and supervision;
2. Trade unions must be allowed to appoint safety representatives from within their membership. Management have no say in these appointments;
3. Employers must prepare and revise, where appropriate, a written statement of policy in respect of health and safety (safety policy). This applies where an employer employs more than five people.

Information, instruction and training

The provision of information, instruction, training and supervision ties in very closely with your common law duty to provide competent staff. Not only so that the interests of fellow employees are guarded but also so that the individual employee is better equipped to take care for their own safety. You should not overlook the training of supervisors when considering this particular section.

These provisions include such things as fire extinguishers, first aid equipment and facilities, protective clothing and equipment, guards on machinery and so on.

The safety practitioner now has an opportunity to compare the responsibilities and those duties at common law.

It is important to recognise the extent of the employer's duties in relation to those of the employee. It would seem that the employee will only be liable is he/she does something outside the control of his/her employer and/or unknown to him/her, or in direct contravention of instructions given by his/her employer.

The amount of reasonable care or co-operation to be expected of the employee is going to depend heavily on the amount of instruction, training and information he/she has been given. The amount of supervision necessary will equally depend upon these three things.

As the amount of information, instruction and training given to the employee increases the amount of supervision will decrease. This does not mean to say that supervision is no longer required but that it may be reduced to take account of the skill and experience of the individual employee.

Law of statute to non-employees

So far we have only discussed duties of employers to their employees but employers also have a duty under statute to people who are non-employees. There are two aspects of this duty.

1. Employers and self-employed

Responsibilities involving the actual operation of the business and working practices

2. Occupiers of premises

Responsibilities involving the premises and ownership of plant and materials. The relationship between the employer (as a client) and independent contractors has been the subject of much debate. Where the organisation's employees are called to work jointly with the employees of contractors, one of the questions which might arise is that of responsibility for the provision of information, instruction and training for the two groups of employees. To some extent the judgment in the following case has answered this question.

Leading case 1.34

In *Regina v Swan Hunter Shipbuilders Ltd* ([1979] ICR 831), an accidental fire, in 1976, occurred on board a ship, HMS Glasgow, under construction at the Swan Hunter yard, which caused the deaths of eight Swan Hunter men and injured three others who were working on it.

A leak of oxygen from a hose left below deck at the end of shift, occurred in the period September 22–23, causing oxygen enrichment (about 40%) of the atmosphere on one of the lower decks. A fierce fire resulted on the morning of September 23 when a welder struck an arc.

Instructions to Swan Hunter employees included a requirement to bring oxygen and fuel gas hoses to the top deck at the end of shift, though there were no notices posted to this effect and it was known that the practice was not consistently observed.

In relation to non-employees, i.e. contractors and subcontractors involved in the welding operations, Swan Hunter did nothing to ensure that they were aware of the hazards of oxygen enrichment and the precautions to be taken. Furthermore, they did not satisfy themselves that safe practice was observed and had no procedure for monitoring the practices adopted by contractors.

The Committee of Inquiry recommended that Swan Hunter introduce a system to monitor precautions in the use of oxygen and fuel gases by both employees and contractors, ensure that all concerned are aware of the hazards and that sufficient instruction is given to enable danger to be avoided.

As a result of the accident Swan Hunter were prosecuted under sections 2 and 3 of the HASAWA on the basis that if the provision of a safe system of work for the benefit of employees involves information and instruction of the potential dangers being given to persons other than employees, then the employer is under a duty to provide such information and instruction.

It is, therefore, important for employers to ensure that the provision of information about dangers peculiar to their places of work or processes extends to persons other than their own employees who may be affected by them or whose actions may affect the health and safety of their own employees.

In addition it would be advisable to provide instruction on the safe use of equipment available on the premises or on the proper precautions to be observed to minimise the risk of accidents occurring. It may also be necessary to give verbal or written instruction, to provide safety manuals or information leaflets and, in special circumstancès, to provide training to persons other than direct employees.

We would expect these responsibilities, however, to include the following. Typical areas of responsibility:

- Ensure that staff are trained and competent to carry out their tasks.
- Ensure that sufficient information and instruction is given.
- Ensure that plant, machinery and equipment in your department is safe and properly maintained.
- Ensure safe access and egress within your department.
- Ensure a safe place of work.
- Ensure that fire precautions are taken.

Regulations

Regulations proposed by the Commission, accepted by the Secretary of State and duly laid down before Parliament become the law of the land and are duly enforceable through the courts. Breaches of duties imposed by health and safety regulations (where they cause damage) are actionable in civil proceedings unless they specify otherwise. For example, the HASAWA specifically excludes sections 2–9 from being actionable at common law for breach of a statutory duty. New regulations may place an absolute duty on employers in the same way as some existing provisions do, or they may be limited by the use of phrases such as 'so far as practicable' and 'so far as reasonably practicable'. 'Reasonably practicable' on the other hand enables account to be taken of differing circumstances.

Where the word 'practicable' is used it is generally taken to mean that which is possible in the light of current knowledge and invention. For example, it is impossible to take precautions against a danger which is not known to exist, or to take precautions which have not yet been invented.

Approved codes of practice

The Commission's power to approve and issue codes of practice is contained in section 16 of the HASAWA. The objective of these codes is to provide practical guidance on the requirements contained in sections 2–7 of the Act, or in health and safety regulations, or in any of the existing statutory provisions. The precise statutory requirement to which the approved code is supplementary must be indicated in the code itself.

The purpose of the code of practice is to:

- Specify in greater detail or in a more liberal style than is practicable

or desirable in regulations, the precise technical and other requirements to be observed in a particular set of regulations or other
relevant statutory provisions.

- Explain what in particular circumstances would be considered to constitute satisfactory compliance with the requirements of a general
obligation.

It was the intention of Parliament that an approved code of practice
should enjoy a new and special status and would in effect provide a simple
and flexible extension of the law. This special status is given by section 17
which states that failure to observe any provision of an approved code shall
not of itself render a person liable to criminal or civil proceedings, but
where in criminal proceedings a person is alleged to have contravened a
statutory requirement or prohibition, the court is required to admit in evidence any provisions of an approved code which appear to it to be relevant.
Further, where the court considers that provisions of the code are relevant,
then failure to observe those provisions is to be taken as proof of a
contravention unless the court can be satisfied that you have complied with
the requirement in another way.

Approved codes will usually be generated by the Commission, the
Health and Safety Executive, industry advisory committees set up by the
Commission, or possibly in conjunction with such a body as the British
Standards Institution. Codes generated elsewhere will not normally be
approved by the Commission unless they are felt to be a necessary and
suitable extension of the law.

Hybrid offences

All other offences specified by the HASAWA are triable either way, for
example:

- Failure to discharge a duty imposed by sections 2–7.
- Contravention of sections 8 and 9.
- Contravention of any health and safety regulation.
- Contravention of an improvement or prohibition notice.
- Illegal disclosure of certain kinds of information.
- Making a false statement or entry to a register or document, or
forging a document with intent to deceive.
- Impersonating a factory inspector.

Only certain offences actually carry the full sanction of a prison sentence
and these are as follows:

- A breach of the requirements of a prohibition notice.
- A breach of the conditions of issue of a licence.
- Attempting to acquire explosives.

- The disclosure of information given under certain circumstances by the Health and Safety Commission.

The first ever prison sentence as a result of a prosecution under the HASAWA was given in 1985 to a company director who 'demonstrated a cynical disregard for the dangers to health'.

The individual was also personally fined a total of £1,500 along with fines to his company totalling £2,000. The director failed to comply with a prohibition notice served on the removal of asbestos lagging. His one-month prison sentence was suspended for two years.

Other forms of guidance

Other means of guidance and advisory literature will generally fall into one of the following categories:

Guidance notes by the Commission

These will be authoritative in so far as they carry the Commission's backing but they will fall short of approval of any particular course of conduct by an employer.

Guidance notes by the Executive

These will be essentially working notes of guidance. They will for example include advice on requirements to be followed and action to be taken by employers in order to comply with the law, technical data about specific hazards, and the interpretation of biological data by medical officers.

Guidance notes by industry advisory committees

These will originate in the form of reports which will carry the authority of the individual committee.

Guidance notes issued by industry generated notes of guidance may come from manufacturers and other associations providing technical and common sense instructions on how to cope with various situations in particular workplaces. The Commission or the HSE will normally not wish to give any official recognition to these notes of guidance. Failure to comply with the requirements may lead to prosecution for breach of a statutory duty. Most safety cases are heard in the magistrates' court summarily but the more serious ones are heard on indictment in the Crown Court. Do not forget, unlike common law there does not have to be an injury before action can be taken by the HSE inspector.

Health and Safety at Work Act 1974 (HASAWA)

Background

The HASAWA is likely to impinge most directly on managers who are held primarily responsible for the compliance with this Act in their company. The Act determines specific standards of safety in a number of areas through a number of regulations issued under its provisions. The Act imposes a number of legal duties on employers, the self employed, employees, suppliers and owners of premises, to ensure that their workplaces are safe and offer no risk to health. The Act has four basic aims:

1. To secure the health, safety and welfare of persons at work;
2. To protect persons, other than persons at work, against risk to health and safety arising out of or in connection with the activities of persons at work;
3. To control the keeping and use of dangerous substances;
4. To control the emission into the atmosphere of noxious and offensive substances.

To achieve these aims the Act established one comprehensive, integrated system of law dealing with health and safety and welfare of people at work and the public who may be affected by such work activities, and in so doing:

1. Places general duties on the employer, ranging from providing and maintaining a safe place of work to consulting with employees;
2. Places duties on employees to take reasonable care of themselves and anyone who may be affected by their work activities, and to co-operate with their employer and others in meeting these obligations.

The Act is a piece of enabling legislation which allows the Secretary of State to define a system of regulations and approved codes of practice which will progressively replace the existing legislation, but maintain or improve the standard of health, safety and welfare established by the Act. Thus the regulations can be amended to keep pace with developments.

Implications of the Act

1. Accountability

It can be seen that the Act in sections 2, 3 and 4 imposes wide ranging and far reaching duties on the organisation by virtue of its position as employer and controller of premises. However the Act does not stop with the inanimate 'body corporate'. Section 7 makes it the employee's duty to have a care for himself and for others who may be affected by his acts or omissions at work, also placing on him a duty to co-operate with the employer to enable the requirements of sections 2, 3 and 4 to be complied with. Sections 33, 36 and 37 make it an offence for an individual to fail to discharge the duties placed on him by sections 2–7 and remove the 'protection' afforded by the body corporate. Not only can the organisation be prosecuted for offences under the Act, so can the managing director and his subordinates right down the management chain, where it can be established in law that they have failed. Therefore, wherever a person holds a management position, the responsibility conferred with that post includes responsibility under the Act commensurate with the status of the post. Further to this, section 8 refers to 'persons' who shall not interfere with or misuse anything provided in the interest of health, safety and welfare. Thus any person who misuses or vandalises a first-aid box or fools with a fire extinguisher can be prosecuted under this section of the Act.

2. Control of premises

Section 4 of the Act is applicable in the situation where persons who are not employees of the organisation including members of the general public, are on the premises of the organisation. The plant or substances can range from an ordinary chair to an arc welder, or from water to a radioactive isotope.

3. Safety information and training

Section 2(2)(c) requires the employer to provide information, instruction, training and supervision. Much of the requirement devolves on the manager as follows.

Information
This will be passed from the department or section. Where applicable and relevant, this information must be brought to the notice of affected employees by the responsible manager. Additionally, information applicable to the safety of a particular process or piece of equipment must be readily available for employees to study.

Instruction and training
The basis of much of health and safety is effective instruction and training. Whilst much of this will originate from and be organised by the responsible department or section, the manager has to ensure that all members of his staff receive the relevant and required instruction and training. Additionally, because of sections 3 and 4, in certain circumstances 'persons not employees' may also need to be trained.

Trades unions see this training as purely their province and representatives are entitled by law to attend a TUC approved course; this principle
has been tested in an industrial tribunal. However, this should not be the
beginning and end of their training. Union courses should be supplemented
by in-house training dealing with specific issues involved in the organisation's work. Ideally the training should produce a balance between all three
roles previously mentioned.

Supervision
The appropriate level of supervision must be exercised at all times. It is not
sufficient to provide information, instruction and training without
adequate supervision in safety matters. Such supervision must be primarily
directed at ensuring that all subordinate safety staff comply. Managers must
consider the adequacy of the level of supervision in possible hazardous
areas, particularly in the light of the experience of the employees involved.

4. Duty not to charge

Section 9 places a duty on the employer, not to charge the employee in
respect of anything done or provided in pursuance of any specific requirement of the relevant statutory provisions. Thus, where there is a statute law
in the form of a regulation requiring certain matters to be done, such as
the Protection of Eyes Regulations which require operators to have eye
protection, this must be provided free of charge. Where practicable all
protective clothing should be provide free of charge.

5. Duty of manufacturers

Section 6 places a duty on the manufacturer and the supplier broadly to
make and supply articles and substances which are, as far as is reasonably
practicable, safe and without risk to health for use at work. Employers and
individual managers must ensure that instructions provided by a manufacturer or supplier are brought to the attention of and obeyed by employees.

6. Suppliers duties (section 6)

One aspect of the HASAWA which we have not discussed so far is the
responsibilities it places upon the supplier of equipment and materials. In
fact section 6 covers the responsibilities not only of suppliers but also of
designers, manufacturers, importers and installers relating to articles and
substances for use at work. These are:

● To ensure that these articles and substances are safe and without risk
  to health when properly used.

- To carry out tests or examinations as may be necessary to ensure that they are safe and without risk to health when properly used.
- To provide any information necessary to ensure that they are safe and without risk to health when properly used.

Installers of equipment are under a similar obligation to ensure that anything they install is safe and without risk to health. These duties can only be relieved by a written undertaking from the user that he/she will personally take steps to ensure that the article or substance will be made safe.

Initially you may feel that these duties have no relevance to you or your organisation or may even relieve you of your responsibility as a user of equipment. There are however two important factors which you must consider.

First as a user of equipment you have a responsibility to your employees to provide (so far as is reasonably practicable) equipment and materials that are safe and without risk to health. You cannot rely upon the integrity of the supplier in every instance to protect the safety of your staff. It is necessary for you, the user, to request information from the supplier, etc. to enable you to use the article or substance safely. Furthermore if an article or a substance has a defect or is a risk to health and safety and it can be shown that you were (or should have been) aware of this, it is no defence to argue that it was supplied in that condition. You may share liability with the supplier.

Second, the organisation may itself be a supplier of articles or substances for use at work and consequently may incur the liabilities imposed by section 6. This often happens where items surplus to inventory are concerned and disposed of by selling them to others who may intend to use them at work.

Safety policy

One of the legal provisions of section 2 of the HASAWA requires employers who employ five people or more to prepare, and keep up to date, a written statement of their policy regarding the health and safety of their employees.

Your policy may consist of one complete manual or it may be a compilation of several individual documents relating to particular areas of your activity. Whatever form it takes it should comprise three separate and distinct parts:

1. General statement of policy;
2. Organisation and responsibilities for carrying out the policy;
3. Arrangements for ensuring safety and health of employees.

Many organisations produce a general statement of intent and require individual departments, cost centres or directorates to develop safety policies which appropriately reflect the day-to-day activities of the department.

By looking through the policy you should find an indication that the organisation will provide resources for health and safety along with the provision of safe plant and equipment, safe systems of work, training for staff and supervision. In fact, you should observe a resemblance to the general duties laid down by section 2 of the HASAWA.

As far as responsibilities are concerned, these should include the duties of employees at all levels in the organisation.

Safety representatives and committees

A unionised employer has a duty to consult with safety representatives appointed by the appropriate trade union. Where two or more safety representatives require the formation of a safety committee, an employer must undertake the establishment of such a committee under section 2(7) of the HASAWA and the Safety Representatives and Safety Committees Regulations 1977, reg. 9(1) within three months of the request being made.

A safety representative is an employee nominated by his trade union to represent his colleagues in discussions with the employer on matters relating to health and safety at work. He may carry out surveys or inspection of the workplace with the object of identifying hazards or potential dangers. Employers are required to disclose to such representatives all information necessary for them to carry out their duties and functions. Details of the information can be found in para. 6 of the Approved Code of Practice on Safety Representatives and Safety Committees. At the same time, health and safety inspectors are also required to provide safety representatives with technical information obtained as a result of a visit to their workplace. This must include details of prosecutions, improvement notices, prohibition orders, and any correspondence to the employer on health and safety matters. All action considered by an inspector as the result of a visit must be discussed with the safety representative.

As far as the safety practitioner is concerned, the safety representative/s within an organisation are an extremely valuable asset. They must be met regularly, involved directly within the decision-making process and considered an extension of the overall health and safety programme.

For safety committees to be effective they must not be too large otherwise their ability to make decisions effectively is diminished. They must be made up of senior management, trade union safety representatives with the secretariat being provided for by the safety manager or one of his members of staff. Chairmanship of the committee should follow normal electoral procedure and a constitution should allow for periodic changes to the structure to take place. Decisions taken by the committee must be adhered to and carried out as soon as is reasonably practicable. Merely having a safety committee because the regulations say you have been requested to have one is a severe waste of resources if it is not permitted to make an effective contribution to the well-being of the organisation.

Decisions concerning new laws and regulations affecting working practices should be placed before the safety committee for discussion. From this, all matters concerning the planning, implementation, monitoring and evaluation of policy can be discussed openly and widely. These and other issues are discussed in Chapter 5.

These regulations came into force on October 1, 1978 and gave trade unions the right to appoint safety representatives to perform the following functions:

- To investigate potential hazards and dangerous occurrences at the workplace and to examine the cause of accidents.
- To investigate complaints by employees in relation to health, safety and welfare at work and to make representations to the employer on these issues.
- To take up general matters of health and safety at work and to represent employees in consultation with HSE inspectors.
- To attend meetings of the safety committee when and if necessary.
- To carry out a workplace inspection every three months after giving reasonable notice to the employer of intention to do so.
- To carry out workplace inspections (after consultation with his employers) when there has been a change in conditions of work, or new information has been issued concerning relevant hazards. The employer is entitled to be represented at these inspections if he wishes.

The idea of workers being involved in these activities has been debated for many years and was actually resisted by many trades unions because they suspected that such involvement might relieve employers of some of the responsibility to health and safety.

It is important to note therefore that the activities outlined above are merely functions which the representative may carry out. They do not relieve the employer of any responsibility whatsoever and do not confer any legal liability on the appointed representative.

The regulations specify a number of other provisions relating to the training of safety representatives and the provision of information relating to safety and health at work. Your organisation's safety policy may specify the local arrangements made to enable safety representatives to perform these functions.

Safety representatives are an important influence in the provision and maintenance of a safe and healthy working environment.

Enforcement of the health and safety provisions

The safety laws within the organisation premises are enforced by the HSE. Primarily this agency will seek to advise and assist employers in meeting the appropriate standards although they do have broad powers of enforcement.

The HSE inspectors have a number of powers available to them and when appointed they are issued a warrant card which specifies the range of these.

These powers include:

- To enter premises at any reasonable time.
- To take a constable if necessary.
- To take any authorised person and equipment, for example, gas, electricity engineers.
- To examine or investigate accidents or dangerous occurrences.
- To require premises or the scene of an accident to be left undisturbed.
- To take samples of suspect substances, etc (they must leave an equivalent sample for independent analysis should you wish it).
- To dismantle or test any dangerous article or substance.
- To take possession of any dangerous article or substance for examination or for use in legal proceedings.
- To require information facilities and assistance to carry on these duties.
- To require the production of any relevant books or documents.
- To seize destroy or render harmless any article or substance which is a source of imminent danger.
- To interview employees, take statements and require a written declaration of the truth of these statements.

The following offences carry a maximum £2,000 fine on summary conviction.

- To prevent or hinder a person appearing before an inspector.
- Intentionally to obstruct an inspector.

Enforcement notices

The HASAWA brought about an innovation in the enforcement of safety legislation by giving inspectors the power to issue improvement or prohibition notices. Each serves a specific purpose.

Improvement notice

An inspector may serve an improvement notice where he is of the opinion that a contravention of a statutory requirement has been or is about to be carried out.

This requires the person on whom the notice is served to make the necessary improvements to reach the desired standard. The inspector may specify appropriate remedial action and give a time limit of not less than 21 days in which to comply.

The minimum time period is important because it is the time allowed for the person to appeal to an industrial tribunal against the terms of the notice.

Appeal may take two forms:

1. Appeal on the grounds that the notice and remedial action is not reasonable;
2. The time allowed is not sufficient in which to comply.

When an appeal is lodged it has the effect of suspending the notice until the appeal is heard and decided.

It is interesting to note that an improvement notice cannot be served where the breach has already taken place and is not likely to be repeated. Under these circumstances the inspector may choose to prosecute.

Prohibition notice

A prohibition notice can be served where an inspector is of the opinion that an activity being carried on or about to be carried on may give rise to serious personal injury. There does not have to be a breach of a statutory requirement.

The notice takes effect immediately but unlike the improvement notice an appeal (within 21 days) does not have the effect of suspending the notice.

A failure to comply with either notice is an indictable offence and will result in prosecution with severe penalties. For example, on conviction, a person shall be liable to an unlimited fine and/or imprisonment for a term not exceeding two years.

The lesson here is not to ignore a notice once it has been served just because you disagree with it. This is an offence in itself even if the notice is unreasonable! The best approach under these circumstances is to lodge an appeal and argue the issue of reasonableness in front of a tribunal.

Prosecution

An inspector may choose a third course of action and that is to prosecute the person responsible for committing the offence. This person may be the employer, the employee, individual managers and directors, or any other person assigned responsibilities by the HASAWA.

Summary offences

- To contravene a requirement imposed by an inspector under section 20 or 25.
- To prevent a person from answering an inspector's question.
- To obstruct an inspector from carrying out his/hers duties.
- A contravention of a requirement imposed by a committee of inquiry or to obstruct a person acting under its direction.

The main factors to be considered when deciding whether reasonable care has been taken are the magnitude of the risk involved in the activity and the cost of the precautions necessary for averting the risk.

Other factors to be considered are the obvious nature of the risk and also whether or not the risk is inherent in the job, for example steeplejacks, miners, etc.

Aspects of personal liability

Our general duty as employees is covered by section 7 of the HASAWA which says that each employee shall take reasonable care for his own health and safety, and that of other people. We are also required to co-operate with our employer to enable him to carry out his statutory duties. This applies to all employees regardless of status, be they operators, managers or directors.

However, if your job involves instructing other people in what they must do then the HASAWA places an extra duty on you to avoid causing these people to commit an offence. Section 36 says:

> 'Where a person by his act or default causes another person to commit an offence then he, as well as that other person may be charged with the offence.'

Hence if you instruct one of your staff to do something which is a contravention of one of the statutory requirements you may be found guilty of the offence. Several managers have fallen foul of this section illustrated by this typical case.

The issues relating to senior managers and directors are a little more complex. It is recognised that employers are merely organisations of people and that offences committed by the organisation may have been due to the act of one or more of its senior managers.

Section 37 says:

> 'Where an offence committed by a body corporate is shown to have been committed due to the consent connivance or neglect of a director or senior manager then he as well as the body corporate shall be guilty of the offence.'

Someone then, must make or neglect to make the decisions that affect the safety and well being of the organisation and its employees, and that individual must be accountable in law.

In a case arising from a serious accident in which the injured party lost four fingers when they became trapped in the rolls of a copying machine, section 37 was used to prosecute the senior office manager. He was given the responsibility of checking the safety of the machine guards by his company's safety policy.

The HASAWA has therefore provided a vehicle for the prosecution and punishment of individuals who break the safety laws and put themselves and others at risk.

An important consideration, along with the responsibilities placed by the HASAWA, is the extent and domain of responsibility given to individual managers and directors by the organisation's safety policy. The purpose of assigning these responsibilities is to maintain standards of safety in the workplace by giving individual specific tasks relating to the safe performance of their activities.

In fact where these responsibilities are clearly defined by the policy the individual may incur criminal liability for failing to discharge them.

A director was prosecuted following a fatal accident to one of his employees on the evidence that he had failed to perform a duty of which he knew or ought to have known. He had, in fact, failed to comply with a company circular requiring him to devise a safety policy for his department and to inform and train his employees in the requirements of the HASAWA.

More recently the first ever prison sentence was imposed upon a director of a company who ignored a prohibition notice issued by an HSE inspector. The court said 'You have demonstrated a cynical disregard for the dangers to health. I am satisfied your motive was profit'. The prison sentence of one month was suspended for two years.

Safety then, is the employer's responsibility, but is clearly seen as the responsibility of the management in any organisation or business.

Managerial responsibility

Typical managerial duties set down in a safety policy may include any or all of the following:

- To ensure that you and your staff understand and implement the organisation's health and safety policy.
- To ensure that you and your staff are aware of their legal and common law duties relating to health and safety at work.
- To ensure that any special regulations which apply to operations

carried out under your control are made known and observed, and to see that all procedures are properly carried out.

- To see the job safety requirements are listed and made known to operatives by satisfactory safety training.
- To assist your staff in resolving health and safety problems and seek assistance as appropriate from the organisation's safety officer.
- To ensure that you and members of your staff attend regular meetings at which health and safety can be discussed.
- To make sure that the reporting of all accidents and dangerous occurrences is done in order to enable investigations to be carried out and to accept the advice given to prevent recurrence.
- To ensure that there are provided adequate levels of supervision suitably qualified and knowledgeable on safe working procedures and practices.
- To ensure that all employees within your control are provided with such information, instruction and training to enable them to work safely within organisation and statutory safety requirements, both at the induction stage of employment and during all employment activities.
- To ensure that all required safety equipment is made available for use by those employees who have a requirement to use.
- To conduct periodic safety inspections or contribute to safety inspections of the area for which you are responsible and to implement improvements as required. This management involvement is crucial to the success of the safety policy.

When judging your safety record you probably looked at the number of accidents you have had over a specified period of time, and compared this with the organisation's accident rate. If you used this measure you might relax in the knowledge that your department has relatively few accidents. However, while this may be comforting news a more important question to be answered is 'how much is this good accident record related to the amount of activity you have undertaken in promoting and maintaining safety standards?

Measuring performance

To begin an examination of your performance you should start by answering the following questions which are typical of those asked in management audits. The questions may be listed under the four main heads listed below.

Consider your activity in each of these areas over, say, the last 12 months and answer these questions.

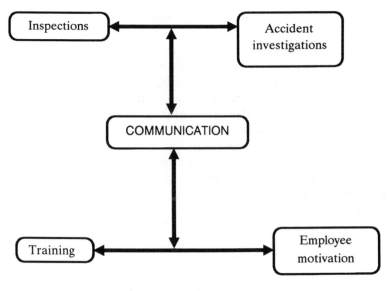

Figure 1.4

Performance appraisal

Inspections

- How many safety inspections have you made?
- How many unsafe conditions were found during these inspections?
- How many of these unsafe conditions were corrected as a result?
- How many unsafe behaviours were observed?
- How many of these behaviours were corrected?
- How many unsafe conditions were reported to you?
- How many of these reports did you respond to?

Your answer to these questions will be some indication of your personal involvement in hazard spotting and correcting problems in the area for which you are responsible. You should be taking the lead in the supervision of safety and ensuring that your staff comply with the safety rules.

Inspections should be carried out frequently, how often really depends upon the magnitude of risk involved in the work. Safety representatives are entitled to carry out their own inspections and you should be prepared to respond to their reports appropriately.

Accident investigations

- How many accident investigations did you carry out (in relation to the number of accidents)?

- Were these investigations made promptly or were they made subsequent to an injury benefit claim or safety officer's enquiry?
- How many times did you discover the true cause of the accident? For example, if you ascribed the accident to operator error what factors such as training, supervision, etc led to this error?
- How many causes could be attributed to failure in the management system?
- How many causes were remedied successfully?

Before choosing to investigate an accident a number of factors are generally taken into account such as the frequency of the occurrence, the severity of the injury, or just the unusual nature of the incident.

In fact there is a duty on all employers under the Social Security (Claims and Payments) Regulations 1979 to take reasonable steps to investigate the circumstances of all accidents notified to them. This investigation should be the starting point in seeking the root causes leading up to the accident itself. If you have relatively few accidents there is no reason why you should not make a serious investigation of them all.

Training

- How many new employees were trained in safety matters, for example fire procedures, first-aid facilities, accident or hazard reporting, safety rules, etc?
- How many existing employees have had refresher training in safety matters?
- How many safety briefing sessions have you given or arranged?
- How many of your staff have attended safety training courses?
- What improvements have resulted from this training?

If you found it difficult to answer these questions it may be because you have no tangible record of what has been done over the last year. It is important to keep a record of all training done however small for without this it will be very difficult to demonstrate compliance with the HASAWA.

Employee motivation

- How many employees were contacted personally about safety matters?
- How many positive reinforcements of behaviour were given?
- How many negative reinforcements of behaviour were given (reprimands or corrections)?
- What media have been utilised for this purpose, for example, films, posters, letters, etc?

Your personal contact with employees is important in generating an awareness of health and safety. The more interest you show the more likely employees are to co-operate with you in promoting health and safety.

Safety is the responsibility of management and should be managed the same as any other activity within the organisation. However, whilst management normally accept the responsibility of dealing with matters such as production, industrial relations and the utilisation of plant and equipment etc, they are generally not so careful about ensuring compliance with the safety rules. This is often because the internal penalties for failure in this area are not so clearly defined – managers rarely get sacked for a poor safety record. This should not, however, encourage you to relax your activities in this area.

Selection of contractors

All the effort you put into providing for the safety of your staff may be undone by the activities of contractors in your workplace. It is important to:

- Take reasonable care to select competent contractors.
- Supervise the activities of contractors where their work brings them into contact with your employees.

The common law places an obligation on occupiers of premises to take reasonable care in the selection of contractors. If part of your job includes the hiring of contractors to carry out certain activities this responsibility falls on you. You may be helped in this by your organisation's policy on the employment of contractors. Many specific organisations now carry lists of approved contractors who can be relied upon to work to an acceptable standard. These contractors must be used whenever possible.

In the absence of clear guidelines you should ensure that, in the right circumstances, they have a safety policy outlining the arrangements and procedures their companies have made for safe working.

Where the contractor is required by law to have a safety policy you should ask for it to be presented with the tender for the contract. If the contractor has less than five employees they are not required to have a written safety policy and therefore should be required to give assurances about safety when they are carrying out the work.

These contractors should be required to work in accordance with your organisation's safety policy and given information, instruction and training where necessary to enable them to carry out their duties safely. Where there is uncertainty you may find it helpful to consult your organisation's safety adviser.

1. Supervision and monitoring

Where the work is carried out in an area under your control you are responsible for ensuring that your staff and members of the public are not put at risk. You will be faced from time to time with decisions relating to the work of contractors.

2. Permission to start work

All contractors should report to the manager of the affected area before work is commenced. (There will also be a requirement for them to report to the clerk of works or engineering department for longer contracts.)

3. Use of organisation equipment

Contractors are expected to provide their own tools, plant and equipment necessary for the satisfactory performance of the work in hand. Use of the organisation's equipment should be by written permission of the organisation's representative.

Contractors should also ensure that their employees are provided with any necessary personal safety equipment, for example helmets, goggles, etc.

4. Fire extinguishers

Contractors should familiarise themselves with the location of fire extinguishers in the area in which they are working. If additional extinguishers are required these should not be obtained from other locations but from the engineering department.

5. Fire alarm systems

Contractors should make themselves aware of the positions of the fire alarm call point and the organisation's fire procedure.

6. Interference with fire equipment

Except for use in an emergency, any interference with the electrical wiring and other mechanism of automatic fire detection and extinguishing apparatus, or of the audible fire warning system should be prohibited. Requests for temporary resetting of such equipment must be made to the engineering department.

7. No smoking areas

The no smoking rules in all areas where smoking is forbidden should be strictly observed. Consideration must also be given to the use of welding equipment, blow lamps, etc and also to the safe storage and use of flammable materials.

8. Warning of danger

Care must be taken at all times to protect the organisation's employees, property and work in progress from danger, and any circumstances which give rise to such danger must be reported immediately.

9. Accidents

All accidents, injuries and dangerous occurrences should be reported to the manager.

10. Unused materials

Contractors should be required to remove all unused materials and leave the site clean and tidy on completion of the work.

11. Housekeeping

Contractors should ensure that the workplace is kept tidy with no dirt or refuse being allowed to accumulate.

These points are relevant guidelines to be applied to contractors where their work interfaces with the activities of your employees. Other, more technical, aspects that need to be considered which take into account the needs of both employees and members of the public include:

1. Electricity, gas, air mains. On no account should use be made of the organisation's electricity, gas or compressed air mains, without the permission of the organisation. Where permission is granted the method of connection should be approved by the engineering department.
2. Excavations. Before any excavation work is begun, the architects or technical services should be consulted about the existence of electric cables, drains, air, gas, and water mains.
3. Fencing excavations. Excavation or projecting equipment should not be left at any time without taking the necessary safety precautions. All excavations, and openings, should be securely fenced and these and any obstructions marked by a sufficient number of lamps during hours of darkness. During the excavation of all such work, the surrounding area should be maintained in a state of tidiness. Loose materials of whatever kind should not be left about or allowed to obstruct roadways, gangways or working areas.

4. Building operations. All building work should be carried out strictly in accordance with the regulations made under the Factories Act in particular complying with the requirements for scaffolding and access equipment.

These provisions, though not exhaustive, may form the basis of a supervision checklist which you might use to assess the activities of contractors.

Remember, just because they are not your employees does not mean to say that you have no responsibility for them. Many of these duties are interrelated but in principle it is the responsibility of the party in control of, or carrying out the activity to foresee any possible harm and take reasonable steps to prevent it. This is complicated by the fact that some areas of responsibility may be shared by two or more parties so that clear procedures need to be laid down to avoid confusion. This is particularly so where contractors are working alongside your own employees and members of the public.

Above all there is a need to ensure that all parties are aware of the risks involved by providing information, instruction and training, and by ensuring that their activities are supervised and monitored.

By considering all these points you will not only help to ensure the safety of employees and others, but also help to avoid incurring liability on both yourself and your employer.

Control of Substances Hazardous to Health (COSHH)

The COSHH Regulations introduce a new legal framework for the control of substances hazardous to health in all types of businesses, including factories, farms, quarries, leisure and service activities, offices and shops. The Regulations require you to make an assessment of all work which is liable to expose any employee to hazardous solids, liquids, dusts, fumes, vapours, gases or micro-organisms. Assessment means evaluating the risks to health and then deciding on the action needed to remove or reduce those risks.

The responsibility to make the assessment rests with you – the employer. As the employer, you could do or lead the assessment yourself or give the task to someone else with the authority and ability to get all the necessary information and make correct decisions about the risks and the precautions that are needed. That person should know the point of the various requirements of the COSHH Regulations and have access to a copy of the Regulations and approved code of practice. Whoever does the assessment, you should make sure that managers, supervisors and employees' safety representatives are fully consulted about the work processes, about what workers are doing (or are liable to be doing), and about the risks and the necessary precautions.

In some cases, particularly if you are in doubt over the answers to the next questions, you may need to consult your supplier or trade association or even obtain expert advice about what substances are involved in the work. Ask yourself if employees are liable to be exposed to hazardous substances in your workplaces. Include service activities as well as production processes.

How can substances hazardous to health be identified?

- For substances brought in, check the safety information on the labels and the information for safe use provided by your suppliers (they are required by law to do so).
- Use your existing knowledge (eg past experience, knowledge of the process, understanding of current best practice in your industry, information on work related health problems in your industry).
- Ask your trade association and other employers in the same business for their experience and advice.
- Check COSHH: is the substance mentioned in any of the Regulations or Schedules? Is it listed in HSE Guidance Note EH40?
- Examine published documentation, trade data, HSE guidance material.

What is brought into the workplace? What is used, worked on or stored? What is given off during any process or work activity? What substances are produced at the end of any work process?

Check: Corrosives Acids Solvents Consider: Dust Fumes Gases Residues

Figure 1.5

A typical check list

- Check Part IA1 of the approved list issued under the Classification, Packaging and Labelling of Dangerous Substances Regulations 1984: anything listed as very toxic, toxic, corrosive, harmful or irritant comes under COSHH.

Do the ways in which each substance is handled or is present in the workplace give rise to any risks to health in practice now or in the future?

Observe, find out about and consider

- Where and in what circumstances substances are used, handled, generated, released, etc. What happens to them in use?
- Is their form changed (e.g. solids reduced to dust by machining)? Identify places (e.g. handling departments, storage areas, transport).
- What people are doing; what might they do?
- What measures are currently taken to control exposure and to check on the effectiveness and use of those measures?
- Who will be affected (e.g. employees, employers, contractors, public)?
- Is exposure liable to occur?
- Is it likely some of the substance will be breathed in?
- Is it likely to be swallowed following contamination of fingers and/or clothing?
- Is it likely to cause skin contamination or be absorbed through the skin?
- Is it reasonably foreseeable that an accidental leakage, spill or discharge could occur (e.g. through breakdowns of the plant or control measures or operators' mistakes)?

Reach conclusions about people's exposure: who, under what circumstances, the length of time they are or could be exposed for, the amount they are exposed to, and how likely exposure is to occur. Combine this with knowledge about the potential of the substance for causing harm (i.e. its hazard) to reach conclusions about the risks from exposure.

Sometimes, of course, the quantities, the exposure time or the effects are such that the substances do not or could not constitute a risk – but you must have the information to back up this conclusion.

Action to be taken

If the assessment shows that there is no likelihood of a risk to health, the assessment is complete and no further precautions are needed.

If the assessment shows that further action is needed, you have to decide what needs to be done to complete the assessment requirements. If it is reasonably practicable to do so, you should prevent anyone from being exposed to any hazardous substances. Where it is not reasonably practicable to prevent people being exposed, you have to ensure their exposure is adequately controlled and their health protected. In such cases you will need to:

- Select the measures to achieve and sustain adequate control;
- Work out arrangements to make sure those control measures are properly used and maintained.
- Make sure your workforce is trained and instructed in the risks and the precautions to take, so that they can work safely. In some circumstances, employees need to be monitored and arrangements made for them to be under health surveillance (check COSHH, HSE guidance notes relevant to your work and trade literature).

Unless you can easily report and explain your conclusions at any time because the assessment is simple and obvious, you should make a record of it. Record or attach sufficient information to show why decisions about risks and precautions have been arrived at and to make it clear to employees, engineers, managers, etc what parts they have to play in the precautions.

If the conclusions alter, for example, the introduction of a new process or machine or a change in the substances used, or if there is any reason to suspect that the assessment is no longer correct, for example, reports of ill health related to work activities, the assessment must be reviewed to take account of these new circumstances.

Assessing what is reasonably practicable

Leading case 1.35

An illustration of the term 'reasonably practicable' is to be seen in the case of *Associated Dairies* v *Hartley* ([1979] 1 RLR 175). A worker was injured when a wheel on a lorry ran over his toe. The employer had provided safety shoes which could be purchased at cost by the workforce. The cost was spread over a period of time. An inspector issued an improvement notice requiring Associated Dairies to issue the shoes free of cost. The employer appealed. The tribunal thought that it would be practicable for the employer to provide the shoes without cost, but that it was not reasonable to expect him to do so. The time, trouble and expense of safety precautions must be weighed against the foreseeable risk and in this case, the expenditure by the employers would be disproportionate to the risk.

Offences under the Act and those other safety and health laws mentioned are deemed criminal and may involve prosecution of an individual or a company in a magistrate's or crown court. It is a fundamental principle of criminal law for the prosecutor to prove beyond reasonable doubt that the offence was committed by the accused. Under section 40 of the

HASAWA, it is for the accused to prove that he did take reasonably practicable precautions as required by the Act and by some sections of the other health and safety laws. This means that if the accused thought that it was not reasonably practicable to take certain steps then it is for him to provide the proof.

It is not possible here to provide an in-depth study into the health and safety legislation in this country. It is intended to remind those already familiar with the law and to provide an introduction to the lay person or student. A reading list is provided for those wishing to learn more about this complex area. Safety practitioners need only a working knowledge of the law as would any professional manager. Expert advice should be sought as and when appropriate owing to the complexities of the law in this regard. Despite the wealth of safety case law in existence at the present time, it is always a communication problem in getting the 'lessons learnt' aspects of the cases across to safety practitioners. Many safety practitioners experience great difficulty in this area. It is essential, therefore, that safety managers have direct access to legal expertise. At the present time, there is a bewildering mass of legislation which lays both criminal and civil responsibilities upon employers. Amongst aspects covered are the style and manner of accident reporting, the safe access to buildings and sites. Particular regulations govern dangerous materials or processes such as asbestos and steam boilers. Special constraints are placed on the employment of children and young persons. Construction and building operations because of their high risk nature are highly regulated. Procedures for the control of industrial major accident hazards and the use and transportation of dangerous substances have all been introduced in the 1980's.

Exceptional care has to be taken in handling the relationship between safety and discipline and unfair dismissal even though employees' duties are tightly defined. Distinct regulations apply to electrical and fire hazards within the Factories Act. Specific provision has to be made for appropriate first-aid facilities. It must be stated that with regard to enforcement, draconian consequences both for civil and criminal liability may be felt by board members down to low level supervisors. Specific controls relating to food handling and hygiene, use of lifting machinery and materials' handling are all covered. Chronic problems which may be felt by employees in terms of noise and vibration, overcrowding or problems of occupational health have all been strengthened in the last three years. Liability may also exist for product and structural safety as well as personal protection. Certain categories of workers including women and those who work at heights or off shore are afforded additional protection under the law.

Within the enforcement area of safety management is that of policing. To ensure that organisations are conducting their business within the terms of the HASAWA, the HSE was set up. At the same time, the Health and

Safety Commission was created to oversee the work of the HSE. The Commission has the general overseeing of the work of the Executive and has power to delegate to it. However, the Executive is a statutory body charged with the responsibility for the enforcement of safety legislation. The Commission cannot give instructions or directions to the Executive about enforcement matters and cannot issue judgments in any particular case.

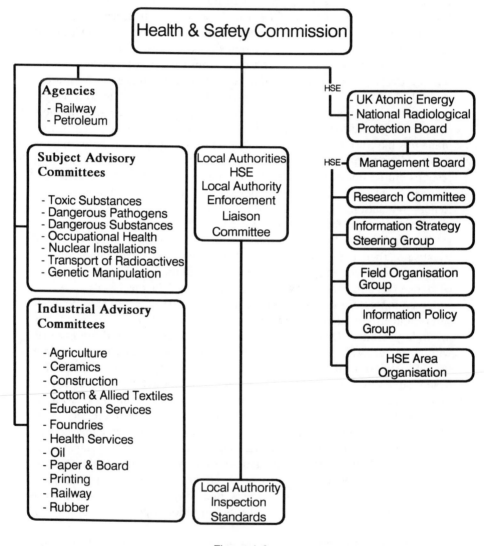

Figure 1.6

An organisational plan of the commission and executive

Both Commission and Executive are rather bureaucratic and cumbersome. To illustrate this, hierarchical structures are given in Figures 1.6 and 1.7. Although the Executive publish a glossy annual report, some statistics and other information collected and issued by them are discussed are Chapter 2.

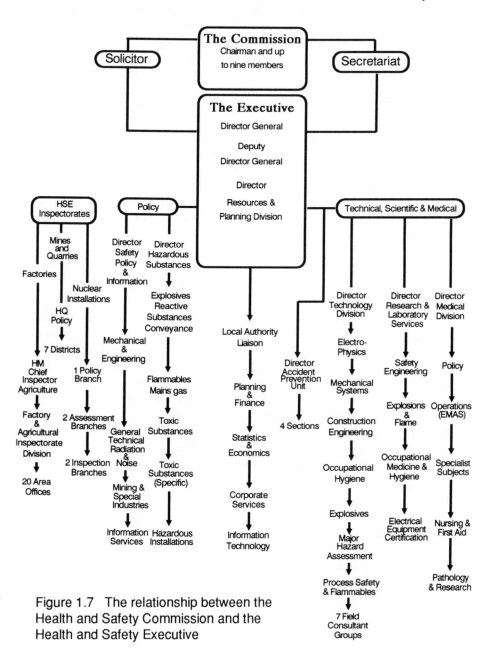

Figure 1.7 The relationship between the Health and Safety Commission and the Health and Safety Executive

In the United Kingdom as in Europe, regulations, directives or decrees are introduced from time to time to deal with issues which have been found to be dangerous or hazardous to health. These regulations might cover such subjects as the use of circular saws or washing facilities. They are usually introduced following evidence to the enforcement agencies that such guidance is necessary. This is an established practice in the western world and covers all aspects of safety. For example, evidence was provided that alcohol was a contributory factor in road accidents. Most developed countries have legislated, or issued decrees or regulations, which clearly point out the consequences of drinking alcohol and driving following evidence gained from accident analysis. In the same way industrial enforcement agencies gather similar evidence which assists in introducing appropriate measures designed to reduce or prevent such occurrences happening in the future. Senior management must appreciate that the rules are made to help not hinder the organisational mission. On the other hand regulating against some malpractice does not necessarily prevent it from happening. People still injure themselves on chain saws, still drink and drive and still suffer ill health carrying on some activity contrary to good advice or legal necessity.

The Council of the European Communities

Since the formation of the EEC, it must not be forgotten that the European Parliament may issue directives which will influence policies and strategies within member states. For example, the Commission to the Council of the European Communities under Article 118A of the treaty provides that the Council shall adopt, by means of directives, minimum requirements for encouraging improvements regarding the health and safety of workers, especially in the working environment. Article 15 of this directive states that member states shall bring into force the laws, regulations and administrative procedures necessary to comply with this directive by January 1, 1991. The directive covers the following areas:

- Objectives.
- Definitions.
- Responsibilities of employers.
- Obligations of the employer.
- Preventative services.
- Information to be collected and held by employers.
- Information and communication with workers.
- Consultation with the workforce.
- Training.
- Obligations placed on workers.

● Adoption of individual directives concerning the workplace, equipment, personal protective equipment, work and visual display units and the handling of heavy loads involving the risk of back injury.

Whilst the law places statutory obligations upon organisations such as those described above it is important that these are implemented efficiently and effectively. In subsequent chapters we shall discuss how this can be achieved.

In summary, the law must be regularly monitored. It is important to establish as early as possible the implication of each set piece of legislation so that appropriate management decisions can be taken. Keeping abreast of current legislation and/or regulations can be time consuming and it is important to know where to seek advice quickly and easily. This will require the establishment of systems and practices designed specifically to inform organisations of their legal obligations at regular intervals. This could include attendance at training courses, seminars and conferences which may be of a national or in-house style. The implications of new regulations upon an organisation are important. The question most likely to be asked a safety manager is in relation to the cost to the organisation. This will require a detailed reply. The procedure for doing this must form part of the daily management plan. These issues are discussed in subsequent chapters dealing with safety management planning and implementation.

With industrial accidents increasing each year it is clear that the law alone is unable to control this epidemic effectively. For effective accident reduction strategies we require a co-ordinated strategy which some refer to as the safety mix or 4 E strategy. This refers to *environmental* strategies, such as making the workplace safer or healthier; *engineering* by making machinery and tools safer; *education* programmes designed to raise the awareness of all problems in the workplace; and *enforcement* which covers the law in this regard. Safety management must be seen as a corporate issue which demands the skills of properly trained safety managers who are capable of utilising all the resources within an organisation. They must have a sound understanding of latest developments within the 4 E philosophy and have sufficient authority within the organisation to implement sound proactive policies.

Further reading

Dewis, M and Stranks, J (1988) *Health and Safety at Work Handbook* (Tolley Publishing Co. Ltd.)

Handley, W (Ed) (1977) *Industrial Safety Handbook* (2nd Ed) (McGraw-Hill)

Stranks, J and Dewis, M (1986) *Health and Safety Practice* (Pitman Publishing Limited)

Howell, R & Barrett, B (1975) *The Health and Safety at Work Act: A Guide for Managers* (Institute of Personnel Management)

Selwyn, N (1982) *Selwyn's Law of Health and Safety at Work* (Butterworths)

Smith, P (Ed) (1989) *Croner's Health and Safety at Work* (Croner Publications)

Health and safety commission leaflets

HASAWA

HSC2 The Health and Safety at Work Act 1974: The Act Outlined
HSC3 The Health and Safety at Work Act 1974: Advice to Employers
HSC5 The Health and Safety at Work Act 1974: Advice to Employees
HSC6 Writing A Safety Policy Statement: Advice to Employers
HSC7 Regulations, Codes of Practice and Guidance Literature
HSC11 Health and Safety at Work Act 1974: Your Obligations to Non-Employees

COSHH

Control of Substances Hazardous to Health Regulations (1988): COSHH Assessments: A step-by-step guide to assessment and the skills needed for it

Introducing COSHH: A Brief Guide for All Employers Introducing Assessment: A simplified Guide for Employers Hazard and Risk Explained

2
Health and safety statistics

Introduction

In the United Kingdom, the Health and Safety Executive (HSE) have an important role in the policing of the workplace in order to ensure that the relevant laws and regulations are obeyed. From time to time it issues general advice concerning certain problems which it has identified as dangerous, unhealthy or injury causing. This will be issued as part of a preventative programme designed either to reduce particular types of situations arising or to warn of specific dangers. It must be remembered that the Executive's main role is that of enforcement and not education, training or publicity; although they may give advice in certain areas. A manager must not, therefore, rely upon the HSE to make his daily management decisions for him, but should use the information that they provide to assist with his strategic planning.

A requirement of the HASAWA is that an organisation will provide certain information to the Executive concerning those accidents and dangerous occurrences which are deemed reportable under the Act. These instructions are found within the Reporting of Injuries, Diseases and Dangerous Occurrences Regulations introduced in 1985 which replaced the Notification of Accidents and Dangerous Occurrences Regulations previously in force since 1980. The regulations are designed to provide a wider definition of injuries, but more importantly, they reinstated the requirement to report injuries causing absences from work of more than three days. The revised regulations did not modify procedures in respect of fatal accidents, details of prosecutions and enforcement notices, ill-health resulting from certain activities eligible for compensation, and death and gas safety statistics. The main changes are in the areas of the 'three-day' injury requirement and the widening of data collected concerning major injuries. The aim of the new regulations is to provide a richer data source which will thus enable the Executive to target its resources more efficiently. From this, it will be able to improve its performance in the areas of inspections and enforcement whilst allowing for the identification of possible sources of occupational danger.

To gather this information the HSE produce a form which is referred to as a Form F2508 which was revised in 1986 to comply with the new regulations outlined above. These forms are purchased in pads of 10 by all organisations required to complete them, i.e. any firm or organisation employing five or more persons. Issued with these are guidance notes which are designed to assist the organisation in the completion of these forms. Detailed guidance notes are provided in another publication referred to as the Health and Safety Booklet HS(R)23. A separate form is required for each person injured. On completion, these forms are to be submitted to the appropriate enforcing authority or nearest HSE office. On receipt of a completed form F2508, the local enforcing authority examines the contents to see if there has been a breach of the law or any of the regulations. It is usual for all fatal accidents to be investigated by the enforcing authority.

From this process, the data collected is compiled and placed onto a computer for subsequent general analysis. The HSE publish data collected via this procedure in their annual report and occasionally publish statistics as a supplement in employment journals. It was not intended to provide data to be used for decision-making by individual managers within their own workplace. One has to look carefully to see how the information produced by the HSE can be used by the safety practitioner.

By the time such data is published, it is usually two years out of date. This information, therefore, can only be used if sufficient company details are also collected and are available to establish relevant trends, but it must be remembered that the objective of collecting this base data in the approved form is to comply with regulations rather than management purposes. At the same time, it is pointed out by the Executive that considerable under-reporting occurs which varies from industry to industry and they estimate this to be as high as 50%. As with most statistics referring to accidents, it has been established that all fatal accidents are reported. From a statistical point of view therefore, using fatal accident data for analysis may be a more reliable alternative providing of course, that the sample size is adequate. In terms of a particular industry or organisation wishing to compare its own performance with that of the national situation, it could be difficult because of the under-reporting. It remains an objective of the Executive to address this problem and for industry to assist with rectifying this anomaly. The Executive has tried to convince industry that cheating or poor compliance with the regulations will not assist in the programme of accident reduction if it is allowed to go unchecked by management. One way of combating this, that is being considered, might be for a closer check between an employee's absence from work under the self-certification scheme and/or a doctor's certificate. If this is introduced companies will have to ensure even greater accuracy in the maintenance of records.

It has been found that some organisations keep no records other than those provided for within the compass of Form F2508. Many do not computerise the data but maintain expensive and cumbersome manual systems. Data collection by some companies is seen as merely meeting the requirements of statutory obligations and few exploit the value of such costly information as a management tool.

The health and safety inspectorate are perceived by many as policemen, and researchers have established that authority figures are considered as 'high status' questioners. It has been shown that people are more likely to be influenced by such questioners because of possible repercussions either to themselves or to their peer groups. For example, some industrial workers have described to insurance companies, on more than one occasion, the strange phenomenon of equipment switching itself on whilst the workforce were on a tea break, in a desperate attempt to limit their liability and apportion blame to someone or something else. Others are tempted to say what they think is required of them and consequently distort certain vital facts in order to cast themselves ina more favourable light.

Other researchers have found that people are more likely to forget facts and may not be able to recall up to half of what they originally perceived when questioned as little as 24 hours after the event. These principles can apply to the role of the safety manager or indeed any manager particularly in disciplinary matters. Whilst the casualty might be excused from recalling certain information concerning an accident because of shock, it is important that procedures are in place which ensure that witnesses are spoken to within 24 hours whenever possible, and that the interview is structured correctly to eliminate some of the problems outlined above.

It must be remembered that it is not uncommon for some organisations to be influenced in the same way and for the same reasons as the individual. To have the Executive or inspectorate crawling all over the place is bad for the image! This might be more important for smaller firms who might have more to lose than the larger company. Whatever the reason, it is now established that the information collected by high status questioners is not reliable and it is no surprise that considerable under-reporting has been identified. This will apply in all situations where there is collection of data for the purposes of possible prosecution. However poor the data collected by statutory bodies such as the HSE is, it is deemed to have sufficient quality to assist with the purpose of law making and for identifying areas for regulation. To be effective the safety manager must devise methods of compensating for these inaccuracies and distortions.

Published information from the HSE is not in sufficient detail to assist the safety manager in programme planning. Contributory factors are not identified in sufficient depth to assist with the identification of trends. Once contributory factors are identified then appropriate remedial measures can be introduced using the safety mix referred to in Chapter 1, i.e. by enforcement, education, engineering, environmental strategies or a mix of some or all four. Making something illegal will not prevent it from happening and there will always be a need to combine enforcement with one or more of the other instruments within the safety mix.

A large number of safety management decisions are based upon opinion and the purpose of using accident data for management decision making and for calculating the safety mix is to reduce relying on 'opinion' as the sole basis for such actions thus saving considerable time and money. It is worth spending a little time familiarising the reader with some basic accident investigation and analytical principles. One of the first problems in collecting data that is both valid and reliable is to define precisely the nature of an accident or dangerous occurrence.

Definition of an accident

There are several definitions of an accident put forward in publications, and the HSE and the Royal Society for the Prevention of Accidents have published their own. In safety management terms, an accident is a random multi-factor event which causes a person or persons to fail to cope with their environment. Likewise, a dangerous occurrence is said to take place when similar random multi-factor events come together in such a way as to cause either a non-injury accident to happen or one that stops short of an accident occurrence taking place.

The word 'random' has a specific meaning and implies the same for accident investigation and analysis work as it does for statistical work generally. Random does not mean 'haphazard' but refers specifically to the premise that every individual accident in a group or series had the same chance of happening. The word chance only refers to truly random events and the application of statistical principles to quantify the probability of certain defined events occurring in the future.

In all accidents one seeks to answer six basic categories of question.

1. *Who?*

   - Who was involved in the accident?
   - Who was the line manager responsible for safety?
   - Who reported the accident?
   - Who was called to respond to the accident?
   - Who was notified?
   - Who should have been notified?
   - Who was responsible?

2. *Why?*

- Why did the accident happen?
- Why were safety practices not applied?
- Why did safety procedures fail to work?

3. *What?*

- What actually happened?
- What were the losses incurred?
- What injuries were sustained?
- What could have been done to avoid the occurrence?

4. *Where?*

- Where did the accident occur?
- Where was the safety officer or line manager at the time of the accident?

5. *When?*

- When did the accident occur?
- When were people aware that an accident could occur?
- When did help arrive at the scene of the accident?

6. *How?*

- How did the event occur? For example, rapidly, slowly, without warning?
- How could safety procedures and practices have been improved?
- How does the organisation learn from the accident occurrence?

There are some basic statistical tests which can be useful for the safety practitioner. These are:

- Frequency tables.
- Probability distributions.
- Sampling Distributions.
- Correlation and Regression.

These are discussed briefly below.

Frequencies

Frequency tables can be illustrated by reference to the following data. The following are times that accidents occurred:

0700	0710	0725	0800	1115	0945	1500	1720	0945	1115	1210	0955	0916
0810	0735	1620	1400	1720	1605	1545	1625	1200	1330	1620	1000	0750
1220	1455	1645	0840	1135	1455	1235	0955	1140	1020	1225	1440	1535

Raw data such as this can be transformed into a more readable form by constructing a frequency distribution as follows:

Accident time	Tally	Frequency
0700 to 0759	/////	5
0800 to 0859	///	3
0900 to 0959	/////	5
1000 to 1059	//	2
1100 to 1159	////	4
1200 to 1259	/////	5
1300 to 1359	/	1
1400 to 1459	////	4
1500 to 1559	///	3
1600 to 1659	/////	5
1700 to 1759	//	2

The groupings into which the times are divided are called classes. The relative frequency of a class is:

$$\frac{\text{frequency in the class}}{\text{total frequency}}$$

Hence the relative frequency of the 1600 to 1659 class is

$$\frac{5}{39} = 0.13$$

Relative frequency is often given as percentage frequency where percentage frequency = relative frequency $\times$ 100. It is possible from this data to present this information in graphical form either by producing a histogram, graph or pie-chart.

Measure of central tendency

The arithmetic mean

This is the sum of all the values in a set of measurements divided by the number of values in the set, i.e. the common average.

The median

This is the half-way value when all the values are ranked in order of magnitude.

The mode

This is that value of the variable which occurs most frequently.

In practice, the mean is the most important of averages; it is nearly always used with a continuous variable. The median is often used in place of the mean since it is so easy to find. The mode is often useful when the variable is discreet, for example when a safety manager would describe the average type of accident as the one of which he had the most.

The concept of probability

The probability that a particular event will occur is measured on a scale between 0 and 1. For example:

One day we shall die	1.0 (certainty)
	0.8
	0.6
Heads or tails?	0.5
	0.4
	0.2
We will never have an accident or	0.1
dangerous occurrence at our works	0.0 (impossibility)

Prior probability

This is based on knowledge prior to an event and rests on the notion of equally likely events. For example, on cutting a pack of cards there is an equal probability of revealing any card. Hence:

$$\text{probability } p = \frac{1}{52}$$

$$p \text{ any spade} = \frac{13}{52} = \frac{1}{4}$$

Post probability

This is based on past experience of the event. Probability can be defined as relative frequency or:

$$\frac{\text{number of times event occurred}}{\text{number of times it was possible for it to occur}}$$

For example, a company found that over a period of several years 20% of its workforce have accidents during training.

$$p = 0.2$$

The addition law

If two events are mutually exclusive (i.e. both cannot occur together) then the probability of either of them occurring is the sum of the probabilities of each event.

(i.e. $p(A \text{ or } B) = p(A) + p(B)$ for mutually exclusive events)

Example: 1,000 enter a safety competition raffle. The safety manager buys 25 tickets and the chairman of the company buys 15. What is the probability that the safety manager or chairman will hold the winning ticket?

Solution:

$$p(\text{SM or Chairman}) = p(\text{SM}) + p(\text{Chairman})$$

$$= \frac{25}{1000} + \frac{15}{1000}$$

$$= \frac{40}{1000} = 0.04$$

Example: If the probability of finding zero defective tyres in the vehicle compound is 0.82 and the probability of finding just one defective tyre is 0.16, what is the probability of finding not more than one defective (i.e. zero or one defective).

Solution: $p(0 \text{ or } 1) = p(0) + p(1) = 0.82 + 0.16 = 0.98$

The multiplication law for independent events

If two events are independent in that one event is no way affected by the other, the probability of both events occurring together is the product of the individual probabilities.

i.e. $p(A \text{ and } B) = p(A) \times p(B)$ for independent events.

Example: A coin is tossed twice. Find the probability of obtaining two heads.

Solution: $p(\text{head and head}) = p(\text{head}) \times p(\text{head})$

$$= \frac{1}{2} \times \frac{1}{2} = \frac{1}{4} = 0.25$$

Example: A piece of machinery contains 10 parts, all of which must function perfectly if the machine is to work safely and not cause danger to the operator. The probability that each individual component will not fail is 0.99. What is the probability that the machine will work safely?

Solution: $p(\text{all 10 parts work}) = (0.99)^{10} = 0.904$

The complementary rule

The sum of the probabilities of all possible outcomes of a situation is equal to 1.0. This rule follows from the addition law. For example, if the probabilities of three possible outcomes of a certain event are:

$p(A)$, $p(B)$ and $p(C)$, then $p(A) + p(B) + p(C) = 1.0$

The conditional probability

The multiplication law also deals with the case where the probability of the second event is conditional on the first event, i.e. where the events are not independent. The rule states that:

'The probability of the joint occurrence of events A and B is the product of the probability of A and the conditional probability of B, given that A has occurred.'

i.e. $p(A \text{ and } B) = p(A) \times p\dfrac{(B)}{A}$

Example: A store room contains 17 serviceable chainsaws and three which are defective. Two chainsaws are selected at random without replacement back into store. What is the probability of obtaining one serviceable (S) and one un-serviceable (U) chainsaw in that order?

Solution: $p(S \text{ and } U) = p(S) \times p\dfrac{(U)}{S} = \dfrac{17}{20} \times \dfrac{3}{19} = \dfrac{51}{380}$

Example: A batch of 30 reflective jackets contains three which are defective. Two jackets are selected at random from the batch and issued to workers. What is the probability that one good and one bad will be selected?

Solution: There are two mutually exclusive ways of gaining the prescribed event; whether a good jacket followed by a bad jacket or vice versa. If A = the good jacket and B = the bad jacket selected then the probability required is:

$$p(A) \times p\frac{(B)}{A} + p(B) \times p\frac{(A)}{B}$$

$$\frac{27}{30} \times \frac{3}{29} + \frac{3}{30} \times \frac{27}{29} = \frac{27}{290} + \frac{27}{290} = \frac{27}{145}$$

The concept of probability distributions

There are a number of standard probability distributions which serve as models to fit particular situations. Three important theoretical distributions are:

1. The binomial;
2. The Poisson;
3. The normal.

The binomial test

This distribution, as its name implies, is concerned with situations involving two 'names' or 'classes'. For example, whether a component in a piece of equipment is faulty or not; whether an employee will be injured or not. The simplest way to understand this situation is whether a tossed coin will land on heads or tails. Suppose two unbiased coins are tossed 16 times with the following results:

Number of heads	0	1	2	(Frequency distribution)
Frequency	6	7	3	

This frequency distribution could be used to construct a probability distribution similar to that illustrated in Figure 2.1A but such a distribution based on post probability and involving a small sample is, not surprisingly, unreliable. This is a situation where prior probability can be used. Given that $p(\text{head}) = 0.5$, it is a simple matter to calculate that $p(\text{no head in two goes}) = 0.25$, $p(\text{one head in two goes}) = 0.5$ and $p(\text{two heads in two goes}) = 0.25$. The theoretical probability has thus been determined. This is a simple binomial distribution. Suppose, therefore, that six coins are tossed, then there is a binomial distribution to give the probability of having no heads, one head, two heads and so on. Once again, work on the premise that $p(\text{head}) = 0.5$.

Taking a practical example, suppose the works' canteen know that in a recent consignment of eggs, 10% are bad. $p(\text{bad egg}) = 0.1$. What is the probability of randomly selecting six eggs and having 0, 1, 2, 3, etc bad eggs in our half dozen sample? Here, the basic premise $p(\text{bad egg}) = 0.1$ is based on post probability (empirical probability) in that someone has tested a large sample, but the distribution is of the same type. It concerns a two state (good/bad) situation or a binomial distribution.

It remains to state the general expression for binomial distribution as:

$$p(r) = \frac{n}{r!(n-r)!} \; q^{n-r} \cdot p^r$$

This formula states that the probability of the event we are interested in happening r times out of a total possible number of n times (the sample

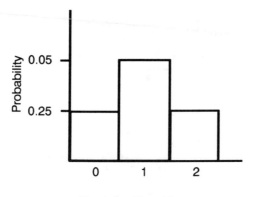

Figure 2.1A

Theoretical probability distribution for
a number of heads obtained in two
tosses

size) when the probability of the event occurring in isolation is p and the
probability of it not occurring is q. $(p+q=1.0)$.

Taking the egg problem, sample size, $n = 6$, probability of selecting a
bad egg, $p = 0.1$, hence:

$$p(0) = \frac{6!}{0! \cdot 6!} \cdot (0.9)^6 \cdot (0.1)^0 = 1 \cdot (0.9)^6 \cdot 1 = (0.9)^6 = 0.531$$

$$p(1) = \frac{6!}{1! \cdot 5!} \cdot (0.9)^5 \cdot (0.1) = 6 \cdot (0.9)^5 \cdot 1 = .6(0.9)^5 = 0.354$$

$$[0! = 1]$$

and so on.

In this way, we can find $p(2) = 0.098$, $p(3) = 0.015$, $p(4) = 0.001$ whilst
$p(5)$ and $p(6)$ are very much less than 0.001. The probability distribution
would be as shown in figure 2.1B.

Example: A further example can be shown by a purchasing sampling
scheme which specifies that a sample of 10 items be taken and that the consignment be accepted only if the sample contains no dangerously defective
parts. What is the probability that a consignment which is 10% defective
will be accepted?

Solution: Given that $n = 10$, $p = 0.1$, $q = 0.9$, what is $p(0)$?

$$p(0) = \frac{10!}{0!10!} (0.9)^{10} \cdot (0.1)^0 = (0.9)^{10} = 0.349$$

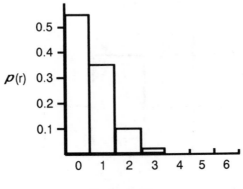

Figure 2.1B

Binomial distribution for $n = 6$

$$p = 0.1$$
$$q = 0.9$$

In other words, 34.9% of such consignments would be accepted by this sampling scheme when the defective level was 10%.

The mean and standard deviation of a binomial distribution

Notation: When dealing with theoretical distributions, or population distributions as opposed to sample distributions, it is usual to use the symbols μ and σ for mean and standard deviation respectively. For binomial distribution we have:

$$\mu = n \cdot p \text{ and } \sigma = n \cdot pq$$

Limiting forms of binomial distribution

A binomial distribution provides a useful tool for the analysis of problems when n is fairly small. When n is large (say >30) then calculations are tedious and tables of binomial coefficients $n!/r!(n-r)!$, are not readily available.

There are two limiting forms of a binomial which can be used when n is large:

- A Poisson distribution when n is large and p is very small (or cannot be defined).
- A normal distribution when n is large and p is neither very small nor very large.

An illustration of the relationship is given in Figure 2.1C.

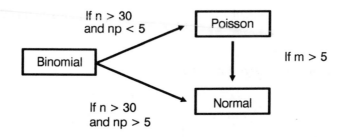

Figure 2.1C

The relationship between distributions

The way a binomial distribution approaches a limiting form known as a Poisson distribution (named after the French mathematician) as n is increased and p is decreased is illustrated below.

n	p	$\mu = n.p$	$p(0)$	$p(1)$	$p(2)$	$p(3)$	$p(4)$	$p(5)$	$p(6)$
4	1/4	1	0.316	0.442	0.211	0.047	0.004	—	—
10	1/10	1	0.349	0.387	0.194	0.058	0.011	0.001	0.001
100	1/100	1	0.366	0.370	0.185	0.061	0.015	0.003	0.001
1000	1/1000	1	0.368	0.368	0.184	0.061	0.015	0.003	0.001
10000	1/10000	1	0.368	0.368	0.184	0.061	0.015	0.003	0.001

This means that provided n is large enough and p small enough, the binomial distribution becomes a fixed set of probabilities for a given value of μ. In other words, if n is large and p is small, the probability distribution can be specified by a single parameter, the mean, where $\mu = n.p$.

Poisson showed that the fixed binomial probabilities could also be obtained from the general expression:

$$p(r) = \frac{e^{-\mu} \cdot \mu^r}{r!}$$

where $p(r)$ is the probability of r events and μ is the mean.

This expression makes it possible to tabulate these distributions easily and so avoid laborious binomial calculations. Individual terms in a Poisson distribution are thus:

r	0	1	2	3	4	...	r
$p(r)$	$e^{-\mu}$	$e^{-\mu} \cdot \mu$	$\dfrac{e^{-\mu} \mu^2}{2!}$	$\dfrac{e^{-\mu} \mu^3}{3!}$	$\dfrac{e^{-\mu} \mu^4}{4!}$	...	$\dfrac{e^{-\mu} \mu^r}{r!}$

It can be shown mathematically that for a Poisson distribution $\mu = \sigma^2$. That is, variance = mean.

Application of the Poisson distribution

There are two main types of application. These are:

1. As an approximation to the binomial when n is large and p is small.

Example: Mass produced safety glass for use in safety goggles of which 1% are defective and are packed in boxes of 100. What percentage of boxes will have:

- No defective goggles
- One defective pair.

Solution: Given that $n = 100$ and $p = 0.1$ $(q = 0.99)$

We have $\mu = np = 1.0$

From the Poisson tables, we have $p(0) = 0.3679$ and $p(1) = 0.3679$. In other words, 36.79% of boxes will have zero defective goggles and 36.79% of boxes will have one defective pair.

Note: It can be deduced from this that 26.42% (100.00 − 73.58) will have more than one defective pair of goggles (use the complimentary probability rule).

2. The second type of application is where p is very small, but difficult to define and n is large and difficult to define. In such cases, the binomial is not applicable but provided the mean can be specified, a Poisson will provide a means of analysis. Typical situations are:

- Accidents per week in a factory.
- Dangerous occurrences per week in a factory.

Each of these examples is concerned with isolated events in a continuum of time and space. The number of occurrences can be stated but not the number of non-occurrences. Thus it is impossible to define n and p. However, the total number of occurrences allows for us to state a mean number of occurrences (μ) in a given unit of time and space, etc.

Example: Fragile parcels arrive randomly at the loading bay at an average of 180 per hour. What is the probability that during a one-minute period no parcel will arrive and what is the probability there will be more than one arrival in a 20-second period?

Solution: For a one-minute period $\mu = 3$
From the tables $p(0) = 0.5$
For a 20-second period $\mu = 1$

From the tables $p(0) = 0.368$
From the tables $p(1) = 0.368$

Hence, p (more than 1) $= 1.0 - (0.368 + 0.368) = 0.264$

It is often necessary to calculate the probability of x or more occurrences of an event and in order to avoid having to add a set of successive probabilities, use can be made of a Poisson summation chart. These allow the safety manager to read off at a glance the probability of at least any given number of occurrences for any stated mean. A summation chart is given in Figure 2.1D.

Example: Using this chart, find the probability of an accident occurring at least three times in the washroom, where $\mu = 0.5$.

Solution: The required probability $= p$ (3 or more occurrences) $= p(3) + p(4) + p(5) + \cdots = 1.0 - p$ (2 or less). On the chart, find the intersection of the curved line $C = 2$ and the vertical line $\mu = 0.5$. From this intersection, take a horizontal reading across to the vertical probability scale to obtain p (2 or less occurrences) $= 0.98$ (approximately). Therefore, p (3 or more) $= 1.0 - 0.98 = 0.02$.

The normal distribution

The binomial and Poisson distributions are concerned with discrete variables, but it is often necessary to work with continuous variables. The

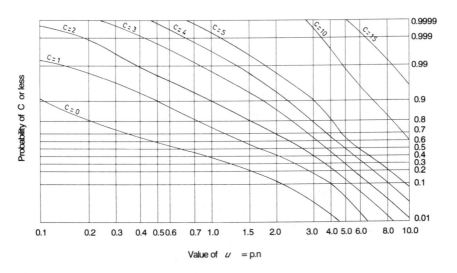

Figure 2 .1 D

Poisson or Thorndyke chart

normal distribution is the most important continuous distribution in statistics since it describes the many distributions of variable encountered in many disciplines.

Normal distributions are characteristically bell-shaped. Just as there are families of binomial distributions prescribed by the parameters p and n, so also are there many normal distributions (an infinite number) prescribed exactly by two parameters known as the mean and the standard deviation.

Example: Steel safety guards are being manufactured to a specification of 30 mm diameter and are acceptable if they are within the tolerance limits 30.1 mm and 29.9 mm. If the actual production indicates that the diameters are distributed about a mean of 30.02 mm with a standard deviation of 0.06 mm then estimate the proportion of safety guards which are acceptable.

Solution: when $x = 29.9$, $z = \dfrac{29.9 - 30.02}{0.06} = -2.0$

when $x = 30.10$, $z = \dfrac{30.1 - 30.02}{0.06} = 1.33$

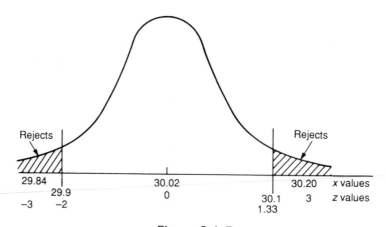

Figure 2.1 E

From normal probability tables, the rejected proportion (i.e. the shaded area) is $0.0901 + 0.0228 = 0.1129$. Hence the required proportion is $1 - 0.1129 = 0.8854$ or 88.54%.

The normal distribution approximates the Poisson distribution when μ is large. The approximation is similar to that of the normal approximation to the binomial distribution except that $\sigma = \mu$. In practice the approximation gives crude results when $5 < \mu < 15$ but it is quite safe when $\mu \geqslant 15$. The approximation improves as μ increases.

Example: The mean number of accidents in a factory is 16 per year. Find the probability that more than 22 accidents will happen in any given year.

Solution: Assuming a Poisson distribution, then since $\mu \geqslant 15$ we may use the normal approximation with $\mu = 16$ and $\sigma = 4$

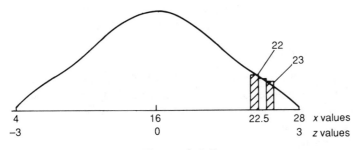

Figure 2.1 F

When $x = 22.5$, $z = \dfrac{22.5 - 16}{4} = \dfrac{6.5}{4} = 1.625$

Hence from the tables, the required probability $= 0.0521$.

The chi-square test

There are several tests concerned with comparing a set of observed frequencies with a set predicted on the basis of some hypothesis. In this way, the hypothesis is tested. The tests depend on the distribution known as χ^2. The shape of the distribution depends on a sample size and so there are a whole set of χ^2 distributions corresponding to different sample sizes. As with other distributions, however, the distribution is not usually associated directly with sample size n, but is associated indirectly to sample size by

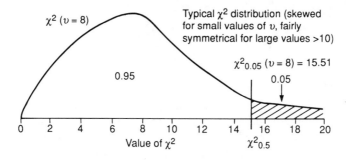

Figure 2.1 G

being described in terms of degrees of freedom (v or df). The number of degrees of freedom depends on sample size. Thus we might refer to χ^2 ($df = 5$); meaning the distribution with 5 degrees of freedom.

Tables of χ^2 give values of χ^2 corresponding to different 'tail' areas (e.g. $\chi^2 0.05$, $\chi^2 0.01$ also, $\chi^2 0.95$) for a range of values of degrees of freedom. In the above example, it can be seen that χ^2 has a probability of 0.5 of exceeding 15.5 when $v = 8$. Its most likely value is about 6.

Goodness of fit tests

Given a set of observed frequencies, $O_1, O_2, O_3, \ldots$ and a corresponding set of expected frequencies of $E_1, E_2, E_3, \ldots$ which have been calculated on the basis of some hypothesis. Are the discrepancies sufficiently great to cause the rejection of the hypothesis?

If discrepancy is measured by:

$$\frac{(O_1 - E_1)^2}{E_1} + \frac{(O_2 - E_2)^2}{E_2} + \frac{(O_3 - E_3)^2}{E_3} + \cdots = \sum \left[\frac{(O - E)^2}{E} \right]$$

then for a large number of repeated samples taken from a parent population $\Sigma(O - E)^2/E$ will be distributed according to a χ^2 distribution. This is not a definition of χ^2 but it is usual to write:

$$\chi^2 = \sum \frac{(O - E)^2}{E}$$

Example: The Safety Manager in a Local Authority has noted the day of the week each of the 100 school accidents occurring in his area took place. He is examining school accidents and wants to know if the apparent high frequency of accidents on Mondays is significant. His data are as follows:

	Frequency
Monday	25 accidents
Tuesday	17 accidents
Wednesday	15 accidents
Thursday	23 accidents
Friday	20 accidents
Total	100 accidents

Solution: These data can be regarded as a sample of accidents and we can set up a hypothesis that it was taken from a population in which frequencies are the same on all days. Sampling from such a population would not be expected to exactly reflect the population; the question is, how much discrepancy can be expected from sampling fluctuations alone?

- Hypothesis 1 = Accidents are equiprobable on all days.
- Hypothesis 2 = Accidents are more likely on some days than others.

Significance level: 0.05

Sampling distribution $\chi^2 = \sum \dfrac{(O-E)^2}{E}$

O	E	$(O-E)$	$(O-E)^2$	$\dfrac{(O-E)^2}{E}$
25	20	5	25	1.25
17	20	-3	9	0.45
15	20	-5	25	1.25
23	20	3	9	0.45
20	20	0	0	0.00
				$3.40 = \chi^2$

Region of rejection $\chi^2 > \chi^2_{0.05}$ $(v = 4)$ i.e. $\chi^2 > 9.49$.

Decision: Accept Hypothesis 1 as the discrepancies are not significant, accidents are equiprobable.

Notes:

Degrees of freedom – the above problem involved frequencies recorded according to one criterion of classification (day of week). The frequencies formed a 'one-way' classification table. For $1 \times k$ tables (1 row, k columns). Here, $k = 5$. For $1 \times k$ tables, the degrees of freedom $= k - 1$. Regard it as the total frequencies (100) therefore freedom exists to specify only $(k - 1)$ frequencies because the last remaining one becomes determined by difference from the total.

There are several other statistical tests which a safety manager might wish to use. Regrettably it is not possible to include them all here and a reading list is provided at the end of this chapter. The above example used the time element within the accident framework. Other factors might be included and an example of how these can be obtained is summarised in the example below.

It is very rare that an effect is brought about by a single cause. In fact, we find in accidents that a combination of circumstances is often necessary and the absence of even one of them can be enough to prevent the occurrence of the accident. For example, examine the factors below which were involved in a recent accident. If such factors are to be collected, then a standard format should be agreed for all accidents (see Chapter 5). Further information concerning sampling techniques is given in Appendix 2 and 3.

A typical accident sequence

1. A toolsetter wakes one morning with a hangover caused by drinking too much alcohol the night before;
2. Because he was drinking until 2 am his blood alcohol level is above that which would enable him to drive a motor car. This does not worry him because he decides to cycle to work;
3. He is late getting up and his wife argues with him about him coming in late the night before. He storms out of the house and makes his way to work;
4. He arrives late for work and the foreman disciplines him for his lateness. His workmates make jokes at him;
5. He switches on his lathe and is heavy handed with his tools because of his state of mind and a consequent lack of concentration;
6. A piece of work drops off the work bench onto the floor. He dusts it and fixes it to the lathe as he is currently working on it;
7. The piece of work was damaged in the fall but the toolsetter did not check his work because he does not feel well and is not alert;
8. He fixes it to his lathe and switches it on. Somebody talks to him and distracts his attention;
9. A piece from the lathe flies out and seriously damages the operator's hands.

An example like this raises many questions and the gathering of the facts is important for accident analysis purposes. Diagrams illustrating the contributory factors involved in an accident are given in Figures 2.2, 2.3 and 2.3A.

Having obtained the contributory factors in several accidents, the chi-square test allows us to reassure ourselves that any observed differences of a proportion are greater than could reasonably be attributed to chance.

Statistically the six categories of question identified above can be linked to certain kinds of measures, descriptions and analysis.

Data for accident analysis can be collected in four forms. These are:

1. *Nominal* where, for example, the sex of an injured party can be noted;
2. *Ordinal* where one ranks processes in terms of their perceived danger;
3. *Interval* where one might note the number of accidents that occur in a week where there can only be a whole number of accidents; and
4. *Ratio* where one can be most precise in measuring a factor such as the exact temperature at which a furnace was operating immediately prior to an accident. Generally the more one progresses through the list the better, as far as the quality of the data is concerned.

Having collected data there are a number of questions that can be posed on the basis of certain common procedures. These are now discussed.

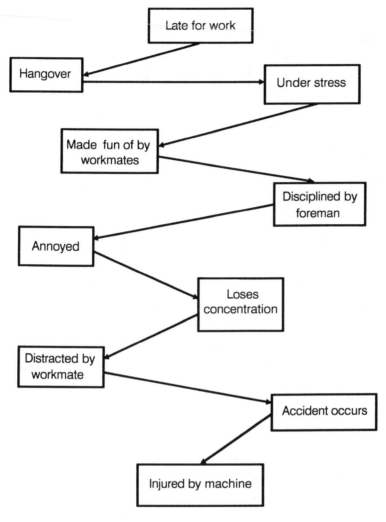

Figure 2.2
Contributory factors in one accident

The first thing that one has to look at in the context of accident data is the frequency and distribution of accidents. This can be amplified by looking at measures of central tendency (averages, means, modes and/or medians) and distribution (variances, standard deviations, percentage or quartile distributions, skew, etc). One then has a formidable array of presenting this data either as graphs, pictograms, histograms, pie charts or more specialist probability charts.

However the real value of the data is revealed when one starts to

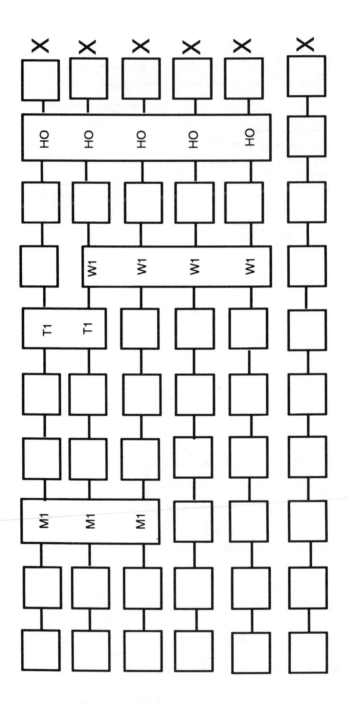

Figure 2.3

How some common contributory factors come together
to form the accident X

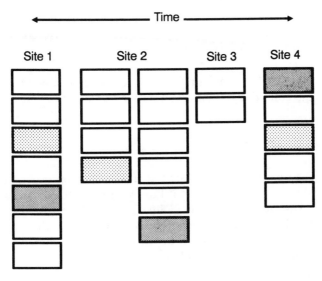

Figure 2.3A

Accident contributory factor groups
distributed by time

tabulate the data in accordance with identified principles in the form of
cross tabulations. For example, in looking at your data one finds that the
majority of accidents happen to employees who have been employed for
less than a year or that male employees are seven times more likely to have
an accident than female employees.

The next set of questions that have to be asked relate to a comparison
of the mean number of accidents that occur. One wants to know if one
plant has a higher rate of accidents than other plants or one company more
accidents than a rival organisation. Similar questions can be asked about
the shape of the distributions of accidents.

More important, one might want to see if an accident is associated with
other factors and a powerful array of correlation techniques exist to help
answer this question.

More advanced statistics enable one to answer questions such as the
following.

- Is it possible to determine why certain events culminate in an
  accident whereas others only result in a dangerous occurrence?
- Are there any common factors which can be isolated to establish the
  cause or consequence of accident occurrences?
- Are there any factors which explain why certain categories of accident
  happen to cluster around certain processes or certain times of day?

- Can one predict how variation in procedures will contribute to accident incidence?
- Can one model or simulate the circumstances in which accidents happen?
- Can trends in accidents or types of accidents be identified?
- Can the collection of data be improved and its reliability checked?

Accident philosophy

Accident investigation considers these events as random occurrences from the standpoint of time and location. For example, if the accidents for any given workplace are arranged on a time scale in the order in which they occurred, it will be noted that the intervals between each accident will vary considerably and will continue to do so whether the component of risk inherent at the workplace is stable or not. From this assumption it may be concluded that accidents occur randomly in time as shown in Figure 2.4.

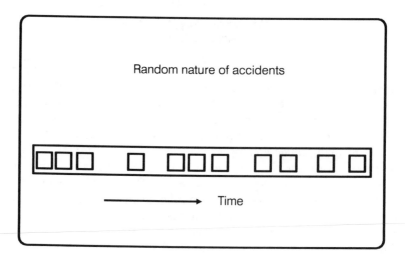

Figure 2.4

If continuous time is divided into equal parts, such as months in any given year, then it will be observed that accidents may be randomly distributed throughout the time scale as shown in Figure 2.5.

This will explain why accident totals will fluctuate randomly above and below the long-term average whether the inherent workplace risk remains the same or not.

If, however, the distribution looked like the second part of Figure 2.5, one might infer that for some reason to be established, the summer months

The distribution of accidents by time

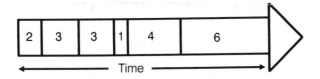

Distribution of accidents by month

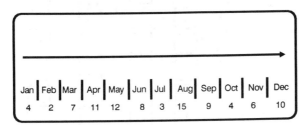

Figure 2.5

of June, July and August were high risk months. The reason might be that concentration is reduced in hot weather, or that people forget safety procedures after a fortnight's holiday, or some other reason that would have to be established.

Cross-tabulation

This basic feature of accidents being random in time is used by many accident investigators particularly those involved in road accident analysis. A basic assessment will highlight any notable grouping of accidents or contributory factors and the use of basic statistical tests can be used to test for any difference in trends from those which were expected. A change in the frequency of accidents by time is a good means of detecting the unusual factor in the occurrence of accidents in a particular group for it can be compared with conditions prevailing at other times. This is the basis for evaluating the efficiency and effectiveness of any remedial measures which are introduced.

Graphical analysis

If the risk attributed to the workplace was constant throughout the day then it would be reasonable to assume that accidents would be randomly distributed by time and location as shown in Figure 2.6.

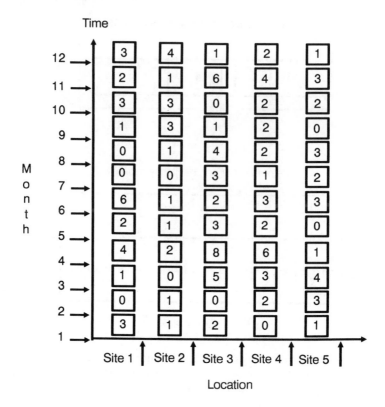

Figure 2.6

Distribution of accidents by time and location

However, research has shown that this is not so and that accident risk is higher at some locations than at others. Where the accident risk is higher at certain locations, then the accidents or dangerous occurrences will tend to cluster at those locations. Such sites are referred to as 'hazardous'.

The multi-factor accident

Many people use the term 'cause' as the sole reason for an accident occurring. Insurance companies in particular like to refer to *the cause* of an accident. Enforcement agencies use the term readily. It has been stressed above that there are no true examples of the sole cause of an accident. Cause must be seen as a global term which will cover the many factors associated with the occurrence of the accident. Each set of circumstances leading up to an accident or dangerous occurrence is unique and as such each accident must be seen to be unique. However, common factors involved in each set of circumstances irrespective of numbers can be categorised into the following very broad headings:

1. The Employee;
2. The Environment;
3. The Equipment.

The environment includes the workplace and equipment includes all dangerous substances.

These basic headings form the link between the various factors which are associated with the actual accident happening. This link, therefore, is considered unique.

The analytical phase

We have seen how the various factors link in the chain of events which lead up to an accident happening where an employee fails to cope with his environment. Using the example used above then, had the employee not drunk so much alcohol and got home earlier, he would probably not have suffered the consequences of his late night out. This in turn may have allowed for his arrival at work on time and in a better frame of mind. He may not have dropped his work onto the floor and his work mates would probably not have distracted his attention thus preventing him from hurting his hand. This chain of events should be considered with groups of accidents at a particular location as a series of events in time. As each set

Accident

	1	2	3	4	5	6
Factor 1	▓		▓	▓		▓
Factor 2	▓		▓	▓	▓	
Factor 3			▓			
Factor 4	▓					▓
Factor 5						
Factor 6		▓				
Factor 7	▓		▓		▓	
Factor 8					▓	
Factor 9						
Factor 10					▓	

Figure 2.7

Contributory factor identification chart

of circumstances in the chain of events, in their entirety, are unique. The clustering of the accidents is indicative of the likelihood that one or more factors may be links which are common to several of the chains of events. A diagram illustrating the chain of events is given in Figure 2.7, and shows how some of the circumstances may be common to some of the accidents.

Here the accident investigator starts his analysis with only the basic data available from the F2508 (or equivalent report form). After verification of those data the investigator will seek to establish and understand the main composition of each set of events in the chain from discussions with colleagues, witnesses or the casualty himself.

Coping with the environment

Research studies have identified human errors and failings contributing with other factors to the vast majority of accidents and dangerous occurrences. Failure to cope with circumstances leading up to and prevailing at the time of the accident will be evident in most situations. It is important that all accident investigations consider human error and it is therefore vital to identify prime factors involving human behaviour as a major part of the study, together with human reaction to unsafe conditions within the workplace, which should also be included.

Objectives of accident investigation

There are two primary objectives of accident investigation and these are:

1. **Accident reduction.** Obtaining sufficient data to facilitate the systematic reduction in the type and severity of accidents in the workplace. These will fall into the four categories identified above as the safety mix and will provide information of sufficient quality to balance the mix to best effect.
2. **Accident prevention.** This relates to the application of safety principles in new design and technology whether it is in the area of automation or improvements to the style and type of manufacturing methodology employed in the workplace.

Both of these strategies have to be based upon recognised opportunities which are available to the designer, engineer, enforcer or general safety practitioner for influencing and preventing all forms of accidents from happening. Both strategies require the co-operation of everyone to succeed and must not be left to one person to solve alone. Only in this way can effective strategies be employed.

It is important that the safety representative is involved in all accident investigations and that he is fully aware of the aims and objectives of the data collection process. It must be appreciated that in certain circumstances accurate data collection can be hampered by the 'high status' phenomenon and care must be exercised so that the investigation is not seen as a purely disciplinary or enforcement procedure. Such investigations may assist in the formulation of rules and safe procedures but should not be seen as a means to an end. Obvious breaches of established procedures, however, must be dealt with in the interests of everyone concerned.

Accident investigation methodology

Good accident investigation techniques require a good data base from which to work. It is necessary systematically to obtain information relating to accidents which will enable the safety manager to identify contributory factors. Chapter 5 discusses some ways that this might be achieved but at this stage it is necessary to develop some further basic statistical methods. The purpose of surveys is to obtain information about accidents. To obtain this information is never free of cost and can be expensive in terms of time and money. Before collecting any sort of data, thought must be given about how relevant it is to the needs of the situation, how it can be analysed usefully and how it can be obtained. The following, is a simple description of a very complex subject and further reading references are given at the end of the chapter.

Terminology

Population

A collection of measurements which forms the subject of the exercise (or part of it). The measurements need not necessarily be related to people but in any case the word 'population' refers to data. The population needs to be clearly specified in advance of any data collection exercise being undertaken.

Element

An object, person or thing on which a measurement is taken.

Census

A survey which examines the whole population.

Sample frame

A list of elements from which a sample can be taken. Ideally, the sample frame should contain all the elements corresponding to the defined population. For example, the electoral register would be a good sampling frame for a study concerned with all the adults in a community but it would not contain all elements because of the impracticability of having a daily updated register.

Sample

A collection of elements drawn from a sample frame. Measurements of various characteristics are made on the sample with the aim of drawing conclusions about those characteristics in the population. That is, sample statistics are determined in order to make inferences about population parameters.

Planning data collection

The population

Deciding on the population might be more difficult than at first thought. In some factory environments the population might mean 'the workforce' but others may have to include members of the public. Consider the population of interest to a trade union official who wishes to determine attitudes to some proposed new piece of legislation. It should be apparent that there are occasions when the population can be defined with precision but the sample frame may present difficulties. There are also occasions when the population exists as a concept only and has an indefinite size. Even if the problem stemming from difficulties in population definition cannot be resolved, it is at least essential to make explicit any assumptions which need to be stated.

What should coverage be aimed at?

Should the aim be to cover the entire population (assuming that the population is finite), i.e. conduct a census, or should the aim be to cover part of the population? For example, should the entire workforce be covered in a survey regarding attitudes to safety clothing or should only specific groups be targeted such as those who have been involved in an accident or incident in the past three years? The advantages and disadvantages of a census v survey are compared in Figure 2.8. Clearly the extent of any differences between a census and a survey will depend on the size of the fraction of the population in a sample survey. A survey concerning 50% of the population will differ little from a census: a survey covering 0.1% of the population will exhibit the difference in Figure 2.8 to a marked degree. The reciprocal of the sampling fraction is sometimes known as the raising factor.

	Census	Survey
1	Exact within the limits of data collection.	Limited precision depending on survey design.
2	Problems of analysis are few.	Analysis is complex.
3	Expensive	Relatively cheap.
4	Slow	Relatively fast.
5	Detail on issues covered is very limited for a given cost.	Issues can be covered in fine detail for a given cost.

Figure 2.8

Census v Survey

What accuracy is needed?

There are three related concepts. These are:

1. accuracy;
2. precision;
3. bias.

The *accuracy* of a particular estimate based on a sample is simply how much it differs from the true population value. Since the population value is not known, the accuracy of any estimate stemming from a survey is not known.

Precision is a concept based upon the idea of a sampling distribution, ie., that sampling fluctuations can lead to varying error when estimating a population parameter on the basis of a sampling statistic. The precision of a sampling device is measured by the standard error of the statistic concerned. Principal determinants of the size of the standard error are:

1. The inherent variability of the characteristic being measured; and
2. The size of the sample used.

High variability and small samples both make for a large standard error and hence lead to estimates having poor precision. For a given required precision the necessary sample size can be calculated given knowledge of (or an estimate of) the variability. Alternatively, given a certain cost limit, the permitted sample size and hence the survey precision can be calculated.

If a mean of the sampling distribution of a statistic is not equal to the actual population value, that statistic is said to be a *biased* estimator (s is a biased estimator of σ; m is an unbiased estimator of μ). Bias can also be introduced to the survey in several other ways. The following are examples:

- Sample frame does not cover the population adequately.
- Non-random sampling (unconscious exclusion of a part of the population OR some sections of the population are impossible to find or refuse to co-operate).
- An error in the data collection process. For example, respondents to a questionnaire give false replies; a misunderstanding involved in abstracting secondary data or an interviewer leads when questioning.

Precision and bias, unlike accuracy, are essentially long term concepts, based upon the idea of repeated sampling. Their importance lies in the fact that it is not possible to state the accuracy of a set of results. In order to examine the accuracy of results it is necessary to examine the validity of the sampling scheme used to obtain them.

Selecting elements from the sampling frame

Two main aims are involved in sample design. These are:

1. To avoid *bias*; and
2. To achieve maximum *precision* for a given cost.

To avoid bias there are several forms of 'probability sample' which can be considered. We have already stated above that 'random' does not mean haphazard, for humans are not very good at picking things at random. Interviewers tend to pick 'average looking' people (less variability than really exists) or do not visit certain types of household or speak to certain types of people.

A probability sample involves a method of selection which gives each of the elements in the population to be covered a calculable probability of being selected. If this condition is not met then the precision of an estimate cannot be assessed. With simple random sampling, each element of the population has an equal chance of being selected. The statistical analysis of simple random samples is relatively easy but it is often possible to devise alternative sample designs which achieve greater precision for a given cost. The most frequently used designs are compared below on page 96.

Pre-testing and pilot surveys

In practice, all survey work should be tested when all the planning phases have been completed. It should already be apparent that a considerable knowledge of the subject-matter and the population is needed *before* the survey can be carried out effectively. If a safety manager delegates this research aspect of his work to another agency he will still need a basic understanding of these statistical concepts in order to assist effectively in the planning phase of the project.

A few test interviews, a few trial questionnaires, a preliminary attempt to abstract data from records, or a trial of the vehicle to be used for collecting the data, are all important and can save considerable time, effort and cost. Apart from certain information given below, which can only be obtained by a pilot study, a pre-test will usually raise a number of issues previously overlooked. The main points to be considered are as follows:

- Adequacy of the sample frame. By actually using the sample frame, its completeness, accuracy, up-to-dateness and convenience can be tested. Check for defects.
- Variability of the population. It is already apparent that some knowledge of the variability (σ) of the characteristic being measured is necessary before the sample size necessary for any given precision can be calculated. A pilot survey will not yield the value of σ, but it will enable an estimate to be made.
- Non-response rate to be expected. A high non-response rate can ruin a survey because of the likelihood of serious bias. If non-response appears to be a problem then modification or a complete change in the method of data collection might be necessary.
- Adequacy of the questionnaire to be used. This often is the most valuable function of the pilot survey. It is difficult to prescribe how to recognise weaknesses, but the investigator conducting the test will be provided with ideas for improvement.
- Coding and analysis. Data processing staff should have been consulted in the planning stages. The pilot survey will provide for a check between the safety manager and the data processing staff that will input the data. Additional and/or alternative types of analysis may be suggested by the pilot data.

Survey design

The objective of a sample survey is to make an inference about the population on the basis of information contained in the sample. Population parameters, such as the mean, μ, and percentage, ¦¦, are typically the subject of study. Three factors affect the quantity of information contained in the sample and hence the precision of estimates of population parameters:

1. The amount of variability of the characteristic being measured;
2. The size of the sample taken;
3. The procedure used in selecting the sample.

The procedure used needs to take into account items 1 and 2 above and is known overall as the *survey design*. Below, the advantages of five basic survey designs are discussed. The task of the investigator is to select from the various alternatives that design which is feasible and which gives the required precision at the minimum cost. Part of the skill in survey design lies in utilising information about the variability of the characteristics in different parts of the population.

Simple random sample

This is the simplest design conceptually, but not necessarily the easiest to implement. It requires that the sample to be taken has an equal chance of being selected. This can be done by assigning a serial number to each element in the sampling frame and then selecting a sample by the use of random number tables. The advantage of this method is that statistical analysis is relatively simple to undertake. The disadvantage is that the method does not make use of any knowledge the investigator may have of variations in population parameters in different parts of the population.

Systematic sample

If a sample is taken by randomly selecting one element from the first k elements in the sample frame and then every kth element thereafter, a one in k systematic sample is obtained. The sampling interval, k, is chosen to produce a sample of the required size. Such a procedure would be convenient for taking a sample of workers from a payroll, for example, or a sample of accident casualties from a sample of accident casualty records. If the listing of items is taken in random order, then this procedure is equivalent to taking a random sample.

If the listing of items is ordered (say in salary order), then a systematic sample often results in a smaller standard error than does a random sample. If the listing has a periodic arrangement and the sampling interval coincides with the periodic interval of the list, or a multiple of it, then a systematic sample will produce very poor results.

The advantages are:

- A very simple procedure for selecting a sample, and, if the listing is ordered better precision is obtained than with a simple random sample of the same size.

The disadvantage is:

- A need to ensure that listing is not periodic.

Stratified random sampling

A stratified random sample is obtained by first separating the population elements into groups, or strata, so that each element belongs to only one stratum. A sample is then taken by independently selecting a random sample from each stratum. The value of this procedure is that the investigator is able to identify, from prior knowledge, groupings (or strata) of elements within which relatively small differences exist with respect to the characteristic being measured and between which substantial differences exist.

Stratified sampling does not require that the sampling fraction is the same within each stratum but this is a common design. It is called proportionate stratified sampling. If the variability differs considerably between strata and/or if the cost of sampling differs between strata it is preferable to use different sampling fractions. The aim of stratification sampling is to make the strata as homogeneous as possible.

The advantages are:

- Better precision than the simple random sampling technique for a given sample size.
- Separate estimates of population parameters can be made for each individual stratum without additional costs.

Disadvantages:

- Requires information on size of population in each stratum.
- Stratified sampling frames may be costly to prepare.

Cluster sampling

In cluster sampling, instead of drawing a simple random sample of elements, the investigator divides the population into regions or clusters of elements and then selects a simple random sample of clusters. Every element in the selected clusters of elements is then measured. Cluster sampling tends to give lower precision than simple random or stratified random sampling for a given sample size. However, this tendency can be countered by careful survey design. With cluster sampling, the clusters should be as heterogeneous as possible.

Furthermore, it is better to have as a sample, a large number of small clusters rather than a small number of large clusters. Cluster sampling is less costly than simple or stratified random sampling if the cost of obtaining a frame which lists all population elements is high or if the cost of obtaining measurements increases as the distance separating the elements increases.

The advantages are:

- Can be used without a sampling frame listing all elements.
- If clusters are geographically determined, costs can be reduced.

Disadvantage:

- Poorer precision than for other probability samples of given size.

Quota sampling

Survey designs discussed above have been probability samples. They have all embodied an element of randomness ensuring that every element in the population has a calculable chance of being included. Quota sampling procedures differ in that once the numbers of different 'types' required in the sample have been determined (e.g. how many males and females, how many in each group, etc), the choice of the actual elements is left to individual requirements. The procedure is commonly used in surveys of consumer reaction research carried out in street interviewing. Quota sampling can be regarded as a form of stratified sampling in which the selection within strata is non-random. This non-random element means that subjective bias can be present and that precision of estimates cannot be measured or controlled. Nevertheless, quota samples are relatively easy to administer, requiring no sample frame and they can be carried out quickly.

Advantages:

- Simple, quick and needs no sample frame.

Disadvantage:

- Prone to contain substantial bias which cannot be measured.

Statistical analysis

Appendix 2 contains the principal formulae for use in connection with the various survey designs discussed above. It is only possible to cover statistical analysis in the context of this book lightly and there is some recommended reading at the end of the chapter. Regrettably, there are no accepted conventions regarding the use of symbols and sampling theorists tend to use Greek letters for population parameters, but the symbols shown are those used quite commonly by students of management statistics.

Experimental designs used in evaluation

The easiest technique to use is to assess the effectiveness after the programme or scheme has been completed. Methods of data collection can vary from asking a few questions to detailed tests. Types of questions which can be asked vary from general ones about whether the safety programme was acceptable and of use to the target audience, to questions which test retention and any behaviour modification. To assess whether a real improvement has occurred, a control group may be used which will increase what can be learnt from an experiment. If a suitable control group can be found then comparisons can be made between the results of those who receive a safety programme and those who do not. Any differences can then be attributed to the programme. One argument against this approach is that the control group may be different from the experimental group but as seen later there are designs available which can overcome this problem. Tests for discovering long-term retention are those made some time after the programme. This period usually varies between one month and six months but sometimes extends to one year after the programme. This illustrates effectiveness and whether there should be a new one or a booster of some kind.

Tests carried out on a target audience before a programme as well as afterwards are of great benefit. The state of knowledge, attitude or behaviour that exists in the target group initially will be known and used as the basis from which a safety programme can start. The change can be measured and this information used to modify and provide feedback for the next time the programme is to run. In Chapter 12, publicity is discussed. Often the effect of publicity is short lived and the peak effect occurs when the campaign is at its height. The only way to judge this is to evaluate the effectiveness during the campaign. If any measure is to be taken during such an event then it helps to have a baseline measure to start with in order to compare any effects of the campaign. So, a before and during study would be the minimum requirement. Testing during the campaign means that there must be staff available to do it properly.

Often it is a good idea to assess the effectiveness of a safety programme while it is going on, as well as before and afterwards. If objectives are going to be achieved then indications of this may appear early on in the campaign particularly where publicity programmes are used. Evaluation undertaken during a campaign can assess the peak effects as well as identifying any drop off effect that might occur as the campaign or programme comes to an end.

Control groups

The use of control groups can increase the power of an experimental design. It ensures that the effects of any variables which are not relevant to the programme can be allowed for. A programme evaluated without the use of a control group means that the assumption has to be made that the group subjected to the programme would not have changed had no programme been run. The problem with this is that people learn by experience and changes observed may have been due to the general learning process rather than the programme. In some cases, it can be difficult to find a suitable control group which is similar to the experimental group but will not be subjected to the programme. The ideal situation is randomly to allocate the sample of people to experimental and control groups but unfortunately this is seldom possible. On occasions, a group of workers have to be found on a completely different basis. It is sometimes possible to involve one site as a control whilst other sites undertake a programme. In these cases it is important that the control group does not learn of the experiment as this can spoil the results.

The ethical problem here is whether one should deprive one group of workers from a potentially life-saving programme. One argument to this is that if it is found to be effective then the control group has the opportunity to benefit from the programme as soon as possible after the positive effect has been identified. Another way of reducing such criticism about depriving control groups of a safety programme is to give them something else beneficial when the programme is being run as long as this does not interfere with the programme being evaluated. The authors usually give workers in such cases a relevant road safety programme which is important to all workers but not directly relevant to the industrial safety programme being studied.

Further reading

Cass, T (1969) *Statistical Methods in Management* (Cassell and Co Ltd)
Greene, J and D'Oliveira, M (1982) *Learning to use Statistical Tests in Psychology* (Open University Press)
Maroney, M J (1975) *Facts from Figures* (1975) (Penguin)
Morris, C (1989) *Quantitative Approaches in Business Studies* (Pitman Publishing)
Yamane, T (1973) *Statistics and an Introductory Analysis* (Harper International)

3

The role of the safety practitioner

Introduction

The title safety officer, safety adviser or safety manager is usually applied to a person employed by an organisation whose job it is to implement efficient and effective measures which would include education, training and publicity designed to reduce the incidence of accidents. The major areas of responsibility should be the formulation, implementation and monitoring of appropriate action. Often the safety practitioner has to manage other staff and as such is faced with the planning, organisation, motivation and control of staff. Following the introduction of the Health and Safety at Work Act (HASAWA) in 1974, organisations have had a statutory obligation to ensure the safety and well being of their employees. This is a general piece of legislation covering broad safety principles whilst other forms of legislation such as the Factories Act 1961 or the Fire Precautions Act 1971 are more specific (see Chapter 1). Some organisations reacted more enthusiastically than others in implementing such legislation. This chapter considers the implications of the HASAWA which placed a broad statutory responsibility on employers to ensure the health, safety and welfare of their employees at work and discusses the daily operational management plan required to deal with this responsibility.

In the actual case studies used to illustrate particular examples, a note should be made of the contributory factors which were resident within the chain of events leading up to the accident.

Case study 3.1

Amalgamated Chemicals, a major producer of a highly toxic resin, employed a safety officer to be responsible for the safety and health statutory requirements of their Mexborough processing plant. This plant employed 950 staff working a three shift system for 24 hours a day. The notification of all injuries and dangerous occurrences was the responsibility of the safety officer. On Friday evening, at 1930 hours there was a chemical spillage of liquid toluene when a delivery tanker arrived later than was expected and pumped the contents into the wrong tank which had inadequate capacity. The spillage was notified to the shift supervisor who notified the duty manager and filled in the appropriate form. Spillages were commonplace and the procedure was routine. The fact that the wrong tank had been filled had not been noticed and the stores supervisor did not check the unloading as the delivery firm employed the same drivers who were familiar with their storage system. On this particular day there was a new driver who had been briefed by the regular driver that morning.

On Saturday, the process plant required more nitric acid for its process manufacturing and pumped off acid from the reserve tank. This too was a standard procedure. Unfortunately, liquid toluene from the wrongly filled tank entered the blending tower. There was an immediate chemical reaction resulting in a tremendous explosion and fire. Complacency with routine procedures is commonplace with everyone believing that it is someone else's responsibility to check.

The role of the safety practitioner is not to be responsible for all safety matters within an organisation. It is to be responsible for making others aware of safety matters and that appropriate safety procedures are followed.

Whilst in management terms all safety related legislation provides organisations with their 'mission', it has been mainly left to the Royal Society for the Prevention of Accidents (RoSPA) and the HSE to provide some leadership and guidance in terms of the strategic and tactical objectives to deal with this problem. Companies have turned to a variety of people for the necessary skills. Some saw the place for safety as an extension of the personnel or industrial relations function whilst others gave it a higher profile and formed safety units within the hierarchical structure. Others chose to give the job to one of the 'engineers' whilst some looked for independent advice. There is no standard approach to safety management and the authors have found some organisations with an intelligent approach and attitude to safety whilst others see it as a necessary burden and do the and do the minimum possible. There are some organisations who employ safety practitioners because they have to, but actively restrict their activities to such an extent that they are ineffective. This is seen by some managements as satisfying the minimum requirements of the law and fails to provide any guidance as to the role of the person responsible for safety within their organisation. The definition of the role of the safety practitioner has been identified as a problem and yet is an issue which has received scant attention in the last 10 years. The same is true of the main management issues outlined in the HASAWA.

Case study 3.2

The Agricultural Manufacturing Corporation had for several years placed the responsibility for safety matters as an extension of the personnel function. After a series of serious accidents, pressure was brought to bear on the company by its insurers to employ a safety officer. An ex-police officer was recruited and employed. The safety officer was given a secretary and an office. He was to report to the personnel officer in line management terms. The safety officer was given no mission and his role was not defined. Even though accidents continued to happen at the same rate, the insurers were satisfied and the corporation continued with its ineffective safety charade.

This company viewed safety as a net cost capable of reducing productivity and profits. It therefore had to be minimised as an unwelcome overhead, provided insurance premiums could be kept to a tolerable level. If the company had developed a proactive safety management programme, the cost of the safety officer and his retinue could have been recouped several times over. Industrial relations would have been greatly improved as would productivity and profitability.

Shanks and Dewis concentrate on the legal requirements of employers and employees and briefly outline a methodology that a safety practitioner might consider when undertaking the provision of a safety service, whilst Simonds and Grimaldi take a more detailed look at the ways in which safety practitioners can improve efficiency and effectiveness. A safety manager should be employed by an organisation in order to carry out the legal requirements placed upon them by the law in an efficient and effective way. His job is to prevent accidents from happening. In reality, this usually means taking steps to reduce accidents within pre-determined cost constraints. The elimination of accidents altogether can be described as his mission but with human behaviour as it is, this can be regarded as an unobtainable goal. More realistic objectives might be to reduce accidents and/or dangerous occurrences by a pre-determined amount for a given cost. However, in order to deal with issues regarding role analysis it is necessary to consider six areas which enable an organisational mission to be met. These are:

1. Collection of information;
2. Analysis and interpretation of this information;
3. Planning of remedial action;
4. Implementation phase;

5. Monitoring phase; and
6. Evaluation phase.

Case study 3.3

RAS Murphy Construction plc, a builder of office blocks, was investigated by the HSE after a coroner's inquest had commented upon the similarity of two previous deaths that had occurred within the past three months. The coroner had enquired as to how many other workers employed by Murphy's had experienced injuries in similar circumstances. The managing director was unable to answer the coroner because he did not employ a safety officer nor did he have a safety committee. He did not collect the most rudimentary statistics on accidents or dangerous occurrences. Serious questions were raised about lack of training and familiarisation with safety procedures. As a result, the HSE investigated the firm and it was successfully prosecuted.

The collection of information

A number of firms opt to use rating or scoring systems as the basis for their strategic model whilst others use their own in-house methods. These are very useful for obtaining information to provide a safety rating or score. Very few base their strategies upon accident investigation and analysis techniques, and are therefore unable to show how effective they have been at reducing accidents or dangerous occurrences from year to year.

For the planning of remedial action, the safety practitioner needs to have access to various types of information such as:

1. The number of injury accidents which have occurred;
2. The number of dangerous occurrences which have taken place;
3. A detailed breakdown of each incident in sufficient detail that will provide for the identification of cause and/or contributory factors;
4. A sufficiently large enough data base to allow for the identification of trends;
5. Supplementary information concerning accidents and dangerous occurrences from similar industries;
6. Relevant national statistics where they are available.

Although these points are dealt with in more detail in Chapter 5, it is important to realise that this type of information is a vital part of the decision making process and provides for efficiency and effectiveness in practice. Generally, safety practitioners need to collect detailed information concerning all dangerous occurrences in their respective organisations. This will include details of all injury accidents.

Previous studies have shown the poor quality of primary accident data collection procedures and that maximum use of the information collected is not made. Despite this, many safety practitioners continue to ignore or realise the value of a good reliable primary data source. A strategic objective here, therefore, must include data collection and to ensure that these data are used for analysis purposes. This must form part of the decision making process.

To do this within practical economic constraints, safety practitioners should establish a system for collecting details of accidents and dangerous occurrences as outlined in Chapter 5. It is known that many organisations spend considerable sums of money in order to meet a potentially dangerous situation. If an objective is to collect all accident information, then steps should be taken to collect this data in a sufficiently detailed form so that potential problem areas can be identified. This will enable priorities to be set and ensure that resources are used effectively. At the same time, supplementary data should be systematically obtained in detailed structured interviews with casualties so that lessons can be learnt. Wherever possible, these interviews should be in total confidence and without fear of any consequent disciplinary action.

We must now consider other forms of information that are required. It has become established practice that the safety officer should be primarily involved in education, training and publicity strategies whilst the engineer or scientist concentrates upon tactical or environmental issues. Such separation should be avoided wherever possible. To enable organisational missions to be met at all, and for efficiency and effectiveness to be improved, both systems should work closely together as each of them plan and implement strategies using the same database for decision making. Both are equally dependent upon the quality of these data and there should be a shared and co-ordinated approach to remedying any problems of unreliability. It is from this premise that other forms of relevant information can be systematically gathered for programme planning and evaluation purposes. It is not intended to delve too deeply into what additional information is necessary for a proactive management style in this chapter. Information gathering, therefore, is of great importance and should be given high priority within the objective setting sequence.

The analysis and interpretation of the database

The majority of practitioners do not have direct access to any database for decision-making purposes. In any case, few have received training in its use. An unacceptably high number are unaware of its value and most have not considered whether their accident trends were a problem or not. Some safety practitioners collect accident data for establishing trends but tend to analyse individual cases rather than establish causes. Furthermore, safety managers do not regularly monitor dangerous occurrences nor are they familiar with statistical packages or research methodology. This is despite government departments, the HSE and the RoSPA regularly encouraging safety practitioners to evaluate their work. Few use basic research tools such as computers. The problem can be compounded because some organisations pursue staff recruitment policies that are not designed to address this problem. In too many cases, they fail to recruit numerate graduates for key management roles or to provide for adequate staff development in the areas of information technology and statistics.

Planning of remedial action

This can only effectively take place after all relevant information has been thoroughly investigated and analysed. Central to the discharge of the safety manager's mission is the planning of appropriate remedial action. By this, the authors contend that education, training and publicity should be the main issues. A number of safety personnel still carry out the practice of preparing occasional visits around the company without defining the purpose or objective for such visits or locating these visits in a broader pattern of provision. Others will write a 'memo' on a subject which may have been raised via the safety committee without establishing whether the subject is a cause of concern reached through data analysis.

Jolly pointed out that for safety education to be effective it had to be continuous and must, therefore, be part of the daily management plan. Clearly the delegation of this responsibility to all staff is necessary. Safety practitioners are not appointed in large enough numbers solely to discharge their duties and responsibilities. The role of the safety manager has to be seen therefore, as that of adviser, supervising the development of remedial measures and their implementation, providing appropriate training and other materials and trying to ensure that safety is given an appropriate high priority on the corporate agenda.

The implementation phase

The implementation of operational objectives needs careful thought in two regards; first, the staff resource, and second, the financial resource. The accident database discussed earlier has to be the prime means of determining priorities. At the end of each year or time period when data is available together with that for the previous two years, or period data, trends can be established and plans of action can be determined for the forthcoming year. The start of the new year or period is an ideal time to be looking at objective setting in a company environment adopting a fiscal year or quarterly period. Managers need to be aware of budget-making policies within their own organisation. A large number of safety managers are not setting objectives or planning from any database, let alone considering operational objective setting as a process. Programmes based upon historical activities and precedent seem to be the norm rather than planning in the light of changing operational requirements. The structured method proposed leads to a series of specific actions and proposals that the safety practitioner should seek to implement with colleagues in other departments within the organisation.

Programme monitoring

Critical to the efficient and effective utilisation of resources is the monitoring phase. There are two areas to consider:

1. Systems management; and
2. Operations management.

Systems management

There must be an orderly and regular review of objectives and their implementation. The monitoring of specific objectives at critical periods is also important. Fluctuating conditions may influence schemes, such as moratoriums on budgets. If these issues are allowed to go unnoticed or unchecked then problems inevitably arise. Problems such as printing deadlines can mean a lost opportunity for example, whilst insufficient staff can affect other issues. Resource systems, therefore, need systematic scrutiny if programmes are to succeed. Shortfalls in the resource base should be identified at an early stage in the decision-making process and their implications should be clearly understood by the safety practitioner. All too often a safety officer can identify what he can do, but is unable to describe what he is unable to do and list accurately why he cannot do it. For example, many members of safety committees, having listened to their safety managers outlining their annual report, may never have asked for the results to be put into perspective or asked whether they were acceptable. It is assumed that safety education and training should be made available to all employees without favour or bias. Management should know whether this is happening and should develop a system whereby shortfalls in organisational expectations can be clearly and easily identified and other priorities set. To quote numbers without qualification is not good management practice.

Operational systems

These are important if projects are to meet their aims and objectives. Training schemes need to be regularly monitored if standards are to be maintained and the operational divisions of the organisations need to be contacted regularly if they are to carry out their programmes consistently and effectively. For example, if an objective is to train each and every member of middle management in a particular area once a year, then this can easily be monitored. If this objective has not been reached then evaluation is needed to show the reasons for this failure. Likewise, if a scheme has been implemented then each stage needs discussion and regular meetings need to take into account any tactical consideration. The majority of safety practitioners do not keep accurate records of their activities. From an operational systems standpoint, information detailing each visit with dates, times, person visited, etc., has immense operational value. In a similar manner, details of other schemes and plans must be recorded. Some safety personnel readily accept that they do not know the extent of dangerous activities being carried out in their organisations and are unaware of the number of dangerous occurrences which happen. If the management system does not seek to quantify this information at the outset then retrospectively-based action plans need to be considered. If a stated objective of the safety unit is to acquire this information then it has to be possible to obtain it.

Evaluation

There are many commercially available safety audit systems which allow for managers to pursue safety policies which are capable of being evaluated. Safety training programme evaluation is a subject which is dealt with later in Chapter 11.

Although the RoSPA and the HSE actively encourage use of all such programmes, it is wrong that 'evaluation' does not feature on any of the current training courses designed for safety practitioners. Moreover, research methodology as an operational tool is similarly lacking from these health and safety courses. The use of statistics does feature in a handful of courses but these are usually academic in nature. In the accident investigation and analysis field there are even fewer opportunities to receive training. At the more basic training level, statistical methods are not covered in sufficient depth, neither are relevant examples used to illustrate their use. The use of information technology and other aids to successful evaluation are sadly lacking in practice in most organisations.

Evaluation can only occur within a framework of clearly defined aims and objectives and if undertaken by properly trained staff. Many safety practitioners argue that safety activities cannot be evaluated, for example because you cannot quantify how many deaths or injuries have been avoided. This is symptomatic of this fundamental issue. Surely, if a particular plan were introduced to encourage the use of high visibility clothing in an unsupervised location, then its results could be measured. If, after the campaign, more people are found to be wearing such material than before, then some degree of success may have been achieved particularly if no such change occurred in the control group. Other areas of behaviour and attitude can be similarly evaluated. Management strategies can also be evaluated for efficiency and effectiveness. It is recognised that specific reductions

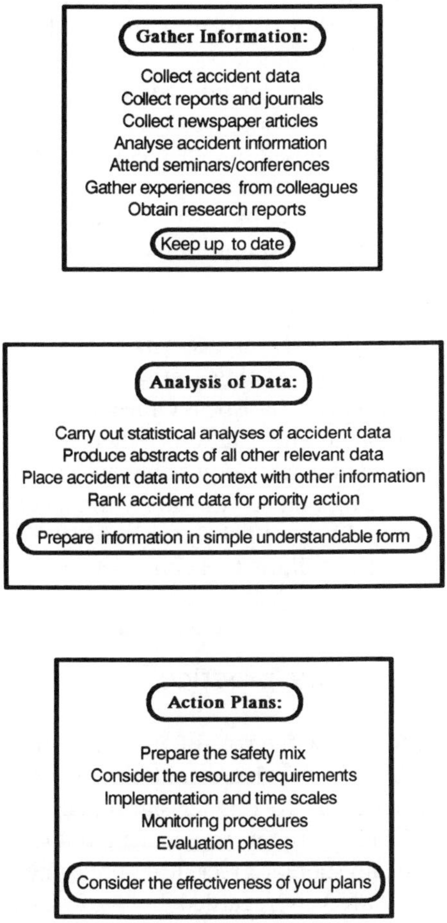

Gather Information:

Collect accident data
Collect reports and journals
Collect newspaper articles
Analyse accident information
Attend seminars/conferences
Gather experiences from colleagues
Obtain research reports

Keep up to date

Analysis of Data:

Carry out statistical analyses of accident data
Produce abstracts of all other relevant data
Place accident data into context with other information
Rank accident data for priority action

Prepare information in simple understandable form

Action Plans:

Prepare the safety mix
Consider the resource requirements
Implementation and time scales
Monitoring procedures
Evaluation phases

Consider the effectiveness of your plans

Figure 3.1
The role of the safety manager

in accidents directly attributable to an education, training and/or publicity programme are very difficult to establish in terms of a simple causal relationship. Nevertheless, the safety manager's contribution to the overall corporate approach in accident reduction is now acknowledged and the long-term value is becoming accepted. For example, a comparison of the number of accidents in relation to the vehicle population in this country would confirm this, particularly when compared with our EEC partners. The safety practitioner, therefore, can be an important and vital part of this corporate plan.

Case study 3.4

Rashid's Oil Company spent millions of dollars on a system designed to carry out safety audits within its many plants and sites. Comprehensive training and familiarisation courses were held regularly for all managers and technical operatives. Fundamental to the system was that it would reduce accidents and dangerous occurrences and subsequent loss of revenue. Regrettably, the firm did not keep adequate or compatible records of accidents, neither were they investigated sufficiently. Thus, no valid database could be constructed that would enable them to measure the effectiveness of their prevention programme in which they had invested so much time and money.

In this context then, the group safety manager or director needs also to compare his organisation's performance with the broader national picture. It is for this reason that the existing statistics collected by the HSE and assembled by the Government Statistical Office in their annual reports have to be qualified and treated with caution. When using these data locally, they must be supplemented wherever possible with information from other sources. It is disappointing that so few safety managers have direct access to such data. This would greatly help and assist programme planning and this may explain the failure to acknowledge the need for effective evaluation.

Some aspects of safety practice

We have attempted to review the role of the safety practitioner within the context of the HASAWA. We have said that some organisations have reacted more enthusiastically to this legislation than others. As a result, there is no standardised approach to accident reduction in this country. There also seems to be no standard recruiting policy nor training provision. We have found that safety is regarded by some as a backwater in the organisation and many firms put 'problem' staff into safety roles; and then the age of many safety practitioners is too old to allow for substantial retraining.

Organisations must, therefore, consider a management style that is not just public relations or law enforcement orientated but actually geared to accident prevention and reduction. This demands a different portfolio of skills. If safety practitioners are to be recruited and trained for the next century, then is it appropriate to recruit people who are too old to undergo sustained professional retraining when compared to other younger professionals, and further, is it wise to recruit people whose personal abilities, experience and attributes are not necessarily best suited to this matter? Could this be the reason why those courses currently available are not well attended or is this because managers responsible for recruitment and training do not really know or understand what the role of the safety practitioner should be?

Several safety practitioners in local government, for example, still act as instructors, and a review of recent advertisements suggests that this is what is expected. In one organisation, 55% of the financial resource base was allocated to an activity occupying only 14% of the accident casualty base yet required 64% of the staff time to deal with it. In this particular company, objectives were not set, accident data were collected but not used and the safety unit carried out their duties in the same way that they had always done.

This may have been 'acceptable' practice in 1974, but it is now time to change. A company must operate within acceptable cost-benefit parameters. Financial restrictions dictate a tighter management approach to decision making and safety personnel now find that they have to be even more accountable than in the past. If they cannot justify their existence, then their relative priority within the company is diminished and provision will be reduced, as has happened in some companies. Regrettably, this poor management and presentation compounds the failure of senior management fully to recognise and comprehend the actual and the potential role of the safety practitioner, to recruit the right staff and train them properly and to provide them with sufficient resources to do the job. The organisational structure may be defective. Safety is no longer the 'Cinderella' area it once was. On the contrary, it should form an integral part of the strategic plan for accident reduction and should be given appropriate priority within the organisation.

The safety practitioner needs to improve the information on which his decisions should be based. This means that he should allocate sufficient resources to meet this requirement. Having spent time improving the quality and reliability of this primary data, consideration can then be given to its analysis for decision-making purposes. From this, tactical objectives can be prepared for operational implementation and monitoring. Within this phase will be the determination of the evaluation criteria and performance indicators to be used. One of the important factors within the objective setting sequence is to quantify what cannot be achieved and to quantify more accurately why goals cannot be reached. All safety practitioners should develop a critical management style that provides for the identification and rectification of shortfalls. Board members, senior managers and members of safety committees should demand this information and it is right that they should be aware of all the relevant issues and not just told about what has been done. Contextual data should be used in these safety reports.

The safety mix

The main aim of the safety manager is to co-ordinate the safety mix. This forms a main feature of the remedial process and successful safety programmes are based upon a mix of some or all of the main ingredients shown in Figure 3.2. It is very rare for one part of the mix to be successful

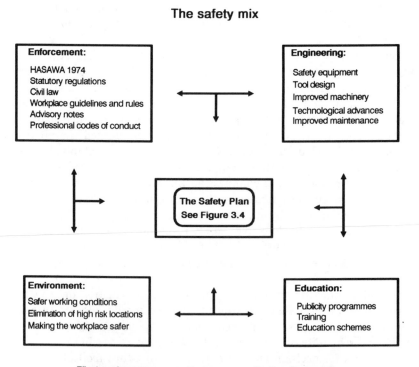

The safety mix

Enforcement:

HASAWA 1974
Statutory regulations
Civil law
Workplace guidelines and rules
Advisory notes
Professional codes of conduct

Engineering:

Safety equipment
Tool design
Improved machinery
Technological advances
Improved maintenance

The Safety Plan
See Figure 3.4

Environment:

Safer working conditions
Elimination of high risk locations
Making the workplace safer

Education:

Publicity programmes
Training
Education schemes

Effective safety programmes will rely upon a combination of one or more of the above elements of the safety mix. It is essential that the mix is correctly balanced and safety practitioners must aim their strategies at achieving this.

Figure 3.2

in isolation. For example, the Department of Transport spent some £30 million attempting to persuade drivers to wear seatbelts. This was conducted via one 'E' of the safety mix, that involving education and publicity. It failed and a further 'E' was necessary in the form of enforcement. The two elements together now account for a 96% wearing rate amongst car drivers. Similarly, speed limits, an enforcement requirement,

Task	Specific Activity
Accident Investigator	To investigate thoroughly all accidents and dangerous occurrences to establish contributory factors
Planner	To plan, implement, monitor and evaluate remedial measures designed to reduce or prevent accidents from happening
Auditor	Carry out regular investigations to ensure safety policy is satisfactory
Trainer	Provide on the job instruction, safe systems of working, indoctrination, workplace rules and regulations, employee responsibilities
Provider	Issue protective clothing and/or equipment A knowledge of legal requirements will be required. Ensure safe environment
Leader	Know your work force. Lead by example and motivate employees and develop schemes to change attitudes and behaviour
Advocate	Establish safety as a priority within your organisation. Secure recognition of importance at board level. Secure sufficient resources to enable tasks to be achieved effectively

Figure 3.3
General tasks for the safety practitioner

are often ignored unless backed up by other measures within the safety mix framework. The task of the safety manager is to develop an appropriate blend within the safety mix framework at local level. This aspect is usually dealt with in the programme planning stages.

Care should always be taken not to rely solely upon the enforcement aspect of the mix as the only means of providing an effective accident prevention strategy.

Whilst the safety manager might consider the planning, implementation, monitoring and evaluation of the safety mix programme within specified areas of operation there are also specific tasks for which he would also be responsible. These are summarised in Figure 3.3.

It is necessary that all these tasks are carried out efficiently and effectively and within clearly defined cost restraints. It is far better for the safety manager to tell the accountants what is to be done rather than the other way round. In Chapter 4, some basic operations management issues are discussed which will assist the safety manager to consider various 'options' and to come to appropriate decisions.

Long-term monitoring – the safety audit or review

The safety audit is a full scale monitoring of policies, procedures, practices and programmes, whilst a safety review is more than an inspection or survey of organisational facilities and tends to concentrate on one aspect of the 4 P's in detail. The aim of both procedures should be to help decrease the risk of accidents happening, and increase productivity. A systematic approach to safety management will help the practitioner set objectives which will be based on priorities designed to improve management techniques, training and development, behaviour and employee attitude.

Such management practice requires measurement and this will need to cater for behaviour and attitude. Measuring these is not too difficult providing both are treated positively. Positive action will produce an activity which is measurable. A good attitude or behaviour must be developed and nurtured by management. This does not occur automatically. A genuine concern for the employee's health and safety is shown not only by management's position, but also by its action. Is management actively involved in accident prevention, or is it seen as a delegated interest? Employees are constantly evaluating the behaviour and attitude of management and this must be seen positively from both sides.

The measurement of attitude and behaviour

A review of safety is geared to determine what action must be taken to achieve a safer, more productive operation. Its function is the gathering of information, but also, is of value to management education and the development of an effective and efficient safety programme.

Many safety practitioners prefer to use the word *review*, rather than *audit*, in order, they say, to avoid the connotation of fault finding and to stress the more positive aspects of an investigative approach. The word review also separates it from any similarity to a financial audit. We have stressed above that there is a distinct difference between a *safety audit* and the *safety review*. The detailed safety audit is too large to discuss here and the safety review is discussed with sample questions to be considered given in Appendix 4.

Safety reviews form a significant part of established management control functions. Via a system of interviews, the attitudes of employees, supervisors and management can be discovered. Any interviews with management should be held with the most senior executive possible. Although he will not be able to provide detailed answers to all questions, it is necessary to prepare well for the exercise. The reviewer or review team must provide an agenda to management in order that information can be gathered and people made available for the review.

There are advantages in obtaining external help when undertaking the first review. These are:

- A consultant can be more objective in respect to the approach, design and concluding phase than someone within the organisation.
- He will not have any biases or be influenced by traditions.
- He will be not be influenced by personalities.
- Independence can be very effective when changes are recommended.

The size and membership of a safety review team will largely depend on the complexity of the facility involved and the expertise that is required. It would be necessary to have periodic reviews every two to three years by an external expert, particularly if there are many changes in the organisation or operation.

Review methodology

It is important to discuss the practicalities of the review process required to assist group executives and location management in the development or evaluation of their accident prevention activities. Although the areas for consideration listed below are summarised, they do outline the general topics required for discussion with senior management. A comprehensive safety review requires that it be conducted by safety practitioners who will draw from their knowledge and experience so that useful information can be obtained. There are generally five review elements to consider:

1. Administration;
2. Accident investigation and analysis processes;

3. Job analysis;
4. Self inspection;
5. Contingency planning.

In addition to these, which are discussed further below, a number (the larger the sample the better will be the results) of supervisors and employees should be picked at random and interviewed to assess their safety attitude and to obtain data concerning their perception of the safety programme. It is important to select these people by occupation or trade rather than by name. This then removes, as far as possible, any prejudices for or against management or its programmes.

A review should start with a conference with senior management in order to explain the agenda and to answer any questions that may arise. The exercise should end with an exit interview so that any recommendations can be fully explained and any differences resolved prior to the final report being published. Where an internal review is conducted, the team should obtain a conclusive response from senior management for each recommendation made. The scope of a rigorous safety review should be to evaluate the above five distinct elements in order to obtain answers to what is discussed below.

Administration

The interest of management and their full participation are the most important factors in any safety review activity. It is important to maintain this situation and secure management involvement. Managers must be visible in the workplace for the promotion of safety as well as for production. In this way, it is possible to unite these two concepts to ensure safe production.

In a complex industrial or mining operation, there are often several facilities tied to an administrative or headquarters-type location. Individual sites sometimes have little or no control over areas of programmes or systems governing their operations, particularly those set up for the whole organisation. Examples might include the safety programme outline, the disciplinary programme or the needs of the workforce. It is important, therefore, that locations are evaluated for those systems which they control and that headquarters type centres are analysed for those that they command in the following ways.

Headquarters or group

- Describe the loss control programme for:

    — employees;
    — processes;

— contractors; and
— equipment.

- What is the senior manager's role in the accident prevention programme?
- Is there a safety manager and to whom is he responsible?
- How often is the accident prevention programme reviewed internally for effectiveness?
- Is there a programme for training supervisors based on established need?
- Does senior management occasionally attend site safety meetings?
- Is there a system which recognises supervisors' and employees' safety achievement?
- Are aims and objectives required for safety performance?
- Are objectives realistic and measurable?
- Are objectives measured?
- What consideration is given to matching man, machine, and the environment in the hiring and placement of employees?
- Outline the programme for the selection and purchase of:

— facilities;
— equipment processes; and
— protective clothing and equipment.

Site or satellite location

- Outline the accident prevention programme for:

— employees;
— processes;
— contractors; and
— equipment.

- What is the role of management in the safety programme?
- Does management recognise supervisors and employees for their safety achievement?
- Does management initiate procedural and motivational communications to staff?
- Does management participate in accident prevention inspections of the facility?
- Does management attend occasional safety meetings with the workforce?
- Are safety aims and objectives set jointly by the entire management team at that location?
- Are the objectives measured?

- Does senior management review all major incidents and subsequent statistical analyses?
- Is there a preventive maintenance programme?
- Is there a system of selection and placement of employees?
- Is there a job analysis programme in operation?
- Outline the training programme for: management development and supervisory safety task training.
- Is there a safety co-ordinator and what are his responsibilities?

Accident and dangerous occurrence investigation

- Are all incidents, including first-aid, investigated for type and contributory factors?
- Do remedial measures attack the factors contributing to the incident happening?
- What system is used to follow up on preventive measures?
- Does the investigation indicate the potential for severity?
- Are all fatalities, major injuries and illnesses, and high cost incidents investigated?
- Does each department head review all incidents in his/her department?
- Does the safety department review and follow up on all incident reports?
- Are thorough analyses made of all incidents for trends? Are these analyses reviewed by senior management?
- Is there a method of determining the number and type of incidents resulting in lost time from off-the-job injuries and illnesses?
- Are off-the-job incidents analysed for type and costs to the facility? Are these analyses communicated to senior management?
- Do employee safety awareness programmes include off-the-job safety?
- Is off-the-job safety information provided to the families of employees?

Job analysis

- Has a priority list of hazardous or high risk jobs been established?
- Are hazardous/high risk jobs analysed by method to determine the potential for accident and the safe work procedure?
- Are the priority listed jobs necessary to accomplish the work aims?
- Who participates in the job analysis?
- Is job or task training based on the completed job analysis?
- Are safe work procedures developed through job analyses?

- Are they used as guides:

  — by employees to perform work?
  — by supervisors to train and supervise?
  — by managers to manage?

- Are the job analyses reviewed when:

  — incidents occur?
  — there is a change in equipment?
  — there is a change in environment?
  — there is a change in the process?

- Are equipment pre-use or inspection check sheets developed using the job analysis procedure?
- Are tags and signs developed and used to support the safe work procedures?

Self inspection

- Is there an inspection team with representation from management, production, safety and employees?
- Does the team have a check-list including all areas of the facility?
- Is there a system of follow-up for the remedy of unsafe conditions and practices observed?
- Does the inspection include the preventive maintenance programme records?

- In addition to the overall plant inspection, are periodic inspections made:

  — by department heads and supervisors of individual areas?
  — by a safety practitioner?
  — by senior management?

Contingency planning

- How many emergency medically qualified personnel are there on each shift?
- How many are trained in first aid?
- Where are the first-aid stations located?
- How often are the first-aid stations checked for operational efficiency?
- Is there a doctor on retainer or designated?
- Are there clear written emergency and communication procedures?
- Are the responsibilities of management and supervisors clearly defined in these procedures?

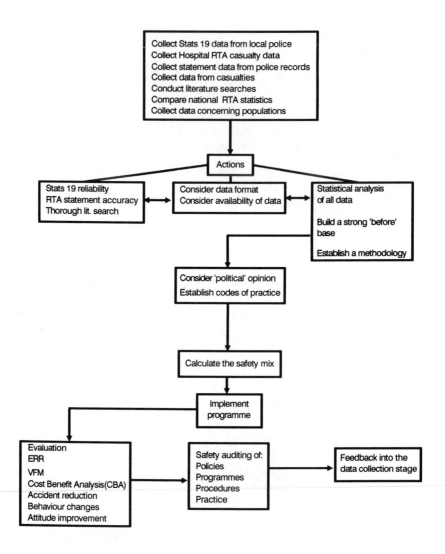

Figure 3.4   The road safety management process

Whatever area of safety a practitioner is engaged in, the safety management process is the same. Figure 3.4 above shows a typical management process for a road safety practitioner. An industrial or commercial safety practitioner will follow a similar process.

- What is the availability of ambulance services if required?
- Who administers or co-ordinates the emergency procedures?

A safety review places the emphasis and encourages the activity where they will produce the best results. Management and supervision are key factors in effective safety programmes. It is the responsibility of the safety manager to ensure that such reviews are held regularly and that the whole workforce including senior management are involved. It is positive action, rather than what is said, which is of vital importance in demonstrating the management position.

Further reading

Henderson, B and Truman, M 'An Auditing System for the Health and Safety Professionals' *Safety* May 1981

International Loss Control Institute (1978) *International Mine Safety Rating* (Loganville, GA: Institute Press)

Jolly, K (1977) *Children and Traffic, Vol 1* (Macmillan Education)

Manuele, Fred A 'How Do You Know Your Hazard Control Programme Is Effective?' *Professional Safety* June 1981

RoSPA (1988) *Health and Safety at Work Handbook* (2nd ed), (Tolley Publishing Co Ltd)

Simonds, R H and Grimaldi, J (1963) *Safety Management* (Irwin Publishing Co)

4

Operations management

Introduction

There are three types of approach to the subject of operations management used by practitioners in industry. Traditionalists tend to concentrate upon the clerical procedures of 'production' type management and use work study, value analysis, standardisation, production control and other similar techniques emphasising the qualitative rather than quantitative aspects of management. Such practitioners lean towards synthesis rather than analysis as their main term of reference. A further type rely mainly on mathematics and the applications of operational research and statistics to management analysis whilst the third type uses a mix of the first two. This type is the one which shall be discussed here.

For our purposes, production function concerns two types of decision. Firstly, those pertaining to the design or establishment of the system, and, secondly, those concerning the operation, performance and running of the system. This philosophy refers to the safety management process and the establishment of the safety management system and its performance. A system is not only an arrangement of physical facilities but also the predetermined manner in which safety related strategies are made and implemented. Decisions relating to system design include such things as the acquisition and arrangement of equipment and determination of safe manufacturing or operational methods whilst decisions relating to the operation of the 'production' process concern the implementation, monitoring and evaluation of safety strategies. These can be regarded in some cases as short term in nature.

Operations management is concerned primarily with the design and operation of efficient and effective systems whose purpose is the provision of goods or, in our case, safety services. Applying the basic principles to the safety training function is shown in Figure 4.1.

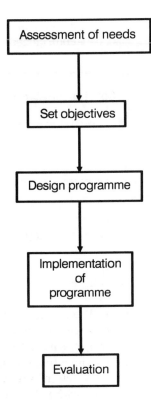

Analysis: breaking the problem into a set of requirements

Synthesis: putting ideas together to form a complete solution

Evaluation: estimating or measuring the degree to which
solutions satisfy requirements

[These issues are further discussed in Chapter 11]

Figure 4.1

Safety training

Problem solving

When a safety problem has been identified then systematic search is often less time consuming, cheaper and offers easier implementation of the remedial strategy/s than a series of plausible guesses which prove fallacious. This is shown diagrammatically in Figure 4.2.

The optimum solution to the true needs of a particular
set of circumstances

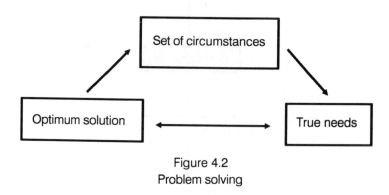

Figure 4.2
Problem solving

The design of jobs has usually always been the responsibility of the production function and effective methods of doing work are essential for the
efficient design of safety systems. The development and implementation of
optimum work methods frequently requires the study and design of workplaces and of equipment. Control is achieved by performance standards
which are obtained after exhaustive investigations into work methods. Such
systems are relevant to the way in which the safety manager may set about
the provision of the safety service within his work environment as well
as to the safety factors built into the general production process for the
workforce in each respective industry.

The traditional frameworks of work study are as follows:

- *Select* the situation to be studied and outline the purpose of the
  exercise.
- *Record* the relevant data, including past records and any specialist
  records.
- *Analyse* the data critically as discussed in Chapter 2.
- *Develop* the most acceptable solution.
- *Install* the new system.
- *Maintain* the new system by control procedures.

The general model used within a work study framework requires the
following phases to be considered.

Diagnostic phase

- Clarify the problem.
- Set objectives.
- Establish the current situation.
- Examine internal and external factors.

Assessing the need to change

- Identify areas requiring change.
- Highlight financial and accident reduction advantages.
- Identify objectives for change.

Developing alternatives

- Assess the degree to which each alternative meets the need and/or objective.
- Evaluate financial and accident prevention savings.
- Conduct feasibility exercise.
- Select the 'best' solution.

Recommendation

- Presentation and selling of the chosen changes.

Implementation

- Actioning change (communication needs).
- Gaining support and commitment for the change.
- Debugging the new systems.
- Provision of training and development for people.

Performance review

- Measuring the degree of achievement.
- Noting side effects and unexpected problems or successes.
- Intervening to change objectives or system operation.

Corporate appraisal

This requires the safety manager to consider the implications of any revised strategy and the effects this will have upon the internal environment. There are many theories relating to this process but for the purposes of practicality the following list of questions will provide a framework on which to proceed:

- Where are we now and why?
- What are the strengths and weaknesses of the safety situation under study?
- What are our objectives? (What should they be?)
- Do we need change? (Threats?)
- What alternatives are open? (Opportunities?)
- What does each alternative offer?
- Which alternatives should be chosen?

A general model showing the clarification process is given in Figure 4.3.

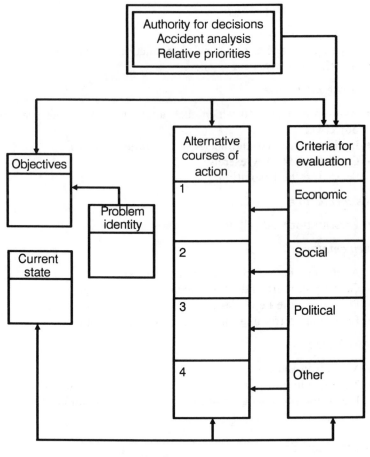

Figure 4.3
Clarification process

Systems approach

This sees all inputs into a safety system, safety organisation or safety process as associated with a set of *needs*. The degree to which these needs are being met by the *process* operation will affect the entry back into the system for future inputs (see Figure 4.4). Also, since the outputs permeate both the substantive and the external environment, they also will affect ability to attract new types of input.

Regulation can only be affected by changes in the inputs or process operation. Choice of inputs is limited by demand for entry again affected by outputs. Process change may be possible with no change in inputs.

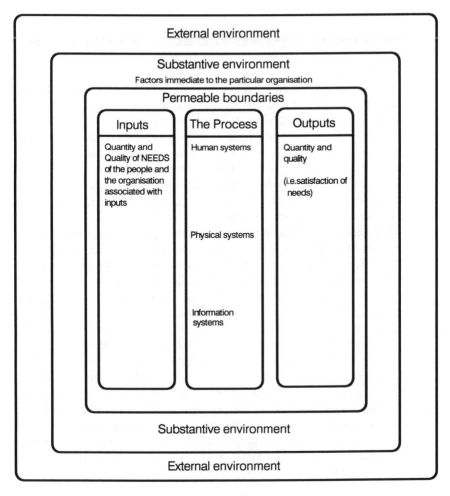

Figure 4.4

Systems approach to problem solving

The approach is to identify inconsistencies between the various elements in the model. For example, discrepancies in satisfaction of input needs by outputs and the interactive effect between factors in both substantive and external environment on inputs.

Characteristics of problem solving

There are seven basic characteristics to consider when problem solving.

These are:

1. Cycling and recycling between stages takes place until the uncertainty in conclusion is at an acceptable level to the safety manager solving the problem;
2. The amount of search is related to uncertainty at the start. A poor strategy is one which leaves the safety practitioner solving the problem still uncertain with information he cannot use;
3. There will be several paths leading to a satisfactory conclusion. However, they are unlikely to be equal in terms of man hours involved, cost, information needs or organisational disturbance;
4. The chosen safety strategy for problem solving should force the safety practitioner to pose and answer the questions which express the uncertainty with which he begins;
5. The measure for balancing the unreliability of information against the cost of verifying it is the penalty which the safety manager expects to pay for making an error in the final conclusion. Sensitivity testing is an integral part of the problem solving process;
6. A good strategy places no constraint on the freedom to change plans in the light of new information and insights as the investigation proceeds. However, at any point in time, one should keep to a particular plan to which one is working. New ideas can be kept separate until the safety practitioner feels it appropriate to review the results of the current investigation and decide whether to continue on the existing path or to develop a new plan for the next part of the investigation;
7. Throughout the problem solving process, value judgements will affect the conclusions drawn and actions taken. Evidence can never give certainty to predicted outcomes, but merely affects the confidence we have in the particular conclusion and the error margin of the predicted outcomes.

Dilemmas in problem solving

There are three basic dilemmas to consider. These are:

1. Which goals or objectives?
2. Which strategy or approach?
3. How to overcome a barrier?

These are now discussed in more detail.

Which goal or objectives?

When a number of different goals present themselves, it is often difficult to decide which goal to go for. It is common for any safety problem to be tackled in several different ways. Some dangers are:

- Choosing too broad a field of investigation.
- Goals which are incompatible in respect of problem solving methods.
- Human change needs.
- Data requirements.
- Development needs of the individual.
- Goals impossible to achieve in the time or the resources available.

Which strategy or approach?

Once the goal has been identified, it is usual for there to be a number of alternative strategies which might be employed to achieve that goal. Some dangers to look out for are:

- Choosing an approach which avoids bringing human problems into the open.
- Following an approach used before for a similar problem and finding it does not succeed.
- Failing to assess the readiness for change and the human environment before making the choice.
- Using a non-participative involvement approach.
- Letting the needs for acceptance of recommendation be the sole influence.
- Approaching the problem bottom up rather than from the top downwards.
- Choosing an original research approach rather than a survey of experience of others first.
- Using primary data inputs rather than secondary data.
- Choosing an approach which within the time available leaves inadequate time for analysis and development of alternatives.

How to overcome a barrier?

In following a particular strategy, a barrier can be met which must be surmounted before the goal can be achieved. In safety practice these are quite common. Some common barriers are:

- Lack of access to reliable accident or dangerous occurrence data.
- Lack of co-operation or involvement of people.
- Lack of ideas for further development or consideration.
- Obtaining evaluation criteria.
- Obtaining interim decisions or approval affecting further progress.

- Lack of knowledge of the principles, systems, concepts and environment.

Some dangers to consider are:

- Failure or refusal to recognise failure in one's personal approach or behaviour.
- Failure or refusal to recognise excessive change gaps as perceived by others.
- Putting off facing up to the barrier.
- Ignoring the barrier and making assumptions to enable progress.
- Selecting a standard solution rather than use or search for creative techniques.
- Assuming co-operation will come when the final safety recommendations are approved.
- Failure to assess the worth of effort to surmount the barrier.
- Perception of the size and cause of the barrier being significantly different in reality.
- Failure to face up to behaviourial problems when involving people outside the safety manager's formal responsibility.
- To accept too readily the impossibility of the situation and give up when it would have been possible to have overcome the difficulty.

In practice, any combination of these situations may exist. The important thing is to recognise the situation(s) and come to terms with them.

Problem solving strategies

There are three main problem solving strategies for the safety manager to consider. These are:

1. Random strategy;
2. Traditional strategy; and
3. Adaptive strategy.

These are now discussed in brief.

Random strategy

In choosing the next step within the problem solving sequence, the safety investigator deliberately adopts a policy whereby the brief is ignored particularly from previous experience and information. The strategy may be a useful one to adopt in very uncertain circumstances which need to be widely explored before taking up any specific aspect in detail (see Figure 4.5).

Traditional strategy

The safety investigator relies as far as possible on reliable accident and dangerous occurrence information that has been specially collected for the purpose. A diagram outlining the philosophy of the traditional strategy is shown in Figure 4.5.

Random strategy

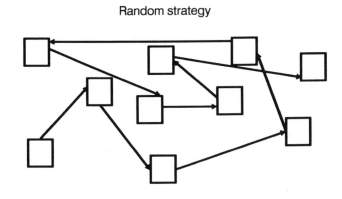

Traditional strategy

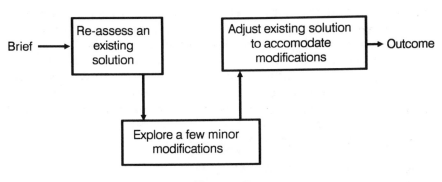

Figure 4.5

Adaptive strategy

The safety practitioner exploits the information generated at each stage as progress is made between uncertainty and decision as shown in Figure 4.6.

Combining logic and imagination, the results of this adaptive approach are kept in one set until such time as enough factual and logical information has accumulated in the other set to test their relevance and value.

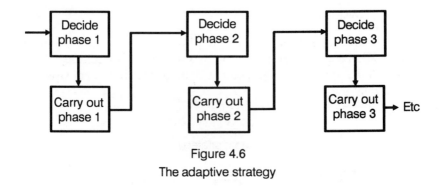

Figure 4.6
The adaptive strategy

The free thinking data are compared with the sequential thinking data as shown in Figure 4.6. The next stage will be either to abandon the insight because it does not fit the facts or to abandon the initial line of approach because it can now be seen to lead in an unfruitful direction. When things proceed well, both insights and sequential sequencing point in the same direction.

Personal elements

Effective safety related problem solving is the result of a balance between vision, judgment and knowledge. These will improve with experience. In Figure 4.7, a diagram is given outlining these three factors and listing those important features within each of the three headings. It should be noted that when applying judgment, one must suppress natural tendencies which may blind one to the truth. A safety practitioner must beware of four areas which researchers have identified as the stereotype syndrome. A safety practitioner should not stereotype problems, solutions, pay-offs or success.

When approaching a problem it is important:

- To question *effectiveness* before *efficiency*.
- That *symptoms* are not *causes* (identify the cause).
- To establish the relative importance of the various problem areas – consider 'pareto analysis'. This is: the law of the vital few and the trivial many! Chronic problems are those which exist continually. They are likely to give more significant returns if solved than will sporadic problems (ones which occur infrequently). Safety practitioners should prevent problems developing into a chronic state.
- That criteria and evaluation are deemed essential if progress is to be meaningful and controlled.
- To take a *system* view of the problem situation.

- To define the boundaries of the problem.
- To be prepared to change the approach, boundaries and criteria for evaluation where necessary.
- To consider all the *life stages* associated with the problem solving situation. For example:

  — the investigation;
  — acceptance/rejection of recommendations;
  — implementation;
  — ongoing operation and maintenance;
  — performance review;
  — growth; and
  — modification and change of the safety programme.

- To establish the *needs* for solution to the problem. For example:

  — to establish a prime need which the safety solution must satisfy;
  — to rank needs according to the importance of them being satisfied;
  — the needs will be associated with all the stages of the problem solving and its resolution.

- To be aware of the *hypotheses* (unsubstantiated assumptions) upon which the safety approach will be based.

It is important during the analysis phase of the safety investigation to remember the following six points:

1. Examine facts as they are, not as you feel they should be or are said to be. Validate evidence in accordance with perception v truth practice;
2. Avoid fitting the evidence to preconceived solutions and challenge everything;
3. Judgment must be part of every selection of alternatives. Do not use judgment when facts can replace it;
4. Look for ideas, hunches – try to innovate – but don't be unrealistic;
5. Involve others particularly those who will have to authorise and operate the final solution. Analysis is a learning process;
6. The right questions produce good answers quickly.

The philosophy concerning the examination of problem areas is summarised in Figure 4.7 whilst the critical examination of *what*, *where*, *when*, *who*, *how* and *why* discussed in Chapter 2 is applied to problem solving too and is summarised in Figure 4.8.

A standard critical examination sheet or 'roulette wheel' is shown in Figure 4.9.

There are some common reasons why safety management solutions might be inadequate and it is only by studying how past solutions were

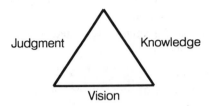

Vision

* all the related systems
  and circumstances.

* of the changed situation
  as a whole.

* discovering new meanings
  and interpretations.

* reconciling and recalling
  past events.

* idealising.

* self - projection
  into a situation.

Judgment

* truth and relevance of
  advice and information.

* capabilities of persons on
  whom one relies.

* appropriateness of action
  plans.

* demand, priorities, relationships
  in a situation.

* significance of observed factors
  and relationships related to known
  problems, difficulties or actions.

* when to go further.

* realities of a situation.

Knowledge

* Knowledge of oneself and of others involved.
* Knowledge of the situation.
* Knowledge of outside field of study.
* Knowledge of techniques and approaches.
* Knowledge of the procedures, policies, processes
  and capabilities of the systems related to the situation.
* Knowledge of relevant theories involved.

Figure 4.7
Personal elements

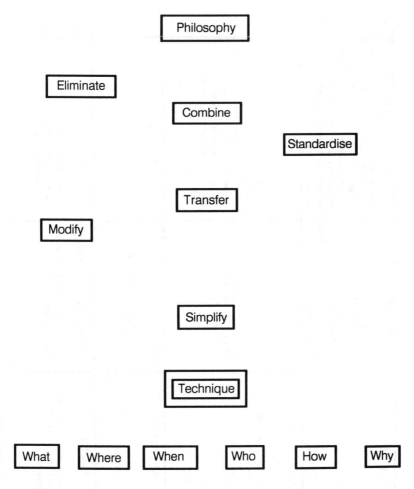

Figure 4.8

Examining problem areas

arrived at and made, that the thinking process can develop so that future results can be improved. Some of the most common categories into which unwanted outcomes can be placed are:

- Failure to identify true needs.
- Starting to develop before a satisfactory specification of needs is prepared.
- Inadequate knowledge of techniques, systems, people available, their costs, skill requirements, strengths and weaknesses and pay-offs.
- Lack of knowledge or awareness of basic principles and concepts.
- Lack of knowledge of other management functions.

Primary questions

	Why?	Alternatives	Selection for development
What is achieved? Consider the element in isolation. Bear in mind the subject of the chart. NB: What is achieved, NOT how it is accomplished or why.	**Why?** Reasons given may not be valid. True reasons must be uncovered.	What else could be achieved? The answer to this section is never 'nothing'. Three main alternatives must always be considered: non-achievement, part achievement and the avoidance of the necessity for achievement.	What should be achieved? It is helpful to divide into the long and short term. Under long term can go suggestions for future research, customer education and the like. The aim is elimination or modification as a second. The economics of the situation must be thought about at all levels.
How is it achieved? Information should be tabulated as simply as possible under these main headings with all relevant details. 1. materials employed 2. equipment employed 3. operator's method, posture & environment 4. operating conditions including SAFETY procedures	**Why that way?** Reasons should be investigated for each of the tabulated items under each heading.	How else could it be achieved? Consider all conceivable alternatives for each main heading.	How should it be achieved? Each heading should be considered first in isolation and selection made of the most appropriate items. Consider the economics. The selected items should then be knitted together to produce the best, SAFEST and cheapest method.
When is it achieved? What are the previous and subsequent significant activities and what are the time factors involved. What is the frequency?	**Why then?** What determines a) the sequence; and, b) the frequency.	When else could it be achieved? All conceivable alternatives should be considered.	When should it be achieved? Consider the economics.
Where is it achieved? Since the fundamental questions have been cleared at the selection stage, only the defined position in the factory, plant or area is required. Where appropriate, give reference to location and distance from previous and subsequent activity. NB: Remember the three dimensions.	**Why there?** What governs the location today and what were the original reasons?	Where else could it be achieved? All conceivable alternatives should be considered.	Where should it be achieved? Answer might be in relation to some other activity. Consider limitations and cost of building designs and services, etc.

Figure 4.8A

Examining the problem areas		
Primary questions		Secondary questions

The present facts	Why?	Alternatives	Selection for development
Who achieves it?	**Why that person?**	**Who else could achieve it?**	**Who should achieve it?**
1. Number of operators 2. Grade (e.g. skilled, male) 3. Employment type (night worker) 4. Designation or name 5. Wage scale and incentive scheme where appropriate	Give reasons for each heading	All possible alternatives should be considered	It may be possible to select the individual without work measurement and recommendations as to wage scale and incentives will normally be made at the development stage

Figure 4.8B

- Lack of knowledge of alternative established approaches.
- Lack of time to make the best decision.
- Taking decisions in areas where one's own knowledge is insufficiently developed.
- Lack of knowledge by those implementing change of what is required of them.
- Inability to overcome personal prejudice.
- Failure to determine priority areas for effort and stick to them.
- Failure to make contacts or to use them.
- Lack of data search.
- Lack of adequate accident and other relevant data collection.
- Failure to communicate between those who are involved in the diagnosis and development of new approaches.

Mental Roulette!

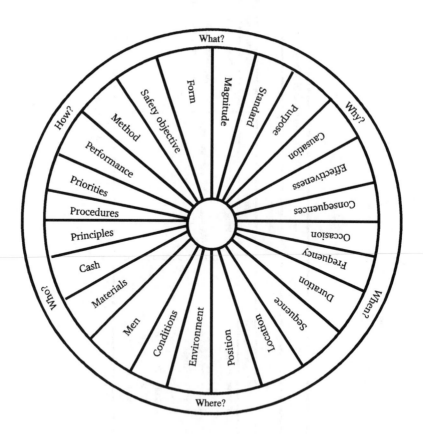

Figure 4.9

- Inability to profit from past mistakes.
- Lack of interest in increasing personal capability by adding to, questioning, re-arranging one's beliefs and understanding of personal mental process.
- Failure to make maximum use for other purposes of every element of work done.
- Shortage of relevant data.
- Inadequate management policies, plans and controls.
- Inability to fix realistic targets and to check achievements.
- Striving for an inadequate concept of good solution.
- Allowing temporary expedients to become permanent.
- Poor human relations and motivation.
- Inadequate selection and training of staff.

Client relationship in problem solving

Safety managers must sometimes bring in outside help when problem solving. It is also common for a specialist safety manager, say from head office, who arrives at a distant outstation to be known by name only. In such circumstances the safety manager then adopts the role of consultant as far as the outstation is concerned. Additionally, it is recognised that certain areas within the scope of the general safety practitioner may sometime require expert help in a specific area outside the general terms of reference of the safety personnel available. Outside help will mean employing a consultant and there are several stages to consider when developing a consultancy relationship irrespective of whether the consultant is 'in-house' or from a completely external source. There are six basic stages to this which are:

1. Initial entry;
2. Contracting;
3. Diagnosis;
4. Action planning;
5. Evaluation;
6. Withdrawal.

Initial entry

It is essential that trust, confidence, credibility and integrity are established and there must be mutual feelings and understandings about the problem to be solved. This will necessitate the clarification and understanding of skills and experience being offered. Gaining mutual confidence that you are the person best suited to help is important. It is hoped that the desired outcomes are:

- Understanding of the problem.
- Mutual wish to work together.
- Beginning of a relationship.

Where an external consultant or internal safety manager is concerned it is crucial that their involvement is widely seen by the workforce as one employed purely to solve a particular safety problem and not for any 'other' reason.

Contracting

Developing an initial contract on both a business and psychological basis is important. At this stage it is helpful to define helper/client roles, agree authority and responsibility aspects of the project and to agree the success criteria. From this stage it is possible to come to a formal contract, produce a plan of action, reaffirm commitment and the 'client' accepts the 'consultant' as the legitimate help.

Diagnosis

The 'consultant' plays the lead in determining who is the real client and what the specific problem(s) is/are and provides an opportunity to share new approaches, ideas and viewpoints on the problem. This is so that a joint definition of the problem can be published, ownership of the problem identified and agreement upon the evaluation criteria agreed.

Action planning

This stage commences with a joint lead involving the safety manager and 'external' consultant although the input from the latter diminishes as the action plans are implemented. This allows for the exploration of alternative methods and plans and for assessing consequences. At the same time leverage points can be identified before deciding upon methods and plans for the first action steps and the development of feedback systems for monitoring results. Outcomes from this stage should provide for a shared knowledge of all alternative strategies, a commitment to the selected plan and permits the weaning policy to be established (i.e. for a move away from dependency).

Evaluation

This will allow for the monitoring of people's reactions to plans as well as technical performance of safety programmes. At the same time, there should be assessment of resistance to change so that plan modification or success criteria can be achieved. In safety terms, this stage provides an opportunity to cultivate people's awareness of your concern and appreciation of their problems and to evaluate the level of dependency. This process will allow an opportunity for further action and also allow a reduction of people's worry levels. An openness and constructiveness in response is hoped for which is a basis for reducing 'consultant' dependency.

Withdrawal

This stage will cater for the evaluation and the development of resources necessary for a 'no dependency' state to occur. At the same time, the client

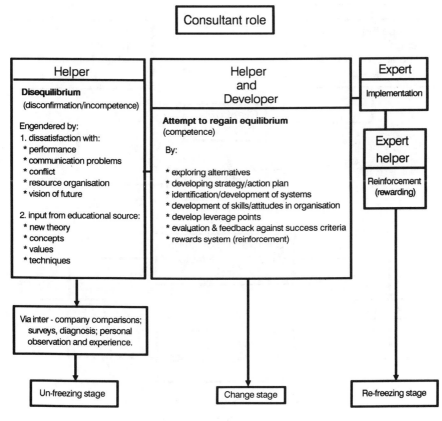

Figure 4.10

Change process in organisations

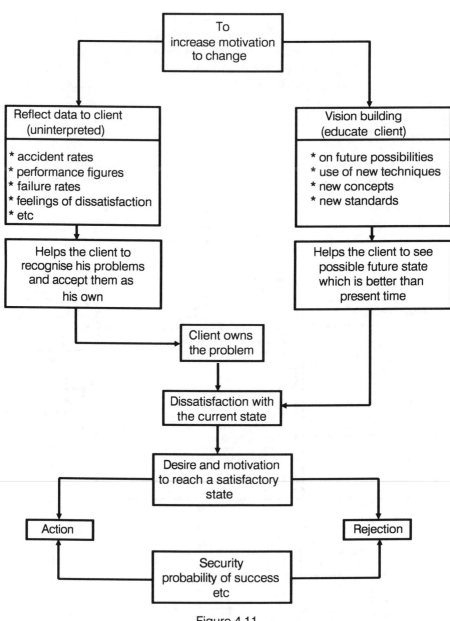

Figure 4.11

Increasing motivation to change

may come to an agreement concerning the planned withdrawal of the consultant whilst also assessing the organisation's self-confidence. It is hoped that such withdrawal will be without any side effects although there will be provision for re-entry where appropriate but above all for the continued successful operation of safety systems after withdrawal.

Changes in people can be classified under two headings. These are:

Gap bridging. Against an overall goal, a strategic need for change is established and the aim is to bridge the gap from where we are now to where we wish to be. The danger in many change situations arising during problem solving is that the 'gap' is seen as too large for those involved and the associated goals are refuted.

Incremental change. This is geared to reducing areas of unpleasantness, hurt, weakness but this process oscillates and is unrelated to an overall goal.

The change process in organisations is shown in Figure 4.10. Some notes summarising how to increase the motivation for change are given in Figure 4.11.

Preparing for entry

When visiting an outstation as a 'consultant', or when the safety manager is undertaking duties in a consultative role, it is important to get the behaviour right. By thinking through some of the issues listed below, behaviour can be selected more appropriately. This may help to avoid some major pitfalls.

1. Get agreement on:

   - Objectives – mutual understanding is important.
   - Who will be there? – do not be assailed without being ready.
   - Who should be seen? – for what purpose?
   - How long will it last? – people are busy, therefore keep interviews as short as possible.

2. Think through:

   - Own objectives, needs and goals – what action is required?
   - Criteria for assessing help levels – commitments, skills, learning, payoffs for the organisation, for the consultant, for the department, etc.
   - Internal state at the moment – problems which are experienced from other internal/external people which may interfere with the meeting.
   - Preparing to be non-defensive (exploring attacks and resistances rather than fighting back).

3. Try to predict:

- Client's needs and goals – underlying feelings (e.g. use to which the consultant is being put).
- Criteria for judgment – comparable experiences, appearance, sociability, self-confidence, publications, record of success.

Some common mistakes made by a safety consultant or outside safety expert can be summarised as follows:

- Losing professional detachment.
- Imposing own values.
- Becoming trapped in one part of the project.
- Unacceptable attachment to the client.
- Failing to seek help.
- Failing to recognise or analyse personal client resistance.
- Not being sufficiently candid.
- Not appreciating client's wish not to change.
- Changing only one subsystem.
- Unbalanced use of structural v process change.
- Attempting an unbalanced change.
- Creating a change overload.
- Not recognising change resistance factors.
- Failing to recognise full implication of accident analysis findings.

Operational safety management

The problem with operational safety management is to develop a satisfactory conceptual framework which will enable organisations having different objectives but similar problems to be studied together. In theory, all operating systems can be regarded as being either input, transformation or output systems. This is sometimes called the *conversion subsystem*. The most common application of operational safety management is in manufacturing industries where the operating system is usually called the production system. However, the types of problems which occur in manufacturing industries also occur in service industries and organisations generally. For example, these can also be represented by the input, transformation and output model. Operating systems also have a controller feedback loop sometimes referred to as the *controller subsystem*. The feedback system consists of sensor, comparer, memory and effector functions. Operating systems are composed of smaller systems which may be connected in various ways such as in flow (series) systems or parallel systems.

Techniques are required to deal with problems of designing, planning and controlling safety operating systems. In practice there are three major reasons why manufacturing safety systems can be different from service safety systems:

1. Production is insulated from the environment;
2. Manufacturing safety systems do not usually involve the public;
3. The production function is usually more readily distinguishable.

The use of operations safety management for decision making is best illustrated by example.

Example 4.1

A local transport depot has the problem of purchasing salted grit for spreading on its goods yards when weather conditions make them dangerous through the build up of ice. The supply situation for grit is both uncertain and subject to seasonal price fluctuations. Because of this, transport firms tend to buy in summer and autumn rather than wait for winter to arrive. The problem is deciding how much grit to buy to meet the safety objectives of the transport group.

The amount of grit needed in one winter depends primarily on two factors:

1. The level of gritting service given; and
2. The severity of the winter.

The transport head office decide that all heavy goods areas must be regarded as primary treatment areas, factory roadways and loading/ unloading areas as secondary treatment areas and car parks and other slippery areas (footpaths, etc) as domestic treatment areas. All primary treatment areas must be gritted if the weather is bad whilst secondary and domestic areas are gritted at the discretion of the safety manager. For one group gritting operation, 10 tonnes are needed for primary treatment areas, 20 tonnes for secondary treatment areas and 5 tonnes for domestic areas.

This particular transport group classify winters by the number of times it has to grit between November and April each year. Mild winters have up to 20 gritting days, normal winters have between 20 and 26 gritting days and severe winters have over 26 gritting days.

Past records show that in the past 20 years there have been:

Seven mild winters with an average of 15 gritting days.
Eight normal winters with an average of 23 gritting days.
Five severe winters with an average of 30 gritting days.

Grit may be purchased by the company during the winter if stocks run out but the cost is much higher.

For next year, price forecasts are given below:

Out of season price	£20 per tonne
Mild winter price	£20 per tonne
Normal winter price	£25 per tonne
Severe winter price	£30 per tonne

Any grit remaining at the end of the winter is stored in three dump areas around the works. The costs of storage are, in practice, very large since capital is tied up at a cost of about 20% of the grit. Furthermore, about 50% of the grit evaporates over the summer. Thus only about 30% of the cost of remaining grit can be reclaimed for future use. Therefore, if 100 tonnes are purchased at £20 per tonne and 50 tonnes are left at the end of winter then the original costs can be reduced by 30% of the cost of the remaining grit, so total cost is as follows:

$$£(100 \times 20) - 0.3(50 \times 20) = £1700.$$

The task for the safety manager is to advise his organisation on how much grit to purchase in order to meet the safety requirements of the organisation. For the purposes of the example it will be assumed that it is now mid-summer.

The safety management decision

The first task in any decision situation is to decide what the decision boundary is. For example, in this particular case, there appear to be two separate decisions. First, what level of service to provide and second, how much grit to buy. It is necessary to define clearly the area of concern. The level of service decision would seem to be basically a policy decision which would need to be made before any decision regarding actual quantities of grit is made. However, the buying strategy can be regarded as being independent of the actual quantity of grit necessary.

The criteria

The actual criterion on which the decision will be made can profoundly affect the outcome of the decision-making process. Cost of the grit would seem to be the most obvious criterion and, since there are no data as to how levels of benefit could be assessed from the gritting process, then cost will be used.

The alternatives

There are many alternative buying strategies. These range from buying as much grit as we like now (mid-summer) to buying no grit at all at present.

To illustrate the procedure to be used it is necessary to examine three alternative strategies. These are:

1. Buy enough grit for the average mild winter;
2. Buy enough grit for the average normal winter;
3. Buy enough grit for the average severe winter.

The states of nature

The most obvious area of uncertainty is the severity of the winter. Again, although this is a continuously variable factor, it is assumed that only three types of winter occur. These are:

1. Mild;
2. Normal;
3. Severe.

Outcomes

Since there are three alternative strategies and three states of nature, there will be $3 \times 3 = 9$ possible outcomes to consider.

Assuming only primary treatment areas are considered then requirements will be as follows:

- A *mild* winter will need $\quad 15 \times 10 = 150$ tonnes
- A *normal* winter will need $\quad 23 \times 10 = 230$ tonnes
- A *severe* winter will need $\quad 30 \times 10 = 300$ tonnes

1. Let it be assumed that 150 tonnes be bought: If the winter is *mild* then sufficient grit will be held and the total cost will be:

$$£20 \times 150 = £3000$$

If the winter is *normal* then an additional 80 tonnes will be required at £25 per tonne. The total cost therefore will be £3000 plus $£(80 \times 25) = £5000$.

If the winter is *severe* then an extra 150 tonnes will be required at £30 per tonne. The total cost will be £3000 plus $£(150 \times 30) = £7500$.

2. Let it be assumed that 230 tonnes be bought: If the winter is *mild* then a surplus of 80 tonnes exists. The total cost is 230 at £20 = £4600 less 30% of the cost of the surplus. This is $80 \times 20 \times 0.3 = £1380$. £4600 less £1380 = £3220. All other outcomes can be similarly calculated.

The matrix

All the outcomes can be put into the form of a matrix as shown in Figure 4.12.

All the outcomes can be placed in the form of a matrix:

Strategies	Mild (p=0.35)	Normal (p=0.4)	Severe (p=0.25)	Expected outcome
Buy 150 tonnes	£3,000	£5,000	£7,500	£4,925
Buy 230 tonnes	£4,120	£4,600	£6,700	£4,957
Buy 300 tonnes	£8,100	£5,580	£6,000	£6,567

Expected outcomes is the sum of the outcomes weighted by the probability of their occurrence.

Figure 4.12

The decision matrix

Points to note

- Of the three strategies examined, buying 150 tonnes of grit has the least cost.
- As more grit is bought, the less risky the decision becomes. The difference between the highest and lowest outcomes gets less. This would then mean going for 230 tonnes.
- The difference between the expected outcomes of the three strategies is not that great in this case. The consequences of being wrong are not that great.
- The expected consequences of not choosing the optimum strategy will become greater as the seasonal price change becomes higher and the proportion of the reclaimable grit gets lower.
- In practice the decision will be more dynamic in so much as grit could be bought every month rather than just two opportunities as assumed above.
- In practice the price forecasts would also have to be regarded as probabilistic.

Decision making in operational safety management

The problem is to provide useful conceptual tools to aid the decision-making process. Making operational decisions is usually done in conditions of uncertainty or unreliability. Decisions are made in the context of the objectives of the organisation and these are both value and functional objectives and shape the criteria on which choice is made. The decision situation has five basic elements which are:

1. Strategies (alternative options);
2. States of nature (described by probability distributions);
3. Outcomes (for each combination of a strategy and a state of nature);
4. Forecasts (the probability of each state of nature);
5. Criteria (often conflicting).

The decision situation is formalised in the form of a matrix and for each strategy, all the various outcomes for possible states of nature are calculated and weighted by their probability of occurrence. In this way, the *expected outcome* for each strategy can be calculated. Also, the *risk* inherent in each strategy can be assessed together with the *degree of difference* between the expected outcomes of the different strategies. In practice, some states of nature do not apply to all strategies. There are usually more than one criterion which often are conflicting or non-quantifiable. The usefulness of the 'answers' depends on the accuracy of the forecasts.

Decision theory can provide valuable insights into a decision situation. It does not, however, make decisions on your behalf.

Example 4.2

A manufacturing company manufactures five products and has 11 different departments. The products are transported between departments on trolleys of a standard size but the products vary in size as follows:

Product	A	B	C	D	E
Quantity per month	1000	2000	500	10000	1000
Items per trolley	20	20	2	100	10
Loads per month	50	100	250	100	100

Each department requires the following floor area:

Department	1	Receiving	500 sq ft
Department	2	Stores	400 sq ft
Department	3	Saws	200 sq ft
Department	4	Engineering lathes	600 sq ft
Department	5	Turret lathes	150 sq ft
Department	6	Drills	500 sq ft
Department	7	Mills	1050 sq ft
Department	8	Grinders	500 sq ft
Department	9	Assembly	800 sq ft
Department	10	Finished goods	500 sq ft
Department	11	Despatch	500 sq ft

Each product follows the routes shown below:

Product	A	route departments 1, 2, 3, 5, 7, 6, 9, 10, 11
Product	B	route departments 1, 2, 7, 8, 6, 9, 10, 11
Product	C	route departments 1, 2, 3, 4, 7, 8, 9, 10, 11
Product	D	route departments 1, 2, 4, 6, 10, 11
Product	E	route departments 1, 2, 3, 4, 7, 8, 6, 4, 7, 9, 10, 11

This company are to move to a new green field site and so have some freedom over the shape of their new building. The safety management task will be to work with the production director to devise a layout for the new building which will provide for maximum efficiency and safety. To do this it is necessary to:

1. Develop a summary chart showing the flow between each department;
2. Represent each department by a circle and the flows between them by lines manipulating the circles until the flow between each department appears to be minimised;
3. Translate this schematic representation into a realistic layout.

In these cases it is a good idea to summarise the departmental load requirements. This is given in the table below.

Load Summary

Department		1	2	3	4	5	6	7	8	9	10	11
Receiving	1		600									
Stores	2			400	100				100			
Saw	3				350		50					
Eng. Lathe	4						100	450				
Tur. Lathe	5							50				
Drill	6				100						150	100
Mill	7						50		450	100		
Grinder	8						200			250		
Assembly	9										500	
Fin. Goods	10											600
Despatch	11											

An initial solution is presented in Figure 4.13.

A final solution to the problem is presented in Figures 4.14 and 4.15 which shows the areas associated with the departments.

The layout can be fitted into a rectangular building with approximately the same area requirements and idealised flow pattern providing maximum safety. This is shown in Figure 4.15.

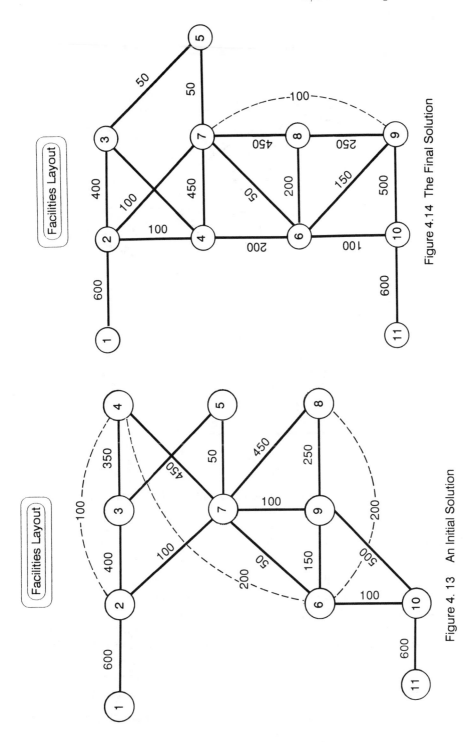

Facilities Layout

Figure 4.14 The Final Solution

Facilities Layout

Figure 4. 13 An Initial Solution

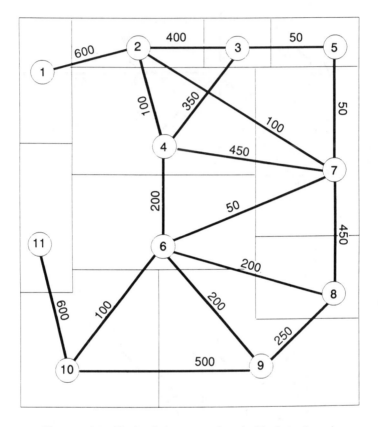

Figure 4.15   Final solution associated with departments

Facilities survey

The problem here will be to locate productive or service facilities together relative to each other so that some measure of system effectiveness is maximised. This includes the safety requirements.

The objective in most facility layout situations is to minimise total flow of either material or people. The less movement involved usually indicates the least cost incurred for the maximum safety – an objective we all strive for. Zoning constraints also influence which facilities can be placed next to each other. Classically, there are three pure types of layout. These are:

1. The *process* layout, whereby all similar facilities are placed together;

2. The *product* layout, where all facilities needed for one particular product or output are placed together;
3. The *fixed position* layout, where facilities are brought to the product.

Tasks associated with *product layout* are concerned with allocating problems to positions so as to *balance* the line whilst problems associated with *process layout* stem from the combinatorial complexity of the situation (i.e. for N facilities, there are $N!$ ways of locating them relative to each other). Techniques tend to be mathematical or heuristic and information is usually summarised on *cross charts* or *relationship charts* which enable facilities with strong links to be noted. Computerised heuristics packages are available.

Facilities layout is largely a matter of manual manipulation of the problem whilst the combinational complexity of the problem prohibits any pure optimisation technique.

Work measurement

It is necessary to know how long a job will, or should take so that manning levels can be calculated, labour costs can be estimated, machine loading can be done in safety and payment schemes can be devised. Work measurement attempts to establish times for jobs under conditions of:

- Qualified workers.
- Specified jobs.
- A defined level of performance.
- Safety.

The technique involves basic times for jobs which can be obtained by any of the five methods employed in work measurement. These are:

1. Time study – using a stop watch;
2. Synthesis – from existing elemental data;
3. Predetermine motion – time systems;
4. Analytical estimating;
5. Activity sampling.

Standard times for jobs are obtained by adding relaxation allowances to the basic times. In practice, different techniques have different advantages depending on whether *accuracy* or *consistency* of times is required. The process of *rating* is still a very dubious procedure and it should be remembered that job timing can cause industrial disputes. Here the safety manager must ensure the fine balance between the need for his organisation to be as efficient as possible and the need to remain within the maximum safety limits available. An example of work measurement for synthesising times for laying gas mains is given in Figure 4.16.

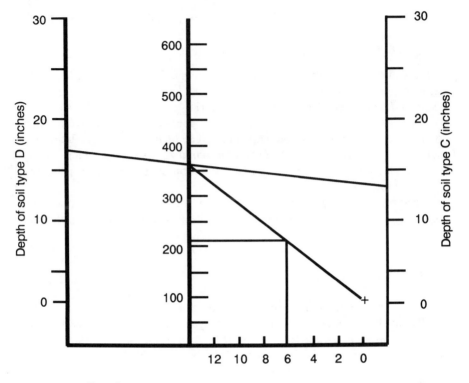

Example:

A 6 ft length of pipe is to be laid 29 inches deep into the ground consisting of a 13 inch top layer (type C) and the rest (16 inches) type D. A line is drawn from 13 on scale C to 16 on scale D. The place where the line cuts the standard time scale is marked and a line drawn from this intersection to the cross. From this line, the time X for laying 6 ft of pipe can be read off.

A nomograph for synthesizing times for laying gas mains.

Figure 4.16
Work measurement

Method study

The problem here is to develop an approach by which safer, more effective and lower cost methods of work may be devised. There are six steps to consider in method study. These are:

1. Select;
2. Record;
3. Examine;
4. Develop;

5. Install;
6. Maintain.

Whilst these are self-explanatory, notes are attached below which may be added to these areas.

Select

This concerns the task or tasks to be studied. Monitoring of various tasks will highlight potential or substantiated danger.

Record

Note each existing method. This can be done in either of two ways:

By Charts:

- Outline process chart.
- Flow process chart.
- Two-handed process chart.
- Multiple activity chart.

By Diagrams:

- Layout diagrams.
- Flow diagrams.
- String diagrams.
- Memo-motion (time lapse).
- Micro-motion photography.
- Cyclegraphs.
- Cronocyclegraphs.

Examine

All methods should be examined together with obtained data and information. Use critical examination technique.

Develop

Develop new method which will employ the principles of motion economy, safety and schemes for collecting ideas (brainstorming).

Install

Install new safe method. Problems can be reduced by consultation with all concerned parties from the first stage when selecting jobs for study.

Maintain

As expected it is necessary periodically to check and update methods.

Ergonomics

It is necessary to establish guide rules for the safe design of the physical environment and of equipment. Ergonomics is concerned with the physiological characteristics of people and how they interface with the equipment they use and the physical environment. The man-machine interface is concerned with information flows through displays and controls. The man-environment interface is concerned with how performance varies with environmental conditions. Techniques include information on:

- Effective designs of displays.
- The speed, accuracy, loading and range controls.
- The physical characteristics of people referred to as anthropometric data.
- Acceptable standards of heating, lighting and sound levels.
- General health and safety.

In practice, the redesign of equipment and working environment can be expensive. Designers find that designing for a range of physical sizes and individual preference can prove difficult.

Job evaluation

This concerns the process of determining without regard to personalities, the worth an organisation places on one job in relation to that of another. The International Labour Office (ILO) states that job evaluation may be defined as an attempt to determine and compare the demands which the normal performance of particular jobs makes on normal workers without taking account of the individual abilities or performances of the workers concerned. There is a need to evaluate jobs because most people have strong feelings about 'fairness' or 'equity' of relative wage levels. Comparison of the contents of different jobs tends to influence attitudes. Workers doing the same job with equal efficiency under the same conditions should get the same wage and differences in the content of jobs should be reflected in the rates of pay for those jobs.

Job evaluation considers five fundamental issues:

1. A thorough examination of the job to be assessed;
2. The preparation of a job description to record its characteristics fairly;

3. The comparison of one job with another by an approved method;
4. The arranging of jobs in a progression;
5. Relating the progression of jobs to a money scale.

There are five common methods for job evaluation and these are:

- Ranking.
- Classification.
- Analytical methods.
- Factor comparison methods.
- Points rating method.

Safety should feature in all these methods but is sometimes overlooked by the job evaluator. Some safety audit processes use the point rating system therefore an example using this type of job evaluation method is given below.

Example 4.3

1. Previous experience

First decide if any previous experience is necessary before the operator can perform the job in question. Unskilled or repetitive operations are not expected to require any previous experience and are catered for in item 2 below. When previous experience is necessary, decide what experience a new operator should have when applying for the job in the first place.

Points range: 0–28

2. Learning period

This is a measure of the time required for an individual to become familiar with new surroundings. Where no previous experience is required, it is necessary to consider the time that the 'average' untrained labour would need before the operator could produce enough to earn the minimum wage. Points may be awarded as follows:

    2 months   8 points
    3 months 10 points
    4 months 12 points

Points range: 0–12

3. Reasoning ability

How does the job require the operator to think? Is it a process that can be performed subconsciously or must the operator reason out a sequence of events?

Points range:

Low	0–4
Medium	5–8
High	9–16
Very high	17–23

4. Complexity process

The extent to which the operation requires the mastery of an unusual number of details or the memorising of large numbers of variations.

Points range:

Low	0
Medium	0–3
High	4–7
Very high	8–11

5. Manual dexterity and motor accuracy

This is included to consider the unusual quickness or deftness which may be required to do the work successfully.

Points range:

Low	0
Medium	0–4
High	5–9

6. Materials

Measure the potential damage that can be caused to the materials or components of the product. This does not include tools or equipment.

Points range:

Under £100	0
Under £1,000	3
Over £1,000	6

7. Effect on subsequent operations

Consider whether lack of care might make work on subsequent operations more difficult or might necessitate additional operations.

Points range:

Low	0–2
Medium	3–5
High	6–8
Very high	9–12

8. Equipment

Refers to the damage that might be caused to machines or other items that assist in processing the product. It is necessary to evaluate the damage that can be caused to the equipment by carelessness. As a useful guide and depending upon the type of industry involved, say 1 point per £1,000.

Points range:
$0-x$

9. Teamwork

Does the job demand close co-operation and adjustment of movement with other workers?

Points range:
2 in team 1
5 in team 2
10 or more 3

10. Attention to orders

To what extent does the job demand an ability to follow the details of a written order, a specification or the detail of a drawing?

Points range:

None	0
Occasional (simple)	1–4
Occasional (complex)	5–8
Constant (simple)	5–8
Constant (complex)	9–12

11. Monotony

This will consider whether the job is boring, tedious or irksome.

Points range:
0–7

12. Abnormal position

Are there any unusual or cramped positions required which cramp or strain muscles to an abnormal degree?

Points range:

Standing with little body movement	0–1
Frequent stooping or reaching	2–3
Continuous stooping, reaching/confinement	4–5

13. Abnormal effort

Is the work heavy to such an extent that the job is unattractive or that unusual physical strength is required? The actual weight to be lifted is not the important factor here but the physical effort needed.

Points range:

Lifting 20 lb frequently or 50 lb occasionally (low)	0–3
Lifting 50 lb frequently or 100 lb occasionally (medium)	4–7
Lifting 100 lb frequently or 150 lb occasionally (high)	8–10

14. Disagreeableness

This concerns the degree to which the job is made particularly unpleasant by the presence of wet, heat, cold, noise, dust and fumes.

Points range:

Low	0–2
Medium	3–5
High	6–8
Very high	9–15

15. Accident

Here the probability of risk must be assessed and then the potential severity of injury to the operator. It is recommended that the severity of injury is less important than the number of accidents occurring as the criteria for what makes a minor accident more serious are difficult to define.

To deal with this aspect equitably, company accident records must be consulted and a minimum of three years data should be used in calculating any trends. As a general guide the following pointing system might be considered:

Points range:

Less than 5 reported accidents/dangerous occurrences in past year	0–5
More than 5 but less than 10	6–10
More than 10 accidents (2 points per accident)	$11-x$

16. Disease

To what degree are the working conditions harmful to health or conducive to an occupational disease such as dermatitis, skin cancer, silicosis, poisoning by lead or analine, etc? Again a retrospective study of company records is required to assist in weighting this fairly. The weighting can be split between potential v actual. If a company uses known hazardous

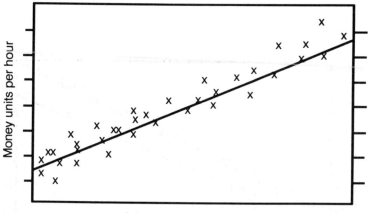

Each job is plotted on a graph, one axis being the points value of the job
and the other axis being the present wage rate for that job

Figure 4.17 A

Points to money

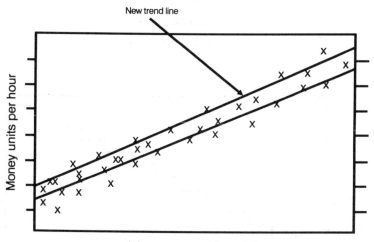

A trend line is drawn through the points using regression techniques.
This represents the present wage trend but many jobs will be above
this line; these are the jobs which are relatively overpaid. Usually, in
order to ensure the smooth introduction of this type of scheme, two
guarantees are given. These are:

1. No person will suffer a reduction in wages; and
2. An increase of x% will be made to the average wage rate.

Figure 4.17 B

Points to money

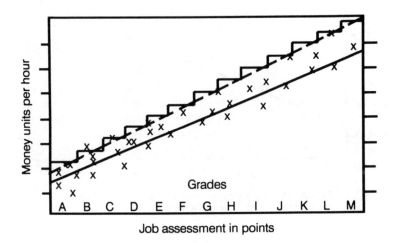

Job assessment in points

A new wage trend line is drawn x% higher than the existing trend line (the dotted line). Job grade steps are then drawn about the new trend line with as many steps as grades that are necessary. This will often leave a few jobs which are still above the step line. These jobs usually have to remain an anomaly until general wage increases absorb them.

Figure 4.17 C

Points to money

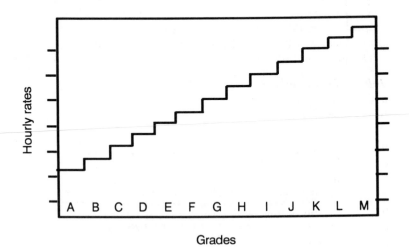

Grades

Figure 4.17 D

Points to money

products but has no record of actual disease then standard weighting will apply. If disease is known to exist then the weighting may double.

Points range:

No recorded diseases	0–6
Recorded diseases	$7-x$

The assessment of manual jobs is usually carried out by a committee comprising of the departmental manager, job analyst, foreman and the workers' representative. Safety managers are not always consulted on these issues and where this happens then the risk of accident potentiality being incorrectly assessed must increase thus invalidating the job evaluation exercise. Methods for converting these points into money vary considerably. A few examples are given in Figures 4.17A to D.

Critical path analysis

This is a method of helping the safety manager understand the various phases of a task and to understand why some tasks have to be undertaken before others. Critical path analysis (CPA) makes a valuable contribution to safety for it provides for things to happen in a logical order. As an example, a factory is to modify its works' canteen and install 'superspud', a new all-purpose automatic chip frying machine. The general manager shows you a list of jobs to be done and seeks your comments as to the safety aspects of installation. Having a copy of the list you also consider the most efficient way of doing the job whilst at the same time maximising safety. The list is as follows:

Job	*Description*	*Duration*
a	order 'superspud'	10 days
b	clear site	1 day
c	reinforce the floor	4 days
d	install pump	2 days
e	install electrics	5 days
f	install overhead chip feed	3 days
g	install chip fryer	2 days
h	set and adjust controls	3 days
i	fit autosalt pump	1 day
j	fit autosalt shaker	1 day
k	connect autosalt pump/shaker	1 day
l	test fry and adjustment	3 days

In such a case it is important to be aware of the relationship between all of the listed activities. For example, activity l (chip tasting) cannot occur until task g (install chip fryer) has been completed. Activity k cannot take place until both j and i have been satisfactorily completed. It may be dangerous to have the electrician laying wires down when men are working off ground fitting the overhead chip feed so e has been placed in front of f. For each activity then we have:

Activity	Preceding Activities
a	—
b	—
c	b
d	e
e	c
f	c
g	a, f, d
h	g
i	e
j	g
k	j, i
l	h, k

A useful way of illustrating the relationships given above is by drawing a network of arrows where each arrow indicates an activity. This is given in Figure 4.18.

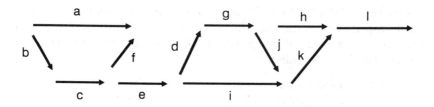

A convenient method of illustrating the relationships is by drawing a network of arrows where each arrow indicates an activity.

Figure 4.18
Critical Path Analysis

More commonly, arrows are used to show activities whilst circles are used to show events as seen in Figure 4.19.

Numbers shown by the arrows indicate the length of time or duration that the activity takes. The whole task described above can be displayed pictorially which makes analysis much simpler to understand. When drawing networks, there are some conventions in general use:

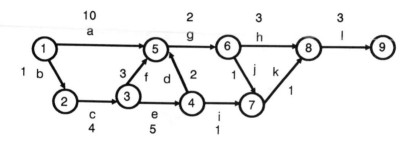

More commonly, using arrows to indicate 'activities' and circles to represent 'events'.

Thus, event (1)   is the beginning of activity a and b

event (2)   is the end of activity b and the beginning of activity c etc.

The numbers by the arrows indicate the length of time the activity takes (its duration).
This is a useful representation of the task in hand.

Figure 4.19

- Networks are composed of events and activities and an event is summarised as of a definite recognisable nature; a point in time. One
event can mark the concurrence of several separate events and can
therefore sometimes be referred to as a node or junction. However,
an event cannot be reached until all activities leading to it are complete.
- An activity is the work or task which leads to the event. On occasions
an activity is not true work since no resources are consumed. For
example, waiting for the delivery of the 'superspud'. This is not a true
job but it is included in the network because the activity is vital to the
project. Events which occur at the beginning and end of an activity
are referred to as the head and tail events.

Analysing the network

A network illustrates *what* is to be done, *when, by whom* and in *what time.*
It also provides a clear statement of policy which can be readily understood
by potential users. If no further action were taken, considerable benefits
would have already been derived. By using simple arithmetic, it is possible
to extract a considerable amount of information. The critical path is the
sequence of events which indicate the shortest time in which the total task
can be completed (i.e. the longest timepath through the network). See
Figures 4.20 A to D.

The importance of the critical path comes from the fact that only on this

Drawing the network

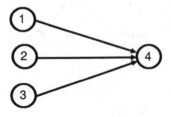

An event cannot be reached until all the activities leading to it are complete.
Event 4 is not reached until activities 1- 4, 2 - 4 and 3 - 4 are all completed

Figure 4.20 A

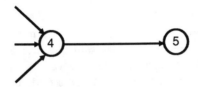

No activity can start until its tail event is reached. Activity 4 - 5 can not start until
event 4 is reached. Two further conventions are that time flows from left to right
and head events have a number higher than the tail

Figure 4.20 B

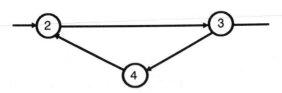

The above situation is logically impossible since event 2 depends on event 3 which in turn
depends on event 4, which depends on event 2 and so on. This is called looping. While
obvious in this small example, looping can be difficult to detect in a larger and more complex
situation

Figure 4.20 C

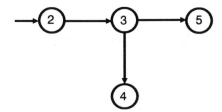

This is referred to as 'dangling' and is a logic fault since activity 3 - 4 leads to nothing.

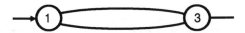

'Dummies' are activities which neither use resources or time and are used on two occasions:

1. When two independent activities have the same head and tail events as above.

To reduce confusion, a dummy is introduced.:

2. When two independent chains have a common event as shown below:

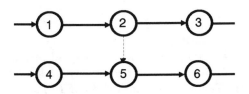

Figure 4.20 D

Understanding the network

sequence of activities will any delay to an individual activity necessarily lead to an extension in the total time set aside for the project (see Figure 4.21). All other activities have some degree of flexibility associated with them and this can be quantified by calculating the earliest time that an activity can begin.

The figure shown in Figure 4.22 shows a critical path from 0 to 1 to 2 to 4 to 5, giving a total project time of 14 days. By dividing up the circles as shown, it is possible to consider the earliest time an event can occur. The earliest event time (EET) of event 0 is 0. Since activity 0–1 takes 4 days, the *EET* of event 1 will be 4. Similarly, the *EET's* of events 2 and 3 are day 9 and day 3 respectively. There are two routes to event 4 since an event cannot occur until all preceding activities are completed, the *EET* for event 4 must be derived from the *EET* for event 2, i.e. $9 + 3 = 12$.

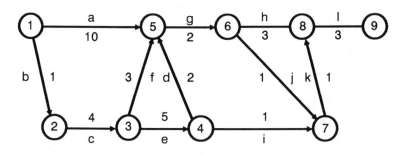

The 'superspud' example shows the shortest time in which the total task can be completed is 20 days. This is the length of the longest path through the network being the sequence of events 1 - 2 - 3 - 4 - 5 - 6 - 7 - 8 - 9, that is, the activities b,c,e,d,g,h,and l. This is the critical path.

Figure 4.21

The Critical Path

If this process is reversed, it is possible to find the latest time an event can occur. Event 4 must not occur after day 12 if event 5 is not to be delayed and so on. These latest event times (LET's) are written in the right hand side of the circles as shown in Figure 4.23. On examining activity 1–2 which is of 5 days duration, we see that this cannot start before day 4 and it must not finish after day 9. This leaves 5 days in which to complete a 5 day task. This is referred to as having no *float*. By examining activity 1–3 it can be seen that this job cannot start before day 4 and must finish before day 9. There are 5 days in which to complete a 2 day job therefore this activity has a $5 - 2 = 3$ days *float*.

Float

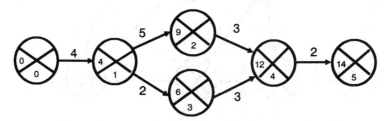

Figure 4.22

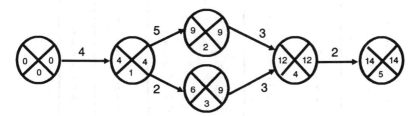

Figure 4.23

No float?

All the events on the critical path have the same
earliest and latest event times. This shows that
all activities on the critical path have zero float

Figure 4.24

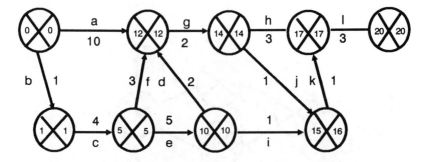

By following the same procedure for the original example it can be calculated that the earliest and latest event times and the float associated with each activity are as follows:

Activity	Start Time		Finish Time		Duration	Float
	Earliest	Latest	Earliest	Latest		
a	0	2	10	12	10	2
b	0	0	1	1	1	0
c	1	1	5	5	4	0
d	10	10	12	12	2	0
e	5	5	10	10	5	0
f	5	9	8	12	3	4
g	12	12	14	14	2	0
h	14	14	17	17	3	0
i	10	15	11	16	1	5
j	14	15	15	16	1	1
k	15	16	16	17	1	1
l	17	17	20	20	3	0

Where an activity has float, its start can be adjusted to suit other factors such as safety requirements or resource allocation. Float is more easily recognised if the network is drawn as a bar or GANTT chart. In Figure 4.26, the 'Superspud' example is drawn out as a Gantt chart.

Figure 4.25

The critical path

Summary

In this chapter an attempt has been made to outline the importance of operations management within the decision making process and to highlight its importance to safety. Many organisations use operations management as a means of maximising efficiency but a danger exists that this could be at the expense of safety with the result of significantly down-grading the effectiveness of the decision. A number of good text books exist on this subject

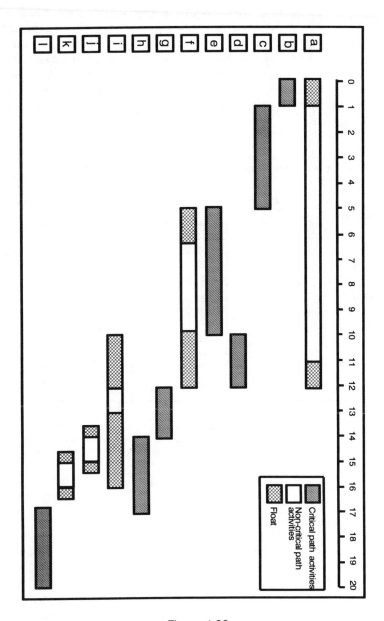

Figure 4.26
Superspud GANTT chart

and a recommended reading list has been added to the end of this chapter for the benefit of those wishing to pursue this subject further.

Those responsible for safety within the workplace must have an input to all operations management studies so that the safety factor can be included within the overall plan. Connected with operations management programmes are matters relating to incentive schemes and other types of payment for reward. These aspects are dealt with in Chapter 6 under a financial management heading as they can have an effect upon safety within an organisation.

Further reading

Faraday, J E (1977) *Work Study* (Pitman Publishing)

Harper, W M and Lim, H C (1982) *Operational Research* (Pitman Publishing)

Lockyer, K G (1984) *An Introduction to Critical Path Analysis* (Pitman Publishing)

Lockyer, K G and Muhlemann, A (1989) *Production and Operations Management* (Pitman Publishing)

5

Data collection and information

Opinion v fact

Everyone will have an opinion on safety matters. Some of these opinions may be informed whilst others will be less so. Some will form an opinion based upon a consensus view whilst others may use experience as a basis for their views and advice. Above all, such comment and advice is well meaning and usually given in good faith. The safety practitioner cannot rely on such an approach. He has to be accountable for his actions and therefore must adopt a more scientific methodology to his decision-making processes. We know that in an operational setting the only completely safe workplace is one that is closed; where people and the worksite are separate from each other. In everything that we do as human beings there is a risk attached to it. In crossing the road, smoking, drinking, eating and so on. All these activities have a risk inherent in them and a decision is taken whether to accept the risk or not. Similarly, in the workplace, such risks should be identified so that appropriate action can be taken by either the individual or the company. Dangers to the individual must be identified and minimised. It is in these areas that opinions have a tendency to form about what is considered hazardous and what is not. Anything which is known to feature regularly in accidents will need a higher priority than those factors which it is merely thought might contribute to the occurrence of an accident. This is particularly important in the larger organisation where accidents are more likely to occur. Not because they are more dangerous but because the more employees there are employed within an organisation, the more likely the incidence of accidents is to increase.

Management will require periodic reports from its safety professionals in order for it to meet its statutory obligations. These reports should contain sufficient information to enable appropriate management decisions to be taken. Such information should be factual wherever possible and subjective issues liable to interpretation should be kept to a minimum. Decisions based on this information are important in that the application of inappropriate safety measures may affect production and profitability. Some senior management executives fail to recognise the importance of the safety processes and show little enthusiasm for them. Safety, therefore, must be conducted and presented in terms that can be simply understood and the various implications affecting the organisation should be quantified wherever possible leaving opportunities for opinion based decisions to an absolute minimum. This in turn can promote the importance of safety within the boardroom and can create enthusiasm for certain options. Being told to do something without a detailed explanation or without choice of options is not exciting and will not create interest or enthusiasm. In order to assist those responsible for advising managements on efficient and effective safety measures, information to aid the decision-making process has to be systematically gathered. Here we need to discuss the types of information to be gathered. Its subsequent analysis for decision-making purposes is discussed in Chapter 7. It is only once this process has been completed and the analysis of the facts has been studied that personal opinion can be called upon.

Information gathering

The most important part of the safety practitioner's operational daily plan is the systematic collection of accident and dangerous occurrence data for analysis purposes. It should be remembered that many dangerous occurrences happen in reality but never get reported. This may be due to a feeling of failure by the person concerned, and threats of disciplinary action for breaches of safety codes and practice will not encourage the reporting of such incidents. Some organisations have set up confidential telephone lines in an attempt to combat this problem. Some of these firms can show an increase in the reporting of dangerous occurrences but admit that they may not be aware of all such instances. Safety management, therefore, must have a structured and systematic approach towards the gathering of dangerous occurrence data. Whilst the confidential telephone idea is a sound approach to the problem it should not be relied upon as the only method of gathering information. Confidential information forms can also be used and these can be structured in such a way as to collect contributory factors required in the subsequent analysis. An example of a sample form is given in Figure 5.1. At the same time, the safety manager should have sufficient standing within the organisational structure to be able to interview any member of staff involved in a dangerous occurrence in total confidence. This method is also an important way of obtaining data. It is very likely that an employee involved in such an incident may feel worried by it. He may even feel fright or shock. When a dangerous occurrence takes place it is usually regarded as a good learning vehicle but this practice must not be encouraged! At the same time, if a lesson has been learned by both employee and employer what need is there of disciplinary action?

Having given thought to primary data obtained for decision-making purposes, these should be supplemented wherever possible with other data published by government departments including the HSE, the Department of Social Security, the Government Statistical Office and the RoSPA equivalent abroad. The HSE in the United Kingdom annually publishes accident and disease types data but does not publish those contributory factors evident in each accident, disease or dangerous occurrence. In fact, the current official data collection form F2508 does not seek such factors contributing to these incidents. It will be necessary, therefore, to collect these locally if the safety mix is to be correctly planned, implemented, monitored and evaluated efficiently and effectively. To provide for the simple evaluation of data collected, it should be gathered in a standardised form. Bearing in mind that the results may be placed upon a computer, thought needs to be given to the coding of the results. To facilitate this, we may break our data collection process into the following broad headings:

1. Accident details;
2. Casualty information;
3. Details of attendant circumstances.

For administrative purposes, provision will need to be made for the identification of accidents individually and for general recording purposes. Data required by the enforcement agencies need to form a part of this process.

Accident details

In general terms, this section must describe what happened, when the incident occurred and where the location of the accident site was. Within this section it is important that details of all equipment involved at the time of the accident are also recorded. At the same time, accident damage is noted both to equipment and surrounding environment together with details of independent witnesses. It is also important at this stage to note any procedures adopted and whether appropriate safety precautions were taken and that issued safety clothing was worn. Whether procedures were not carried out or clothing not worn is not at issue here. Questions relating to why certain factors exist are dealt with under attendant circumstances and are deemed to be contributory to the accident or occurrence.

A. Subject of Report:

Fatality ☐   Specified major injury ☐   3 Day injury ☐   Dangerous occurrence ☐   Flammable gas Incident ☐   Dangerous gas fitting ☐

1   2   3   4   5   6

B. Person or Organisation Making the Report:

Name and Address

[ ]

Post Code [ ]

Name & Telephone Number of Contact

[ ]

Type of Business

[ ]

Role of Company at time

[ ]

Main Site Contractor ☐   Sub - contractor ☐   Other ☐

Is injured member of your family? ☐ Yes   ☐ No

C. Date, Time and Place of Accident or Incident:

Day Month Year
[ ][ ][ ]

Time of Accident [ ][ ]
24 hour clock

Location of accident [ ]

Normal activity carried out at site [ ]

D. The Injured Person:

Name & Address [ ]

Age ☐   Sex ☐   Employee ☐   Trainee ☐   Self - employed ☐   YTS ☐   Other ☐

Trade or Occupation [ ]

Nature of Injury [ ]

Figure 5.1

Sample accident form

E. Kind of Accident:

Contact with moving machinery ☐	Injured while lifting/carrying ☐	Trapped ☐	Exposure to explosion ☐
Struck by moving object ☐	Slip/Trip/Fall same level ☐	Drowning ☐	Contact with elec. ☐
Struck by moving vehicle ☐	Fall from height ☐	Exposure ☐	Injured by animal ☐
Struck against fixed object ☐	Distance fell ☐ metres	Exposure to fire ☐	Other ☐

F. Agent(s) Involved:

Lifting equipment ☐	Process plant ☐	Live animal ☐	Ladder scaffolding ☐
Portable hand tools ☐	Stored materials ☐	Moveable container ☐	Construction formwork ☐
Vehicle ☐	Deficient atmosphere ☐	Working surface ☐	Electricity equipment ☐
Other ☐	Pathogen infection ☐	Building Mining ☐	Entertainment sports equip. ☐
Describe factors indicated [　　　　　]		Any other agent ☐	

G. Account of Accident or Dangerous Occurrence:

Describe what and how the incident happened. In the case of an accident, state what the injured person was doing at the time:

Signature of person making report [　　　　　　] Date [　　　　　]

Casualty information

Here it is necessary to record details of who was involved in the incident and the levels and type of injuries received. Generally, it is thought necessary to record those killed or injured. Few accident investigators support the classification of injury types at this level. In an accident a person is either killed or injured. A non-injury may be deemed a dangerous occurrence. It is difficult to identify those separate factors which contribute to a serious injury rather than a minor injury or what makes an incident a minor one rather than a serious one. For example, in two identical instances two people fall from scaffolding 20 feet in the air. One lands on his head and is seriously injured while the other lands on his feet and suffers minor lacerations. In this case, one employee was off work for three months whilst the other returned to work the same day. Where scientific research is involved there are accident injury scales for the classification of disease and injuries. It is argued that for the operational management of effective safety procedures and practices, these are unnecessary. It must be remembered that the aim of the exercise is to identify contributory factors present in when an accident occurs. The sole purpose is to identify these and take remedial action. The fact that an employee was injured in varying degrees does not significantly contribute to this part of the exercise. It is for this reason that safety managers need only classify injuries simply at this stage.

Attendant circumstances

This part of the procedure considers those factors which have contributed to the accident or dangerous occurrence. It will include details of the accident site and its immediate surrounds and will cater for factors which led up to and immediately preceded the accident or occurrence. Where a non-injury incident is involved it may only be necessary for a self-certification exercise by the person involved to be carried out. It is recommended that in these circumstances Part 2 of the form, the casualty detail, be suitably modified to ensure anonymity. Care should be taken that all questions that can be regarded as subjective are completed with care. For example, if an accident occurs outside then it might be necessary to explain the meaning of 'high wind', 'rain/drizzle', 'mist/fog' etc in any instructions or in training given. These factors often appear in outside-type incidents. Indoor-type accidents can suffer a similar language interpretation if adequate care is not exercised. For example, the difference between bright light, light and darkness will need care as would matters referring to ventilation such as airy, breezy, windy, gusting, etc. In a recent case during a warm sunny spell, the workforce opened windows and doors to get a cool breeze. The breeze was rather strong and blew over several items of equipment stored in the work area. These fell over and injured a worker's foot whilst another had dust blown into her eyes thus causing the worker to catch her fingers in a machine. Here, the contributory factors are identified as the weather, the open windows and doors, the windy, blustery conditions, the loose materials capable of being blown over, and the dust. The casualty rate could have been affected by the removal of any one (or more) of these factors. Similarly, a person slipped and fell in a car park because it rained for the first time in eight weeks and the rainwater mixed with oil and rubber caused the car park surface to become very slippery. The employee was late for work and in his haste to run into the office to avoid getting wet slipped and broke a leg.

Where man fails to cope with his environment, most data collected for accident analysis purposes can be standardised. There can, of course, be allowances made for those occasional variations which do exist between occupations and industries.

Data collection

Decisions will always be influenced by a person's perception of those elements of the environment, internal or external to the organisation, which are seen as relevant. Thus, a greater understanding of issues and their relevance to a particular decision along with a more realistic picture of the environment will lead to a better basis for decision.

Information is required for many reasons, some of these are to:

- Clarify the request of the client.
- Identify issues relevant to the problem or the decision.
- Enable projections to be made of future behaviour of people and systems.
- Establish the current situation and what has lead up to it.
- Formulate an approach to resolving the problem.
- Check personal ideas against those of others.

There are eight steps involved in establishing a data or information base. These are:

1. An identification of the data requirements;
2. An identification of potential sources of data;
3. A selection of sources to be used;
4. A selection of the method to be used for collecting data;
5. Planning the method of data collection and the analysis which will follow;
6. Collecting the data;
7. Analysing the data;
8. Presenting the information in a clear and understandable form.

Data often exists in a form which has little value as an aid to specific decision making. In converting data into a meaningful form of information, one or more of the following should be considered:

- Aggregation or disaggregation of the data.
- Regrouping and/or ordering of the data.
- Testing relationships between various types of data.
- Trying various methods of presenting the data.

It is often only by trying different approaches to, and combinations of the above, that insight and ultimate understanding can be achieved.

What are data?

This is often thought to be numerical consisting only of such things as sets of numbers, graphs, equations and the like. On reflection, it is clear that this cannot be so since many decisions in our daily life are made on the basis of non-numeric information. Data is anything which describes the attributes of a situation, system, person, object, etc. For example, if we wished to describe the safety department in which we work, it could be done in a variety of ways:

- Number of staff.
- Sex of staff.
- Age of staff.
- Attitudes.
- Hobbies.
- Task undertaken.
- Length of service.

There is almost an infinite amount of data concerned with such a department. Some of this data is objective (such as numbers, sex, age, etc) whilst some of the data is subjective (such as attitudes, etc).

The boundary between objective and subjective is often imprecise and is dependent upon:

1. The particular characteristic chosen; and
2. The form of measurement used.

How could the safety procedures in your organisation be classified?

Equally, some data are quantitative (i.e. measurable, countable), for example numbers.

Some data sets are qualitatives (i.e. rankable, assignable), for example hobbies.

Rigorous mathematical methods of analysis are available for dealing with both types of data.

Sources of data

The establishment of a sound and credible information base is essential for any project evaluation. Common failings in many project and research investigations are:

- A failure to identify potential sources (i.e. insufficient initial research).
- A failure to use sources (being deterred by effort, time, cost or political antagonism).
- Poor choice of sources (using subjective data when objective data is possible; failing to build in validation processes; failing to identify the sensitivity of the end decision to data accuracy).

A simple classification of data sources are:

1. *Primary data* – this is the information which originates from your investigation:
   (a) what people/systems do (observation and experimentation);
   (b) what people say (questioning and expert opinion).
2. *Secondary data* – this information does not originate from the investigation.
   (a) what people have done/said (internal records);
   (b) past performance of systems (external published sources).

Primary data

The fact of gathering data for specific needs often forces greater thought about:

1. What is trying to be done; and
2. What contribution will the piece of data make?

Gathering data in this way often provides the opportunity for personal contact, obtaining specific pieces of feedback or just developing thought in order to provide a greater insight into the nature of the problem. Almost without exception, some cross checks are needed of secondary data via primary data and vice versa.

Observation

These methods use some kind of recorder, either human or mechanical (e.g. video cameras, or the human eye, etc). It is the aim of such methods to avoid any abnormal behaviour of the system due to the observation.

This is far from easy; frequently people have a tendency to settle to 'normal'. Examples of such an approach are:

- Activity sampling surveys (working on a new piece of equipment to record what happens).
- Filming a specific activity in a department.
- Traffic flow counters.
- Visual checks on floor utilisation.
- Safety studies.

Experimentation

The aim is to identify the difference in the outputs of a changed system with those prior to or in, an unchanged situation. The content of the use is in the testing out of a cause effect model which has resulted from assessment of the current situation. Examples of this might be:

- Testing new equipment.
- Testing new procedures.
- Testing safety ideas.

Questioning

This is the most common source of primary data involving the use of interviews and/or questionnaires. Asking questions is a good method of establishing and cross checking causal models and is the only way to get at behaviourial problems in an organisation. Considerable skill in the use of interviews and questioning techniques is required if data is to be obtained which is worth analysing as a basis for useful information. The ease with which this source can be misleading or inaccurate is evidenced by the disastrous results of schemes based almost entirely upon data from such sources. The cost and time attached to the use of this source is influenced by the geographic dispersion of the people involved, the number of people involved and the technique chosen. These issues are discussed later.

Expert opinion

There are certain situations where the processing of data to form information is best done by a particular person. Examples might be:

- Evidence from a scientist specialising in a particular field relevant to the study.
- Production controller estimating delivery of new equipment.
- Union representative on reactions of his members to a new procedure.

The reasons for accepting expert opinion in the main fall into the following three categories.

1. The rules for processing the data to form information are not available outside the mind of the individual.
2. The data cannot fully be established as it is in the subconscious as well as the conscious mind.
3. The worth of extracting the data, etc, is not offset by the benefits of greater accuracy (often a general indication is all that would be required).

Secondary data

Such data tends to be easily accessible and is often a good starting point for an investigation. Desk work based upon such data can be helpful in the following:

- Defining terms, gaining understanding in new fields of knowledge.
- Widening viewpoints on relevant issues.
- Establishing the current 'state of the art' in specific areas.
- Identifying the areas where primary data will contribute.
- Formulating possible approaches to resolving the problem.
- Obtaining some understanding of the environment under investigation.
- Providing a theoretical background to the study.

Internal records

Most organisations keep many internal records, some formally, some informally; these records can be of great value in project work once located and released. Skills in interviewing and gaining personal acceptance are often a pre-requisite to this. As a base internal records can reveal accounts, costings, labour and some accident statistics.

External published data

A large volume of up to date, published data is accessible, some of which is almost bound to be relevant to a specific project. These can sometimes be obtained from professional organisations, trade associations, libraries and colleges of higher education. It is usual for any article to be obtained within 14 days.

Since most problem situations are by no means unique, it is highly likely that there will be some comment in the literature relevant to the problem being investigated. This being so then it is surprising that the use of external published data is underestimated. However, it is important that when using external data sources the context of any findings is assessed for validity prior to local use.

Comparative studies

The result of collecting primary and secondary data will provide a base for formulating a hypothesis about future behaviour of systems or people which will be significant in the recommendations of any change. The use of comparison and analogy can often give further insight and affect the confidence in a model. The utility of this method lies in the suitability of the comparison chosen.

Comparative studies can offer some of the following:

- A cross check on how to solve a problem.
- An indication of similarities and differences in approach.
- Identification of the results and associated side effects to compare with predictions.

Choice of sources of data

Factors which undoubtedly need consideration when choosing the various sources of data are:

- The worth of the data.
- The ability to cross check key information.
- Time to collect.
- Cost of collection.
- Accessibility (particularly internal records).
- Political sensitivity.

Cost benefit aspects should be considered in making the choice. Clearly, subjective judgment will play an important role in this choice as the implication of various data decisions may be unclear.

Planning of data collection and analysis

There is a great need to assess the ability to analyse data prior to collecting it. It is not uncommon to discover, after great effort and expenditure of time, that the following are true:

- There is too much data for manual analysis.
- The form of the data collected is not united with the form of analysis to be applied.

Some common types of analysis are:

1. Significance testing of means and variances;
2. Goodness of fit χ^2 tests;
3. Testing the correlation between variables;
4. Establishing a regression line;
5. Grouping data in various ways;
6. Preparing histograms, pie-charts, graphs, etc.

Accident data collection

A specific example used by some organisations to gather data is shown as Stats Form 1 shown in Figure 5.2. This serves to show the level and type of information which could be gathered which is also sympathetic to Form F2508 required by the HSE. Such a form may need modification depending upon the industry in which it is to be used. The important point to remember is that contributory factors need to be identified and any form design should attempt to identify these. The example form shown as Stats 1 would need an accompanying sheet explaining each question.

The first part of the form should give the employer a reference numbering sequence that will identify each individual accident record but also keep a tally on accident numbers per year. It must be remembered that one accident can produce more than one casualty so care must be exercised when carrying out accident analysis as opposed to casualty analysis. On many occasions board members or safety committee members have been confused over accident and casualty figures. Care must be exercised, therefore, when quoting figures.

A note must be kept of the accident location and this can be eased by using factory, building and room numbers for computing purposes. Individual workstations can also be numbered. Locations showing a high accident rate should be investigated separately. It is useful to record accident costs and there are many conventions used to calculate these (see Chapter 6). It is important to keep a record of accident severity and it is only necessary to distinguish between fatal, injury and non-injury type accidents.

In terms of the *accident details* then, it is important to record the date, time and exact location of the accident clearly. For road accidents, it will be necessary to use the standard grid reference conventions. Numbers killed and injured should be recorded and whether the accident occurred inside or outside. It will be necessary to list activities carried out by an employee whilst carrying out his/her duties. These should then be classified numerically for computer purposes. Activities or manoeuvres would vary with each industry therefore careful planning is required. For example, a

Form STATS 1

Accident and Dangerous Occurence
Reporting Form

Incident record number [ ]   Employee record number [ ]

Department [ ]   Location [ ]   Name [ ]

Employee address [ ]   Post Code [ ]

Incident class [ ]   Severity [ ]   Man days lost [ ]   Lost-time [ ]   Cost [ ]

Part 1: Accident Details.

Date of accident [ ][ ][ ]   Time of accident (24 hour) [ ][ ]   Location [ ]
                 Day Month Year

Number of casualties [ ]   Severity [ ]   Number killed [ ]   Number injured [ ]   Damage only [ ]

Indoor/Outdoor [ ]   Activity [ ]   Accident type [ ]   Agents involved [ ]   Flammable [ ]

Part 2: Casualty Details.

Sex [ ]   Occupation [ ]   Age [ ]   Status [ ]   Injury type [ ]   How long employed [ ][ ]
                                                                                    Years Months

Qualified [ ]   Training [ ]   Date of last course attended [ ][ ][ ]   Course subject [ ]
                                                            Day Month Year

Course type [ ]   Previous accident history [ ]   Date of last accident [ ][ ][ ]   Previous accident type [ ]
                                                                       Day Month Year

Health at time of accident [ ]

Part 3: Attendant Circumstances.

Light conditions [ ]   Weather [ ]   Ventilation [ ]   Temperature [ ]   Medications [ ]   Alcohol [ ]

Equipment in use at time of accident [ ]   Date equipment last checked [ ][ ][ ]   Checked by whom [ ]
                                                                      Day Month Year

Equipment type [ ]   Activity [ ]   Supervision [ ]   Other [ ]

Signature of person making report [ ]   Status [ ]   Date [ ][ ][ ]
                                                           Day Month Year

Figure 5.2

Casualty statement

Signature [   ]   Date [   ]

Witness statement

Signature [   ]   Date [   ]

scaffolder may have an activity chart as follows:

00   Loading scaffolding from depot into vehicle
01   Securing load to vehicle
02   Travelling to/from site
03   Road traffic accident
04   Vehicle accident off the public highway
05   Unloading materials on site
06   Erecting scaffolding on site (ground level)
07   Erecting scaffolding on site (above ground level <15 metres high)
08   Erecting scaffolding on site (above ground level >15 metres high)
09   Carrying out safety checks on completion
10   Climbing up
11   Climbing down
12   Dismantling scaffolding
13   Removing scaffolding from site (ground level)
14   Using tools during assembly/dismantling
15   Other (please specify)

Accident type may follow those conventions used by the HSE and as outlined in Section E of their Form F2508 as would agents involved and matters referring to flammable items.

Casualty details should be straightforward and should provide information concerning the person injured or involved in a dangerous occurrence. Base data should also include questions relating to the experience and professional competence of the casualty and their ability to carry out their tasks adequately and in safety. Injury type should be simple and might follow the following format:

00   Head
01   Neck
02   Collar bone
03   Shoulder (left)
04   Shoulder (right)
05   Chest
06   Arm (left)
07   Arm (right)
08   Wrist (left)
09   Wrist (right)
10   Hand (left)
11   Hand (right)
12   Waist
13   Hips

14 Leg (left)
15 Leg (right)
16 Ankle (left)
17 Ankle (right)
18 Foot (left)
19 Foot (right)

Further codes could be added to identify cuts, fractures, bruising, etc. It may be appropriate to seek medical advice prior to setting up individual injury type codes.

Information concerning a casualty's previous accident involvement is an important consideration as are details of training courses undertaken. Course titles should be listed in a similar manner to those listed above under 'activity'. It has been found necessary by some industries to ascertain an employee's health at the time of the accident and some organisations are able to carry out their own medical examinations periodically. In these cases it is usual to include on the form the date the last company medical examination took place.

Attendant circumstances in the Stats form example (Figure 5.2) list 'light conditions' as the first question. In some industries adequate lighting is important particularly in outdoor activities such as building sites, or in the clothing industry where sewing machines are in use. In an outdoor situation, it might be appropriate to list light conditions as follows:

01 Cloudy
02 Clear and sunny
03 Dull and overcast
04 Bright
05 Hazy
06 Foggy visibility < 50 metres
07 Foggy visibility > 50 metres
08 Artificial light – streetlighting (all working)
09 Artificial light – streetlighting (not all working)
10 Artificial light – spotlighting (all working)
11 Artificial light – spotlighting (not all working)
12 Artificial light – sodium/security lighting (all working)
13 Artificial light – sodium/security (not all working)
14 Artificial lighting inadequate
15 Other (please specify)

Internal lighting can similarly be broken down as can ventilation. With regards to temperature, internal temperatures should conform to the criteria listed in the Factories Act 1961. For both internal and outside temperatures, the actual temperature as recorded from a thermometer should be used. Weather conditions may be recorded as follows:

01 Dry (no wind)
02 Dry and windy (Beaufort scales 1 to 12)
03 Wet but not raining
04 Raining
05 Fine rain or drizzle
06 Icy (confirmed by temperature reading)
07 Snow (but not snowing)
08 Snowing (no wind)
09 Snowing (with wind) causing drifting

Where medications are prescribed to an employee it must be ascertained whether these can affect an employee's performance. Medical advice should be sought in cases where a casualty has been taking medications thought to have contributed to the accident. Similarly, alcohol should be monitored. Evidence suggests that alcohol in the workplace is becoming a problem and the only way to discover its involvement in accidents is to seek this information at the outset.

Equipment in use at the time the accident occurred should be itemised together with information concerning the correct use of protective and/or safety clothing. Information concerning equipment/safety clothing maintenance is also important and should be recorded as should details of the person responsible for carrying out these checks.

Equipment in use at the time of the accident should be listed according to those used by the organisation. For example, in the agricultural industry one would need to list (similar to an inventory) all those items of equipment used by employees.

These must be coded in a way suitable for computerisation. Within this section it is important to identify whether safety/protective clothing or other measures were used in accordance with laid down instructions. An example might be as follows:

01 Chain-saw used in accordance with laid down procedure and full safety equipment worn or used
02 Chain-saw not used in accordance with laid down procedure but full safety equipment worn or used
03 Chain-saw used in accordance with laid down procedure but full safety equipment not worn or used
04 Chain-saw not used in accordance with laid down procedure and full safety equipment not worn or used

In some cases, certain items of equipment not deemed to be potentially hazardous may be omitted from the listing until such times as they are involved in an accident. For example, at a local school, a pencil was not regarded as hazardous until one injured a pupil. In this case the pupil had just gone to the front of the class to sharpen his pencil in a desk-mounted drum type sharpener. He had obtained permission from the teacher in charge to do this. On returning to his desk, the pupil tripped over the strap of a school bag and fell forwards over a desk on to another pupil, stabbing the pupil in the arm with the recently sharpened pencil. The lead broke off requiring the injured pupil to undergo hospital treatment. Up until this point, pencils were not a feature of the equipment heading within the computerised data collection process. Since they have been added this particular local authority have experienced several pencil type accidents both in and out of school premises. Remedial action resulted in the removal of the barrel type pencil sharpeners and the teachers now provide small hand held sharpeners to pupils whilst in their seats. This action has significantly reduced the pencil related type accidents.

Over a period of time comparisons with the equipment inventory can show those individual items of equipment which feature in accidents against those that do not. This is recognised as a more satisfactory way of establishing which items are dangerous and allows the safety practitioner to build his equipment records on a regular basis.

Having identified the equipment it is necessary to identify in some way the activity being undertaken at the time of the accident. If we take the chain-saw example illustrated above the activity codings may look like this:

01 Tree surgery (above ground level) using safety harness
02 Tree surgery (ground level)
03 Tree surgery (above ground level) using ladders
04 Cutting tree into logs
05 Hedge/bush pruning
06 Hedge/bush removal
07 Cutting other wood types
08 Other (please specify)

It is important to record casualty supervision details. All too often supervisors and managers overlook their responsibilities adequately to supervise subordinates when carrying out their duties. Recent examples concerned the Clapham rail accident and the Zeebrugge ferry disaster. In both cases it was alleged that subordinates were unsupervised. At Clapham a signal repair engineer was said to have left certain aspects of his work in an unsafe condition. His supervisor or line manager failed to notice this omission. Likewise on the Zeebrugge ferry it was claimed that a junior member of staff responsible for closing the bow doors was asleep. His supervisor or line manager failed to notice this and take appropriate action. A general who loses a battle cannot blame his soldiers! With leadership comes a responsibility. This cannot be ignored when things go wrong and those who absolve themselves of this duty show extremely poor management practice. This is particularly noticeable when management blame subordinates, or allow subordinates to take the blame, for not doing their jobs correctly. The process of responsibility must go upwards until it can proceed no further.

It is useful to include on any data collection form a means for obtaining 'other' information which may be regarded as 'special projects'. This can facilitate the recording of information without necessarily requiring a new print run. Although only one box is provided for in the example below, some organisations have as many as six 'special project' or 'other' boxes at any one time.

Obtaining data from people

This concerns two common methods of collecting primary data: the interview and the questionnaire. There are other methods available such as experimentation, observation, self-recording and so on, but these are relatively sophisticated and rarely applicable to operational project conditions.

The choice

The basic decision whether to use the questionnaire or interview is almost always concerned with resources and the scope of the problem:

- How much time and effort and manpower can be allocated to the project?
- Where are the sources of data located?
- What kind of data is needed?

The answers to these questions often mean that one of the methods is rejected and thus eases the decision to be made. Other choices can be eliminated by discussing appropriate advantages v disadvantages whilst in more marginal situations, a choice is made by direct comparison of the two methods.

The questionnaire

Advantages

- It can be administered to groups of people at the same time thus saving time and expense.
- It can be used where the respondents are spread over a wide geographical area.
- The required answers on a questionnaire can be pre-structured thus making the task of analysing much easier.
- Questionnaires can be more reliable than interviews.

- Questionnaires can be made anonymous thus allowing for more freedom of response.
- Questionnaires give the respondent the opportunity to verify factual data.
- Questionnaires avoid interviewer 'error'.

Disadvantages

- Questionnaires often suffer from a low response rate, which give rise to problems of representativeness. Respondents can also avoid answering specific questions.
- Difficult questions cannot be clarified by the respondent.
- Questionnaires are often seen to be impersonal and respondents do not feel committed to filling them in.
- There is no opportunity to ask extra questions on a questionnaire and therefore new data is missed. 'You only get answers to the questions asked.'

The interview

It is important to deal with some general principles of the interview before specific safety examples are discussed. The interview is a face to face verbal exchange, in which one person, the interviewer, attempts to elicit information or expressions of opinion, attitudes or belief from another person or persons.

The role of the interview is to act as a method for collecting data. This may be used:

1. During the early stages of an investigation to help identify the problem areas, the relevant dimensions, to suggest hypotheses and to reveal the natural frames of reference existing in the minds of the respondents;
2. When questionnaires are used, the interview may be employed to pretest the questionnaire form;
3. As the main instrument of data collection;
4. To clarify findings which have emerged from other sources of data.

Advantages

- Interviews increase respondents' commitment.
- They tend to be more valid, encouraging true-to-life answers.
- Interviews often reveal data which would not come out in a questionnaire.
- They allow for clarification of difficult questions.

Disadvantages

- Problems of interviewer 'error' such as appearance, manner and style of asking questions.
- Problems of anonymity or the lack of it.
- Unstructured interviews often provide data in a form which is difficult to analyse.
- Interviews are time consuming.

The structured v the unstructured type interview

A standardised interview is one in which the questions have been decided upon in advance of the interview. The questions are asked with the same wording and in the same order for each respondent. The essential feature of a structured interview is that the interviewer does not have the freedom to re-word questions, to introduce questions which seem especially applicable to the individual case, or to change the order of topics to conform to the interviewer's spontaneous sequence of ideas. In the unstructured interview, the interviewer technique is completely flexible and can vary from one respondent to the next.

Structured interviews

- Incorporate a basic principle of measurement (that of making information comparable from case to case).
- Are more reliable.
- Minimise errors due to question wording.

Unstructured interviews

- Permit standardisation of meanings, rather than the more superficial aspects of the stimulus situation (the question).
- Are likely to be more valid in that they encourage more true-to-life responses.
- Are more flexible.

Questions

For both interviews and questionnaires, it is necessary to relate questions to the problems under study. However, the discipline of refining questions and making sure that they are relevant can be difficult. For example, is a question pertaining to an employee's hobbies relevant to the study?

There are a few basic rules that can be applied to the framing of questions and these are:

1. Avoid ambiguous words or phrases;
2. Avoid long questions;
3. The questions should state as precisely as possible the time, place and context you want the respondent to assume;
4. Either make explicit all the alternatives the respondent could answer or none of them;
5. Avoid multiple questions;
6. Avoid leading questions;
7. Avoid rhetorical questions;
8. Avoid implied values.

It has been widely assumed that the interview is superior in many ways and must be used whenever resources permit. Certainly the interview should be used at the exploratory stages particularly in the area of accident investigation. Because of the seriousness of the accident investigation process and the legal requirements to make all workplaces safer such an interview may be referred to as a statement interview or formal interview. This is discussed below.

Statements or formal interview

If statements are considered as part of the operational plan then it is important that they are taken as quickly as possible after the event and in normal circumstances should be taken within 24 hours of the accident happening. As early as 1932, psychologists have been able to show that a person is likely to forget half of what they originally perceived after 24 hours. To take a statement after this period of time can result in memory loss which may affect important detail, or other factors may influence the casualty thus distorting the facts. For example, some research in 1979 by Clifford showed that a high status questioner can influence a witness. By this it was possible to show that a motorist stopped by the police would think carefully about what he said to the constable because of the fear of prosecution. In this case, the police officer becomes a high status questioner. Likewise, an insurance company receives many reports each year from clients involved in road traffic accidents purporting that trees have mysteriously emerged into the path of their vehicle! In these cases, the insurance company is seen as the high status questioner in that the client's no claims discounts may be involved if they are found blameworthy. In such examples, a distortion of the facts (some refer to this as being economical with the truth) is common.

It should be understood that the taking of statements has a prime objective, and that is to ascertain facts relating to an accident or dangerous occurrence, which will facilitate the introduction of remedial measures which are specifically designed to prevent or reduce the incidence of those events happening in the future. The taking of statements should not be seen solely as a means of apportioning blame or for deciding upon disciplinary action. The safety practitioner conducting such an interview may wish to obtain these facts in total confidence. Some organisations provide confidential phone lines for the reporting of dangerous occurrences. This practice is good and can be recommended.

Disciplinary action must always be used wisely and should only be considered after all the evidence has been presented. It is more important that the interview is taken and conducted in a professional manner. These issues are discussed below.

Conduct of the formal interview

It is unwise to allow an employee to make a statement concerning an accident without supervision. To do so may mean that vital contributory factors are omitted from the report. It is more appropriate to conduct an interview which is constructed in such a manner as to provide a basis for the systematic gathering of relevant factors pertaining to the accident or occurrence. It is important that these interviews are seen primarily as fact finding exercises.

It has been said that there is a wealth of evidence which questions witness reliability but also the reliability of the victim statement can be questioned particularly when the consequences of the accident are understood and possible disciplinary or other punitive action could result. Here the interview technique should be used for fact finding only so that the investigator can learn more about the contributory factors which came together to cause the accident. Geiselman and Fisher (1986) describe three types of interview techniques. These are the cognitive, hypnosis and interrogative type interview. Here, hypnosis means what it says and the interrogative type interview is that which one would expect from the police. The most effective methods found by these two authors were the cognitive and hypnosis methods. The latter was rejected on practical terms due to the length of training necessary to hypnotise people. The ethics of this are also questionable. The cognitive type interview was found to be equally as good and easier to learn. Basically, this method consists of four general points for jogging memory plus several specific techniques which are outlined below. There is no reason why these points could not assist the safety manager to obtain more reliable information from injured members of his workforce. The four points are explained to the interviewee before the narrative report. The first two attempt to increase the overlap of elements between the stored memory and the retrieval mechanisms. The last two encourage the use of several retrieval paths. The four points are:

1. Reconstruct the circumstances

Here the interviewer asks the witness or victim to reconstruct the incident in general terms. Reconstruct the circumstances that surrounded the incident. Get the interviewee to:

- Think about the environment in which the accident happened, such as room layout, furniture locations, weather, vehicles, equipment, lighting and other people or objects.
- Think about what they were doing before the accident happened, how they were feeling and their reactions to the incident.

  It is important to start before the accident happened and it may be necessary to start 24 hours before, as evidence exists to show that stress at home, alcohol and other factors can feature as major contributory factors in an accident happening.

2. Report everything

The investigator should explain that all information may be helpful and nothing, even if thought to be irrelevant, should be omitted. All information should be given. Some people tend to think that some information is not important so they hold back. Do not ask your casualty or witness to edit anything.

3. Recall events in a different order

It is natural to ask the person being interviewed to start at the beginning and journey through to the end. If you have done this, it is worthwhile asking for the information in reverse order or try starting with the point that concerned the interviewee the most about the event. From here you may go forward or backwards in time.

4. Change perspectives

Try to see the event from another person's point of view or adopt the perspectives of others who were present at the scene.

Mental reconstruction of circumstances surrounding a memorable event has been shown to be a powerful aid to memory and visiting the accident site and undertaking accident reconstruction exercises are valuable.

In addition to the four points outlined above, the cognitive interview also uses a series of specific questions to help an accident investigator elicit information following the narrative phase of an interview. The investigator might consider the following:

- Was the casualty qualified to carry out the task being undertaken at the time of the accident?
- Was safety clothing worn?
- When did the casualty last undertake relevant safety training?
- When was equipment involved in the accident last examined?
- Were safety procedures followed?
- Was the casualty fit to undertake his duties?
- Have the contributory factors been identified?
- How could these have been eliminated and how can they be for the future?

These questions are of a general nature and must not be regarded as exhaustive. They are given as a general indication of the type of information which must come out of an interview situation when accidents have occurred. The aim of the exercise must be accident prevention in the future and a decision will have to be taken as to the blend of safety mix required. We know that enforcement on its own is ineffective so taking disciplinary action alone could not be recommended. It must be used with other measures which must be elicited from the investigation.

Further reading

Bartlett, F C (1932) *Remembering* (Cambridge University Press)
Clifford, B (1979) *Eyewitness Testimony: Bridging of a Credibility Gap* (MacMillan Press)
Geiselman, R E and Fisher, R P 'Interviewing Victims and Witnesses of Crime.' *Police*, Vol 7 March 1986 pp 26–34
Gregory, G (1988) *Decision Analysis* (Pitman Publishing)
Loftus, E (1979) *Eyewitness Testimony* (Harvard University Press)
Owen, F and Jones, R (1990) *Statistics* (Pitman Publishing)

6

Financial management and accident costs

Introduction

Safety managers will have a basic understanding of management accounting and its importance within the organisational structure. This will allow for decisions to be taken which provide for maximum safety for a known cost. All too often, safety related decisions are taken which later prove to be too expensive or do not provide an appropriate economic rate of return (ERR). Calculating an ERR will be discussed later in this chapter. Company accountants will need to know the financial implication of all safety management decisions, so it is necessary to spend some time looking at this issue together with some current methods of estimating accident costs and the cost that these incidents can have upon the organisation.

Basically, financial management is a broad term applied to management accounting and funds management. Within the context of management accounting this concerns itself with information that is useful to management. It is defined as the application of accounting knowledge for the purpose of producing and of interpreting accounting and statistical information which is designed to help management in its functions of promoting maximum efficiency and in formulating and co-ordinating future plans and in measuring their execution. This form of accounting practice feeds off financial accounting, cost accounting, budgetary control and capital investment appraisal but the emphasis is on the use of information to assist management to plan and control activities of the organisation rather than upon techniques. Funds management on the other hand, concerns itself with the acquisition and control of funds; with sources of finance and the control of liquidity. As long-term planning proceeds, financial management must assess the implications of the policies proposed in terms of funds required and make arrangements to raise the long-term funds necessary to secure the financial foundations to provide for organisational growth. Short-term proposals are equally important. Irrespective of how big an organisation is and however profitable it might seem, it is still important to have the money available to pay the bills due and the weekly wages. This emphasises the need to try to forecast future cash requirements both in the short and the long term.

Safety managers need to know something about the techniques used to collect and summarise this information but do not need the detailed knowledge that an accountant must have. This chapter discusses basic financial management concepts and does not intend to provide full coverage of a complex subject. Safety practitioners wishing to learn more about the subject should consider the reading list given at the end of the chapter.

The accounting equation

Financial accounting is based upon the accounting equation made up of *assets*, *capital* and *liabilities*. Resources in an organisation are referred to as *assets*, whilst resources provided by the owner(s) are referred to as the *capital* and the indebtedness of the organisation for these resources is known as *liabilities*. This equation can be expressed as:

Capital + Liabilities = Assets; or
Capital = Assets − Liabilities.

It is this equation which is expressed in the financial position statement referred to as the *balance sheet*. The equality of the two sides in the equation will always be true, irrespective of the number of transactions entered into. The actual assets, capital and liabilities may change but the equation will remain true. For example, suppose Mr Bill Bloggs started a safety management consultancy and deposited £40,000 in a bank account. The balance sheet after this opening event would be as follows:

	£		£
Capital	40,000	Assets (cash at bank)	40,000

Bloggs now purchases a computer for his business which costs £5,000. His balance sheet would now be:

	£			£
Capital	40,000	Assets:	Computer	5,000
			Cash at bank	35,000
	40,000			40,000

Bloggs needs to sit down whilst playing with his computer. He needs some furniture. This costs him a further £5,000. He also requires office premises which cost him £29,500. His balance sheet will now look like this:

	£			£
Capital	40,000	Assets:	Computer	5,000
			Furniture	5,000
			Building (Office)	29,500
			Cash at bank	500
	40,000			40,000

Bloggs requires a loan of £1,000 as he is short of ready cash. He negotiates a loan with a bank. Bloggs' balance sheet will now be:

	£			£
Capital	40,000	Assets:	Computer	5,000
Liabilities (loan)	1,000		Furniture	5,000
			Building (Office)	29,500
			Cash at bank	1,500
	41,000			41,000

Each of these transactions above have maintained the equality of the total of the assets with that of the capital plus the liabilities.

Double entry system

Each transaction affects two items. In order to show the full effect of each transaction, accounting must show its effect on each of the two items. From this requirement, the double entry bookkeeping system was developed. Here, each entry will show the effect upon one item and its effect upon the other. One entry is called the *debit* entry and the other is the *credit* entry. Traditionally, each item (whether it is an asset, liability expense, revenue or the capital itself) will have its own account in the ledger (nowadays generally a computer printout). There will be a separate heading for each account, the left hand side being the *debit* side and the right hand side being the *credit* side. Each entry in an account will give a cross-reference to the other account involved in the same transaction. A number of people are confused which account to debit and which one to credit. The reader might find it useful to remember that whenever a transaction includes cash, then the cash account is debited when money comes in and is credited when money is paid out.

Example 6.1

The accounts and entries involved with Bloggs Safety Consultants shown above would be as follows:

Capital Account

	£		£
		Cash	40,000

Cash Account

	£		£
Capital	40,000	Computer	5,000
Loan	1,000	Furniture & Fittings	5,000
		Buildings	29,500

Equipment Account

	£		£
Cash	5,000		

Furniture & Fittings Accounts

	£		£
	5,000		

Buildings Account

	£		£
Cash	29,500		

Loss Account

	£		£
Cash	5,000		

From these transactions entered into the ledger, a debit and credit entry is therefore required. The total of the debit entries will equal the total of the credit ones. All transactions, for whatever purpose, will be recorded in the ledger by this double entry system. Increases in assets, decreases in liabilities or capital and incurring of expenses will appear as debit entries whilst increases in liabilities or capital, decreases in assets or sales including all other income will appear as credit entries. At the end of the accounting period when the final accounts are being prepared, all accounts in the ledger are *balanced off* and the list of the balances are extracted to form a *trial balance sheet*. This is to check that the double entry system has been maintained properly and the total debit entries equal the credit side. Proceeding further to the production of the final accounts some other matters are dealt with. These are matters relating to:

● Accruals and prepayments.

- Stock valuation.
- Depreciation of fixed assets.

The workings of accruals and prepayments have no direct benefit for the safety practitioner but this does not mean that he should not read about these matters in order to gain a further understanding of how his organisation conducts its financial affairs. Students wishing to learn more of this should read the selection of texts given at the end of the chapter. Financial ratios designed to help the safety practitioner assess his organisation's financial performance are given in Appendix 5.

Stock valuation

Stock valuation too would not necessarily be a responsibility of the safety staff but its importance should be understood. This is particularly relevant in industries where an 'ageing' factor is crucial to the quality of the product. In some parts of the food industry, for example, it is far better to operate a *first in first out* (FIFO) policy than a *last in first out* (LIFO) one. There is another common method used in stock valuation which is referred to as the *weighted average cost* (WAC). Whatever method is currently used in a particular industry it will be based upon accounting tradition and the safety manager should be mindful of this when considering a particular safety related strategy which will require contact with stock. This is especially relevant when dealing with items of safety equipment and the costs that these will have upon the organisation. Examples of these three common methods are given in Figures 6.1A to C.

The effect on the calculation of gross profit by using the different methods of stock valuation is given below:

	FIFO	LIFO	WAC
	£	£	£
Purchases	1,440	1,440	1,440
Less closing stock	320	240	296
Cost of goods sold	1,120	1,200	1,144
Sales	1,840	1,840	1,840
Gross profit	720	640	696

It is important to remember that this year's closing stock becomes next year's opening stock so that whichever method is used the profits for the whole life span of the business will be the same although different in each separate year. It shows the importance of any changes in the method of stock valuation.

Month	Purchases	Issues	Stock after transaction	
				£
January	10 @ £30 each		10 @ £30 each	300
April	10 @ £ 34 each		10 @ £30 each and 10 @ £34 each	640
May		8 @ £30 each	2 @ £30 each 10 @ £34 each	400
October	20 @ £40 each		2 @ £30 each 10 @ £34 each 20 @ £40 each	1,200
November		2 @ £30 each 10 @ £34 each 12 @ £40 each	8 @ £40 each	320

In this method, the safety clothing received is deemed to be the first to be issued. In this example, the stock figure at the end of the year would be £320

Figure 6.1 A

The FIFO

Month	Purchases	Issues	Stock after transaction	
				£
January	10 @ £30 each		10 @ £30 each	300
April	10 @ £ 34 each		10 @ £30 each and 10 @ £34 each	640
May		8 @ £34 each	10 @ £30 each 2 @ £34 each	368
October	20 @ £40 each		10 @ £30 each 2 @ £34 each 20 @ £40 each	1,168
November		20 @ £40 each 2 @ £34 each 2 @ £30 each	8 @ £30 each	240

In this method, as each issue of safety clothing is made, they are deemed to be from the latest purchases received at that time. The stock figure at the end of the year would be £240

Figure 6.1 B

The LIFO

Month	Purchases	Issues	Average cost of stock held	Stock value
				£
January	10 @ £30 each		30	300
April	10 @ £ 34 each		32	640
May		8 @ £32 each	32	384
October	20 @ £40 each		37	1,184
November		24 @ £37 each	37	296

Here, each purchase of safety clothing, the average cost of the goods held in stock is recalculated to give a new weighted average cost. Any subsequent issue is then deemed to be at that cost until a further purchase causes the average cost to be adjusted again. For the example given above, the stock figure is shown to be £296

Figure 6.1 C
The WAC

Item	FIFO cost	LIFO cost	WAC cost	Net realisable value
	£	£	£	£
A	40	30	37	50
B	40	30	37	50
C	40	30	37	50
D	40	30	37	10
E	40	30	37	50
F	40	30	37	50
G	40	30	37	50
H	40	30	37	46
	320	240	296	356

On a global or aggregate basis, the cost figures are all below net realisable value but on an individual basis, item D has a very low net realisable value. In fact, lower than the cost figure under any method of costing the stock

Figure 6.2
Summary

Individual valuation

The valuation of stock is normally the lower of cost and net realisable value and the difficulties of determining cost have been seen. There is a further complication here in that should the lower figure be taken for each individual item of stock or should the lower aggregate figure be used? In Figure 6.2, it can be seen how many interpretations of the stock value there are.

The problems of stock valuation discussed here deal only with those associated with the purchasing and selling of goods. How a cost figure is ascertained for a finished product coming into store by way of internal manufacture is not discussed and this usually forms part of the routine costing system.

Depreciation

Fixed assets are things such as land, buildings, plant, machinery, furniture, equipment and vehicles, which have a long life and are held to be used in the business and not primarily for resale. Usually, fixed assets have a limited number of years of useful life and when an asset is purchased and later no longer used by the organisation, that part of the cost not recovered on disposal is called *depreciation*. The causes of depreciation are:

- Physical deterioration such as fair wear and tear, erosion, exposure, etc.
- Economic factors such as obsolescence and inadequacy.
- Time factor like the amortisation of leases, patents or copyrights.
- Depletion like providing for the consumption of an asset of a wasting nature such as a mine or quarry.

Depreciation is the part of the cost of the fixed asset consumed during its period of use by an organisation. It has been a cost for services used in the same way as the cost of wages. It is an expense and will need charging against the profits in the final accounts along with all other expenses. This depreciation can be calculated over the life of an asset as cost less the amount received on disposal. If the item is bought and sold during one accounting period then the depreciation for that period is easy to calculate with accuracy. Difficulties start when the asset is used for more than one accounting period but an attempt has been made to charge each accounting period with the relevant amount of depreciation. There is no one true method of providing for depreciation during the life of an asset. Difficulties involved are considerable. For example, for many assets it is difficult to estimate how long the asset will last and in what condition it will be at the end. Many methods of providing for depreciation exist but there are two main methods we shall consider here. These are:

1. The straight line method, and
2. The reducing balance method.

The straight line method

This method is used by most organisations in the United States and has become more common in the EEC. The method provides for an equal amount to be charged as depreciation for each year of the expected use of the asset. The formula is as follows:

$$\text{Depreciation provision per year} = \frac{\text{Cost} - \text{Estimated Residual Value}}{\text{Number of Years of Expected Use}}$$

For example, an item of safety equipment costing £350 is expected to have a life of four years with the organisation and then be scrapped for a value of £50. A depreciation provision for each year of the four years is:

$$\frac{350 - 50}{4} = £75$$

The reducing balance method

This is less popular a method than it used to be but is still used widely. It follows a similar calculation to that carried out for tax allowances on fixed assets. To calculate the depreciation provision for each year, a fixed percentage is applied to the balance of costs not yet apportioned as an expense at the end of the previous accounting period. This is referred to as a fixed percentage applied to the *written down* value. The formula used is as follows:

$$\frac{r}{100} = 1 - n\sqrt{\frac{s}{c}}$$

Where:

n is the number of years of expected life
s is the estimated scrap value
c is the cost of the asset
r is the rate of depreciation

For example a safety guard for a piece of machinery costing £1,250, expected to be used by the organisation for three years after which it is estimated to be sold for £650, would have a depreciation provision for each of the three years of:

$$\frac{r}{100} = 1 - 3\sqrt{\frac{640}{1250}}$$

$$= 1 - 3\sqrt{\frac{64}{125}} = 1 - \frac{4}{5} = \frac{1}{5}$$

Therefore $r = 20\%$. This can be proven as follows:

  £1,250 less 20% = £1,000
  £1,000 less 20% = £ 800
  £ 800 less 20% = £ 640

 Those supporters of the reducing balance method argue that it helps to even out the total charged as expenses for the use of the asset each year. This is because although this method means high depreciation charges in the early stages and low depreciation charges in the later years, the repair and maintenance bills are usually weighted in the opposite direction. The advocates of the straight line method argue that repair bills are irrelevant to the calculation of depreciation charges and that this method provides an even charge against profits each year and that it is a simple and easy calculation. Any adjustments to the depreciation provisions to cater for over- or under-provisions are made in the year of disposal.

Example 6.2

In order to illustrate the accountancy involved in respect of depreciation a company buys a 'Waterloo Safety Alarm' for £1,000 at the beginning of the financial year. It is expected that the alarm will last the length of the current production run lasting two years, at the end of which it is hoped to sell it for £700. Depreciation is to be provided via the straight line method. In this instance, the alarm is sold after the two year period for £685. Figure 6.3 illustrates the extract from the accounts dealing with this item.

 The aim of making provision for depreciation is to ensure that the cost of the asset is charged as an expense in an equitable way over its useful life in an organisation. Parts of the cost are allocated to different years until the whole of the asset's cost has been expended. This does not necessarily mean that depreciation provisions provide for funds with which to replace the asset when it is finally disposed of. The provisions do, however, reduce the size of the profits and therefore affect the size of the dividends distributed in a company or the size of drawings of a sole trader or partner so that the depreciation provisions do have some effect on retaining cash within the business which will assist with asset replacement if required.

Extracts from accounts

Year 1

Safety alarm account			
	£		
Cash	1,000		

Provision for depreciation on safety alarm account			
	£		£
		Profit and loss	150

Cash account			
	£		£
		Safety alarm	1,000

Profit and loss account			
	£		£
Depreciation of alarm	150		

Extracts from balance sheet (Yr 1)

Balance sheet		£	£	£
	Fixed assets	Cost	Dep	Net
	Alarm	1,000	150	850

Extracts from balance sheet (Yr 2)

Alarm account			
	£		£
Balance b/f	1,000	Disposals	1,000

Provision for depreciation account			
	£		£
		Balance b/f	150
Disposals	300	Profit and loss	150
	300		**300**

Extracts from accounts Year 2 (Continued)

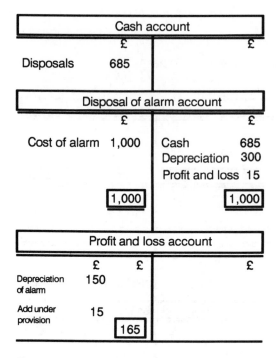

There will be no mention of the alarm on the balance sheet for Year 2
as the alarm is no longer in the possession of the firm

Figure 6.3
Extracts from accounts

An aspect affecting the replacement of assets is inflation. This means in
practice that the replacement cost of the asset will be more than the original
cost. Replacement cost of depreciation is a phenomenon which has
occurred since the end of the Second World War. It has been the scale of
inflation since that time that has caused traditional accountants to accept
the need for some form of inflation accounting. Nowadays, the traditional
historical cost basis for preparing accounts is retained but can be supplemented by a statement showing the main figures adjusted to take
account of the declining value of money as represented by the Retail Price
Index.

Profit is measured by matching revenues of a period with expenses of
that period. This matching process may not always be matching current
values. Profit for a period will always be overstated in a period of inflation
if any costs of one date are matched with revenues of a later date. Particu-

larly relevant in this connection is the depreciation of fixed assets. Depreciation based upon historical costs (i.e. writing off the cost of the asset over its expected life whatever method is used), will not accumulate a depreciation provision equal to the cost of replacing the asset in inflationary times. Perhaps the earliest recognition of accounting for inflation was the decision by some companies to base their depreciation policy on a replacement cost basis. For example, if an item of equipment cost £500 and was expected to last five years and have no scrap value, then under the straight line method of depreciation based on historical costs, the depreciation charged to the profit and loss account would be £100 per year. Under replacement cost depreciation, in addition to the £100, a further amount would be appropriated to a capital reserve which would reflect the amount by which the price of the equipment had risen over the year. This attempts to ensure that sufficient money is retained in the business for the replacement of assets.

A further consideration to the determining of profit in times of inflation is stock valuation. The same quantity of closing stock may have a higher cost valuation than the same quantity of opening stock. This is particularly likely to happen under a FIFO system of pricing out material issues. The result of this different valuation for the same quantity of stocks is to reduce the size of *cost of goods sold* which in turn results in the overstatement of *gross profit*. It is due to these considerations that the LIFO system of pricing out material issues is finding more favour today. It is important that all safety managers are aware of their own company policy in these areas so that they can adjust their programme planning accordingly.

Fund flow and cash flow

To the general manager, financial statements are primarily concerned with profit and loss, and details concerning assets, capital and liabilities. The information presented in these financial statements can be illustrated in a different way to show the sources and applications of funds within the business. This is useful in determining what funds are available and discussing how they are to be used. The information provides an analysis of the reasons for changes in either the company's fund of working capital or its cash resources. It is important for a firm not only to be profitable but also to have adequate working capital and in particular cash resources to meet its commitments as they fall due. Thus many companies prepare flow statements and/or cash flow statements to help with funds management. Some accountants argue that *fund flow* is synonymous with *cash flow* whilst others say that fund flow pertains to the effect on working capital and cash flow refers to the effect on the cash balance.

The sources and applications of working capital and cash are shown in Figures 6.4 and 6.5.

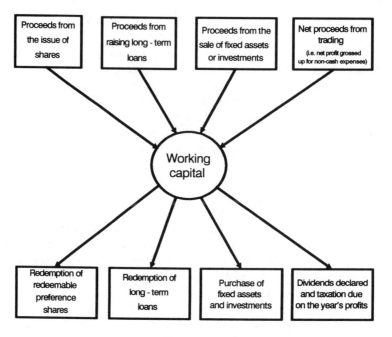

Figure 6.4
Flow of funds

The main external sources of funds for either working capital or the cash balance can be seen to be proceeds from share issues, the raising of long-term loans and the sale of fixed assets or investments. The main internal source of funds for working capital and one of the main internal sources of cash funds is the net profit earned by the organisation. However, it must be remembered that for the concepts of funds flow and cash flow any non-cash expense (such as depreciation) must be added back to the profit figure produced in the final accounts as there is no funds or cash flow generated by the book entry of depreciation. The *funds* or *cash flow* was generated in full at the time of the purchase of the fixed assets concerned. The main applications of funds for either working capital or the cash balance can be seen to be the redemption of shares or long-term loans and the purchase of fixed assets or investments. With regard to dividends and taxation, it is the amount proposed of the former and the amount of the latter assessed due on the profits which affect the size of the working capital. This is because the proposal and assessment reduce the amount of profit that can be retained as a reserve and create a current liability. The actual payment of the dividend and tax does not affect working capital as both a current liability and a current asset (cash) are equally affected. In the case of the

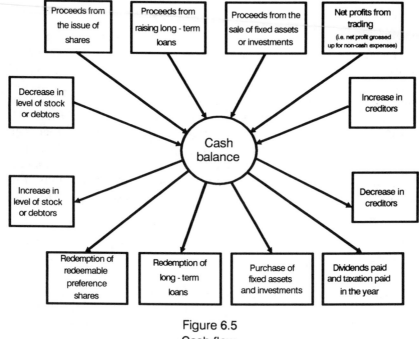

Figure 6.5
Cash flow

cash flow, it is the actual dividends and tax paid in the year that are required.

A cash flow statement is more detailed than the fund flow statement because in the latter all movements within working capital are not shown whereas they are shown in the former. Such movements are usually the increase or decrease of stocks, debtors and creditors. An increase in debtors can be regarded as an extension of credit by the firm to its customers and a decrease in creditors can be regarded as a reduction of credit granted to the company by its suppliers. Hence the effect upon cash flow.

Funds flow and cash flow statements are used in two main ways:

1. As a tool of historical analysis; and
2. As a planning tool.

These are discussed briefly below.

Historical analysis

The statements illustrate the financial policies adopted by the company. They show the extent to which new fixed assets have been financed by internally generated sources and, by deduction, the extent to which external financing was undertaken.

Planning

Forecasted fund flow and cash flow statements are essential for planning the size, timing and nature of new fund requirements. Estimates are made of the uses of funds for new fixed assets, increasing working capital, redemptions of shares and debentures, dividends and taxation. Against these are matched the estimated funds generated from internal sources and the difference gives the estimated requirements of external financing. The size of the external financing requirements may well cause the original plans of capital investment to be revised. In respect of short-term planning, a cash budget is essential. Cash budgets are a detailed cash flow statement. The detail is not only in the make up of the sources and applications of the cash but in a timing of the flows, probably on a monthly or quarterly basis.

Budgetary control

Most safety practitioners operate from a budget allocated to them for carrying out company safety policy. Having very briefly discussed how cash is generated for such activities it is now necessary to see how budgets should be controlled. A system of budgetary control establishes various budgets which set out in financial terms the responsibilities of management in relation to the requirements of the overall policy of the organisation. There should be a regular comparison of actual results with budget forecasts both to try and ensure (through action by the safety manager) that the objectives of safety policy are met and also to form a basis for any revision of such policy.

The crux of the budgetary process is that financial limits are *allocated* to component parts of the organisation. Thus, the safety manager plans activities in line with company policy and within the financial limits. It is important to try to obtain departmental management *agreement* to this financial limit as it is the manager who is going to be held responsible for keeping within it. Experience shows that a safety manager is more willing to accept responsibility for performance against his budget if he has been allowed to participate in the determination of the size of that budget rather than it being imposed upon him.

Primary responsibility for the administration of the budgetary process is normally delegated by senior management to a budget accountant who has the task of co-ordinating the preparation of both the budgets and their reports. These reports may be presented to a special budget committee (particularly in larger organisations) which is composed of the managers in charge of the major functional areas of the organisation. Membership of this committee would normally be extended to the safety manager.

Preparation of budgets

The following steps are typical of those taken in the preparation of the individual budgets and the *master* budget for a commercial organisation. A safety manager responsible for safety at various locations such as a group safety manager, would be responsible for his own master budget. This would then form a part of the overall organisational master budget:

1. A statement of overall safety objectives is prepared on which the individual budgets are to be based;
2. Forecasts are made regarding the general economic conditions and the conditions likely to be prevailing in the industry. Here accident data plays a key role;
3. A safety budget can then be prepared based upon the forecasts and will highlight key task areas for action;
4. A production budget is prepared in conjunction with the above and will require consideration of all materials and other resources required to carry out those key task areas presented in 3. above;
5. The administrative cost budget is prepared for each area of activity;
6. A capital expenditure budget is compiled, covering anticipated changes in legislation or purchase of specialised equipment or other modifications.

The preparation of the budget is shown diagrammatically in Figure 6.6.

Budgetary control during the year

Once the year has started, the control aspect of the budgetary process consists of comparing the actual results to budgeted figures. The chief value of the budgets as a control mechanism in this connection will be achieved through the effective use of regular reports. These reports, co-ordinated by the budget accountant, will show the variances (normally expressed as percentages) between the actual and budgeted figures. Significant variances should be highlighted. Variance control charts can be employed to present control limits to safety staff and these charts will also show up the significant variances as actual results are recorded.

The reports should also make it clear which budget variances were *controllable* by those responsible and which were not. Detailed explanations of the cause of the variances can be based upon the type of variance analysis between standard unit costs and actual unit costs. It must be remembered that budgetary control needs action. The chief value of the reports lies with effective use of reports. Budgetary control thus employs the concept of what may be described as *responsibility accounting*. The accounting system in operation must provide information in line with the budgetary system (appropriate cost centres).

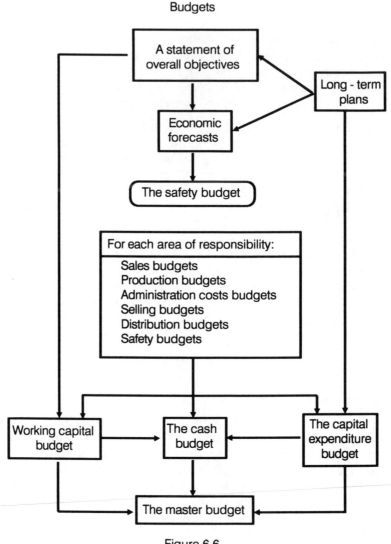

Budgets

Figure 6.6

The preparation of the individual budgets and the master budget for a commercial organisation

Costing an accident

Accidents cost an organisation considerable sums of money and justification for taking positive action within the organisation is based on this fact. As discussed in Chapter 3, the aim of the safety manager is to reduce accidents or prevent them from happening. Showing remedial strategies to be effective in meeting this aim will in turn save time which can be simply translated into monetary terms. There are many methods for estimating the cost of an accident but there are two classes of costs which result from an accident:

1. From insurance (the insured costs); and
2. Uninsured costs.

In theory, an organisation can insure itself against any eventuality but in practice the costs of doing this are prohibitive. Most companies, therefore, insure a part of their activities, such as those required by law, and accept liability for the remainder. For example, a worker who drops a casting onto the floor and breaks a toe will have compensation paid for from insurance sources. The damage done to equipment or the casting itself may have to be borne by the company if such eventualities are not covered by insurance. Let us look at 10 elements connected with an incident which may be regarded as uninsured costs. These are not listed in any order of priority.

1. Cost of wages paid for working time lost by workers who were not injured but whose work output was interrupted by the accident taking place;
2. The net cost to repair, replace, or straighten up materials or equipment damaged in an accident;
3. Cost of wages paid for working time lost by injured workers, other than workers' compensation payments;
4. Extra costs necessitated by the accident involving overtime work;
5. Cost of supervisors' wages whilst their time is required for activities necessitated by the accident;
6. Wage costs due to decreased output of injured worker after return to work;
7. Cost of learning period of any new worker employed during the injured workers' period of absence;
8. Uninsured medical costs borne by the company;
9. Cost of time spent on accident investigations and processing of HSE requirements and compensation type administration; and
10. Additional costs such as equipment replacement, hire of temporary facilities needed until normal state can be resumed. For example, replacement vehicles involved in road traffic accidents.

A safety manager must be in a position to calculate his company's accident costs and company accountants will usually agree the method to be adopted. A sample form used to extract cost data is given in Figures 6.7 and 6.8.

Accident Cost Report

	Hours	Mins
Total Lost Time (1)		
Treatment Time (2)		
First Aid Time (3)		
Grand total (1+2+3)		

Name of Employee [＿＿＿＿＿＿＿＿]   Works Number [＿＿＿＿＿＿]

Date of Injury [＿][＿][＿]   Nature of Injury [＿＿＿＿＿＿＿＿＿]

Department [＿＿＿＿＿]   Operation [＿＿＿＿＿＿]   Hourly rate £ [＿][＿]

Average hourly rate in the Department where the injury occurred   £ [＿][＿]

Wage Cost of lost time by workers not injured (but by employer)   £ [＿][＿]

Number of worker who lost time because they were talking, watching, helping etc.   [＿＿]

Average time lost per worker   [＿＿]

Number of workers effected by the accident or incident   [＿＿]

Average time lost per worker   [＿][＿]
(Hours Mins)

Nature of damage to equipment [＿＿＿＿＿＿＿＿＿]

Net cost to replace or repair damaged equipment   £ [＿][＿]

Wage cost of time lost by injured worker whilst being paid by employer   £ [＿][＿]
(other than employees compensation payments)

Time lost on the day of injury for which the employee was paid   [＿][＿]
(Hours Mins)

Number of subsequent days absence for which the employee was paid   [＿]

Length of shift or number of hours in standard day   [＿][＿]
(Hours Mins)

Number of additional journeys for medical treatment in employers time   [＿]

Average time per journey [＿][＿]   Total   [＿][＿]
(Hours Mins)   (Hours Mins)

Additional lost time by employee for which he was paid   [＿][＿]
(Hours Mins)

Lost production costs (include overtime extra supervision etc)   £ [＿][＿]

Cost of Supervisor's time connected with the accident   £ [＿][＿]

Supervisor's time shown on report [＿][＿]   Additional Supervisor's time required   [＿][＿]
(Hours Mins)   (Hours Mins)

Wage costs due to decrease in output of worker after injury (if rate paid)   £ [＿][＿]

Accident Cost Report

Injury Accident Number

Non-Injury Accident Number

Dangerous Occurrence Number

Date

Department

Name of Injured Worker

(or Name of worker reporting a dangerous occurrence)

Works Number

Please answer the following questions:

1. How many other workers (not injured) lost time because they were talking, watching or helping at the accident?

2. How much time did they lose?

Hours   Minutes

3. How many other workers (not injured) lost time due to damaged equipment in the accident or they required the output or assistance of the injured?

4. How much time did most of them lose?

Hours   Minutes

5. Describe the damage to materials and equipment:

6. Estimate the cost of the repair or replacement of the materials and equipment listed above? £

7. How much time did injured workers lose on the day of injury for which he was paid? £

8. If operations (or machines) were stopped, will overtime be necessary to make up lost production? YES NO

9. Will it be impossible to make up lost production? YES NO

10. How much supervisor's time was used assisting, investigating, reporting, re-assigning work or instructing a substitute or making adjustments to work loads?

Hours   Minutes

Name of Supervisor

Please pass this form as quickly as possible to the Safety Manager

Figure 6.7
A Supervisor's Accident Cost Report

Total time on light work

Employees average percentage of normal output during this period

Where the injured employee was replaced by additional staff the wage cost for this period

Time the new employees was below normal for standard wage expected

New employees average percentage of expected (normal) output

New employees hourly rate of pay

Time of Supervisor in training new employee

Medical cost to the organisation (not covered by employees compensation insurance)

Cost of time by other clerical workers involved in processing accident paperwork

Other costs not detailed above (eg additional costs in renting equipment, public liability etc)

Total uninsured costs

Figure 6.8

Accident Investigator's Cost Sheet

Such data will then allow a company to assess its own average accident costs, which vary from industry to industry, and this will provide for a better basis on which to assess budgetary requirements and improved programme evaluation strategies. It is easier to undertake prospective rather than retrospective studies, although organisations who do not do this may wish to undertake a small retrospective study in order to obtain a sample accident costing. In this case, remember that to help decide how many cases to look at or test the reliability of the averages, compute the standard errors of the averages. It is likely that a two-thirds fiducial probability will give an average for a dozen or more cases of a given type within one standard error of the true average for this type of case in your organisation. The standard error is equal to:

$$\frac{\bar{\sigma}}{\sqrt{N}}, \text{ and } \bar{\sigma} = \sqrt{\frac{\Sigma x - \Sigma x\bar{x}}{N-1}}$$

N = number of cases
x = cost of an individual case
$\bar{x}$ = average cost

In a larger organisation it might be better to look at 25 to 30 cases.

Incentive schemes

There is evidence that some incentive schemes are a contributory factor in accidents. For example, a The Bloggs Delivery Service paid its drivers on the number of delivery collections made during a working shift. The emphasis of the bonus scheme was on speed. It has been known for several years that speed is a major factor in accidents whether on the road or on the factory floor. In the case of The Bloggs Delivery Service one driver lost his life, four drivers were seriously injured and 11 were slightly injured in road accidents in one year. In addition to this, 37% of the fleet of vehicles were damaged in some way during the same year. The cost of all this to The Bloggs Delivery Service was too much and the firm went out of business 18 months later. All incentive schemes involving drivers of vehicles should be based upon low accident involvement and low accident damage factors. For example, a driver completing one year of accident-free driving should be entitled to a minimum bonus based upon the savings in insurance premiums under similar conditions to the no claims bonus operated by insurance companies. Some companies operate the RoSPA Safe Driving Award Scheme but unless this is linked to a financial reward there is little incentive for drivers to take part. Careful recording of accident costs as discussed above should allow organisations to calculate meaningful schemes for their employees.

Payment by results

Some companies operate schemes based upon the number of items or actions produced within a certain time scale. It is common for safety to be ignored from the processes involved unless the safety manager is consulted.

Incentive schemes give rise to much discussion, although this is as much due to the varying interpretations of what is meant by an incentive scheme and to the variety of opinion as to what its objectives are. There are differences in the bases of assessment on which schemes are founded and also in the industrial atmosphere into which they must fit. Inevitably, there are good schemes and bad ones and opinion of them is tempered by personal experience. In Chapter 4, job evaluation was briefly discussed. Through this, each job may be placed into a particular grade for which a specific remuneration is paid. For some jobs, this is all that is necessary in designing a wage payment system. Such a system is referred to as a time rate (TR) or day rate. Payment under such a system involves paying a person according to the time he spends at work rather than directly on the amount of work produced. There are sanctions on payment for work done. If no work is produced at all then it is unlikely that the person would be allowed to continue in the job! Alternatively, if the work done is excessive compared to what is expected, then some kind of reward (whether short term or in the long term) is usually received. The advantages of TR schemes are usually listed as:

- The employee has a guaranteed wage.
- Wages are relatively easy to compute both by employee and employer.
- They provide low administrative costs.
- It is easier to control the quality of the work when wages are not dependent upon output.
- The wage system does not inhibit labour flexibility within a particular grade.
- Day-to-day disputes over earnings are avoided.

The disadvantages of these schemes are:

- There is no direct financial incentive to increase output.
- Usually active supervision is necessary.
- Productivity and therefore unit costs are impossible to forecast accurately.

One of the empirical rules upon which work measurement is based is related to the effort rating of a person working at standard performance. Under incentive conditions, this will normally be about one-third higher than the rating of a person working under non-incentive conditions. There can be no theoretical base for this rule. Its only justification is that it has been found to be generally true. From this, it follows that if one-third more effort is required to achieve standard performance from non-incentive performance, then incentive payment should be one-third higher than non-incentive payment.

When the term *performance* is used, a comparison with our concept of standard performance is implicit. Therefore to quantify performance, it is an expression of the standard time for a job (i.e. the time it will take at standard performance) as a percentage of the actual time in which the job was performed. This is shown as:

$$\text{Performance} = \frac{\text{Standard time}}{\text{Actual time}} \times 100$$

For example, if a person performs a job, the standard time for which is 10 minutes, in eight minutes, then his performance will be:

$$\frac{10}{8} \times 100 = 125\%$$

Many different schemes for payment by results (PBR) have been published since the turn of the century. All such schemes do basically the same thing in that they relate performance to earnings in some way. Explaining the operation of such a scheme is best done in an example.

Example 6.3

Fred Smith is a junior machinist at Bloggs Boot Bazaar, a boot and shoe makers in the Midlands. In one eight-hour shift he performs the following work:

Boot buffing	100 boots
Heel honing	200 boots
Leather lopping	100 boots

He also worked on a workbench cleaning job, which is unmeasured work, for a period of time but he cannot remember whether it was for 20 or 40 minutes. If unmeasured work is paid for at base rate the wrong booking of time to Fred would make the following difference to his pay (payment scheme is shown in Figure 6.9):

Job	Quantity	Standard Minutes (SM)
Boot buffing	100 boots	$\times 3.19 = 319$
Heel honing	200 boots	$\times 10.5 = 21$
Leather lopping	100 boots	$\times 0.94 = 94$
		Total 434 SM's

If 20 minutes' unmeasured work were booked, then

$$\text{Performance} = \frac{\text{SM of measured work}}{\text{Actual time}} \times 100$$

$$= \frac{434}{(480 - 20)} \times 100 = 94.35 \text{ BS.}$$

Since the scheme is a straight proportional one, Fred's pay per hour for measured work will be 94.35% of his target incentive rate.

The incentive rate for Fred is £3.20 (base rate plus one-third) which will mean that measured pay is as follows:

$$0.9435 \times 320 \times 7\frac{2}{3} = 23.15$$

Plus 20 minutes (one third of an hour) at the base rate of £2.40, therefore, total pay = £23.15 plus 0.8 which is £23.95p. However, if 40 minutes unmeasured work is booked then:

$$\text{Performance} = \frac{434}{(480 - 40)} \times 100 = 98.64 \text{ BS}$$

Therefore measured work pay = $0.9864 \times 320 \times 7\frac{2}{3} = £24.18$.

Plus 40 minutes (two-thirds) at the base rate of £2.40 then total pay is £24.18 + 1.60 = £25.78p.

Job	Standard time
Sole searching	1.52 SM per boot
Upper stitching	0.84 SM per boot
Lower stitching	1.35 SM per boot
Boot buffing	3.19 SM per boot
Heel honing	10.50 SM per boot
Leather lopping	0.94 SM per boot
Tongue twisting	3.31 SM per boot
Cap crushing	0.01 SM per boot

Hourly base rates

Rank	Grade	Hourly rate
Safety footwear operative	A	£8.00
Assistant safety footwear operative	B	£6.00
Machinist first class	C	£4.80
Machinist	D	£3.60
Junior machinist	E	£2.40
Cap crusher's assistant	F	£1.20

Figure 6.9
Standard times data

For convenience, earnings can be expressed on a numerical scale where normal day rate or time rate for a job is 75 on the scale. Incentive rate is therefore 100. Figure 6.10A to D shows a performance earnings graph with the most simple of all PBR schemes a 45-degree line starting from the origin. The strength of this lies in its simplicity in that $x\%$ more output means $x\%$ more money. Usually, two modifications are necessary before the scheme can be put into use to protect both worker and management. These are:

1. A minimum earnings level, usually at non-incentive (base) rate to ensure that earnings never fall below the level that would have been received under a time rate system;

2. A maximum earnings cut-off level to ensure that inaccurate standard times do not result in high earnings which are not deserved. This is usually set at a level somewhere between 120 and 130 performance.

The slope of the incentive line dictates how sensitive earnings are to variations in performance. Schemes with a slope lower than unity result in earnings being less sensitive to variations in performance. The slope of the line is usually called the *gearing* of the scheme. Geared schemes are usually used where the nature of the work means that although standard times may, in the long term be accurate, there will be some variations in the short term. In Figure 6.10C a scheme is shown which has a gearing of 0.5 but still passes through the 100-100 point. This scheme is sometimes modified to prevent the bonus part of earnings being paid before 75 performance is achieved (see Figure 6.10D).

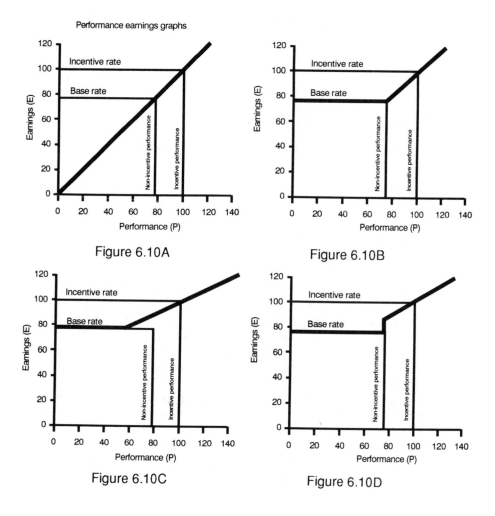

Performance earnings graphs

Figure 6.10A

Figure 6.10B

Figure 6.10C

Figure 6.10D

Cost consequences of PBR

Money earned by a worker is a cost to the company and a firm will be prepared to pay more money for more output. The important measure from management's point of view is the labour cost per unit of production. The relationship between performance and output will be a function of the actual job performed. We can, however derive a simple indication of labour cost by simply dividing earnings (a measure of cost) by performance (a measure of output) for each scheme. In Figure 6.11 a cost curve for the simple 45-degree line scheme is shown indicating the cut-off and minimum earnings modification. For the 45-degree part of the scheme, the cost ratio is unity since output and cost change in the same proportion. When the cut-offs operate, the performance changes but the earnings do not. This results in a hyperbolic cost curve.

Generally, $E = GP + K$ (equation of a straight line $y = mx + c$), where:

E = earnings
P = performance
G = gearing
K = a constant

$$\text{Cost ratio} = \frac{E}{P} = \frac{GP + K}{P} = G + \frac{K}{P}$$

For the 45-degree line, $G = 1$ and $K = 0$, therefore the cost ratio is 1. For the horizontal lines, $G = 0$, therefore the cost ratio is K divided by P (see Figure 6.12).

Calculating the safety factor

Several incentive schemes have been discussed and so far no allowances have been made for the safety of the production process. It should be remembered that all accidents affect performance and thus produce a cost. Therefore, some means of including this within the calculations is necessary. Like incentive schemes generally there are many methods of meeting this provision and most are based upon the number of reported accidents and dangerous occurrences carrying out specific tasks expressed as a proportion of the costs of those incidents. Some tasks will have a greater risk than others (see Chapter 8), therefore it will be difficult to calculate a standard rate to cover every eventuality. Let us look at work measurement techniques.

Work measurement can be described as the application of techniques designed to establish the time for a qualified worker to carry out a specified job at a defined level of performance in *complete safety*. This poses three

Cost consequences

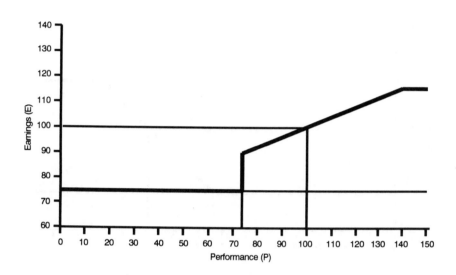

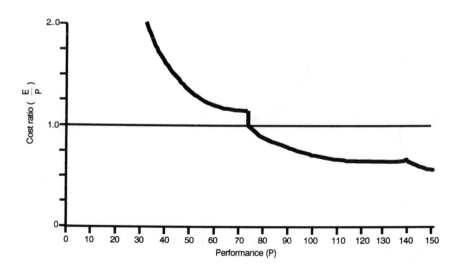

Figure 6.11

Cost consequences

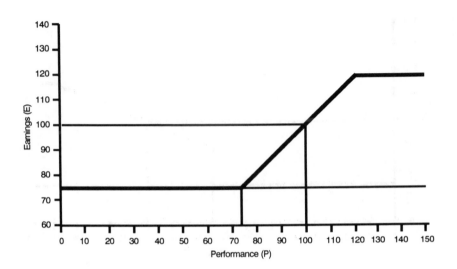

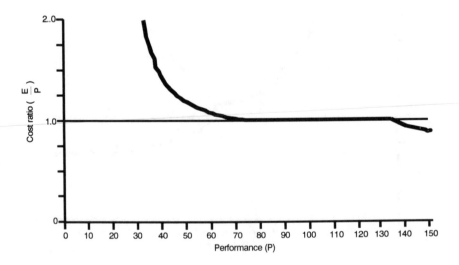

Figure 6.12

questions:

1. What is a qualified worker?
2. What is a specified job?
3. What is a defined level of performance?

A specified job is one for which specifications have been established to define the job such as:

- The quality standard required.
- The method to be followed by the worker.
- The machines, materials and tooling to be used.
- The working conditions under which the job is performed.

Being a qualified worker means one who is accepted as having the necessary physical attributes, intelligence, skill, education and knowledge to perform the task to satisfactory standards of safety, quality and quantity. The term *performance* means a rate of working or alternatively a rate of output expressed as an average over the working day or shift. There are two basic concepts regarding what levels of performance should be. These are:

1. That it should be the level which can be reasonably expected under *motivation* conditions of employment; and
2. That it should be of the level of performance which can be reasonably expected under *non-motivation* conditions.

The British Standard recommendation is that performance should be pitched at the motivation level and the term used to describe this level of performance is referred to as the *standard performance*. This is defined as:

'the rate of output which qualified workers will achieve without over-exertion as an average over the working day provided they are motivated to apply themselves to their work.'

It is not proposed to discuss the principles of objectivity, subjectivity or general relevance of work measurement, but it should be remembered that the above definitions are not perfect and that work measurement has never pretended to be anything but an empirical discipline.

Facts rather than opinions are required to ensure effective planning and control of production. The *work value* of each job is one of the most important facts. The work value of a task consists of two factors. These are:

1. The value of the sort of job; and
2. The time required to complete the job.

The first is determined by:

- The market value of labour.
- Agreements.
- Legislation.
- Job evaluation.

The second is determined by work measurement.

All organisations make some kind of estimate of the length of a job and there are three possibilities. These are:

1. The use of a measuring technique which is systematic and has known, close limits of accuracy;
2. Guesswork;
3. Assume that the time which is taken to do the job is the correct time.

The uses of work measurement are:

- *Methods* to assess the relative importance of different parts of the method and to compare alternatives.
- *Incentives* to provide a fair and realistic basis for incentive schemes.
- *Machines* to determine machine loading.
- *Men* to establish manning levels.
- *Planning* to provide a basis for production planning.
- *Control* to provide a basis for management control.
- *Costing* to provide a basis for standard costing systems.
- *Budgeting* to provide information for labour budgeting systems.

Although there are several uses listed above, the purpose with which work measurement is usually connected is that of establishing incentive schemes. This is why work measurement tends to be such an emotive subject. It must be pointed out that payment is only one use of time standards, although it is the most troublesome.

The majority of work measurement techniques involve the breaking down of the job to be studied into *elements*. For each of these elements, separate standard times are established. The standard time of the job as a whole is then the sum of all the standard times of its constituent elements. Standard times for these, consist principally of three basic parts (although others may be added). These are:

1. Basic time;
2. Relaxation allowance; and
3. Safety factor.

This is shown as an example below.

Example 6.4

Element	Basic Time (Mins)	Relaxation (%)	Relaxation (Mins)	Safety (%)	Safety (Mins)	Standard Time (Mins)
a	0.6	17	0.10	17	0.10	0.80
b	0.4	12	0.05	12	0.05	0.50
c	0.8	2.5	0.02	2.5	0.02	0.84
d	0.3	17	0.05	17	0.05	0.40
Total	2.1		0.22		0.22	2.54

Diagrammatically this is shown in Figure 6.13.

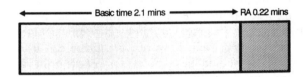

Figure 6.13
Standard time

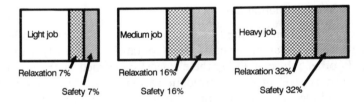

Figure 6.14
Standard units of work

Standard units of work

This should generally be broken down into the following:

- The quality of work in all kinds of jobs can be expressed in terms of the common unit.
- One work unit consists of three parts namely *work*, *relaxation* and *safety*.
- The proportion of each part varies with the type of job but the three parts together always add up to the common unit (see Figure 6.14).

Work measurement uses five techniques which are:

1. Time study;
2. Synthesis from elemental data;
3. Predetermined motion-time systems;
4. Analytical estimating; and
5. Activity sampling.

These are discussed briefly below.

Time study

This is a method of recording the times and rates of working for the elements of a specified job which is conducted under specified conditions and for analysing the data in order to obtain the time necessary for the carrying out of the job at a defined level of performance. The times for the task are recorded using one or more stop-watches on the shop floor which is why time study has met with and still does encounter opposition.

Using the correct approach, however, resistance can usually be overcome. Method study should be a necessary pre-requisite to time study especially if the times obtained are to be used as a basis for incentive schemes. Time study also provides timings for separate work elements which can be used in synthesising times from elemental data.

Synthesis from elemental data

This technique is used to build up the time for a job at a defined level of performance by totalling element times obtained previously from time studies in other jobs containing the elements concerned or from synthetic data. When time elements recurred in various jobs, the times may be recorded and filed so that when those elements occurred, records could be consulted for *all* the necessary elements and it is possible to compile a standard time without having to carry out a time study. This saves work and makes the compilation of standard times much faster and cheaper. When an attempt is made to time elements for synthesis purposes, elements have to be selected so that they have the widest application in the jobs which have to be timed. If the elements are too long and diverse, their field of application will be limited; and conversely if too short may not be easily measurable.

Predetermined motion-time systems (PMTS)

This is a system whereby times established for basic human motions (which are classified according to the nature of the motion and the condition under which it is made) are used to build up the time for a job at a defined level of performance.

Analytical estimating

This technique is a development of estimating, whereby the time required to carry out the elements of a job at a defined level of performance is estimated from knowledge and experience of the elements concerned. Time study is mainly useful to analyse repetitive jobs, but is uneconomical to analyse non-repetitive work. On the other hand, a foreman's estimate or bargaining procedure are rarely satisfactory. Analytical estimating is generally more accurate since it is systematic and based on the study of work. Time is not estimated for the job as a whole but the task is first broken into elements as in time study, although in general, the elements tend to be longer. Times for these longer elements are worked out by a trained estimator. This technique is widely used to estimate times in engineering and construction work. Analytical estimating can give satisfactory results, although they will be less accurate than those obtained through time study or synthesis from elemental data. This method relies heavily upon the skill of the estimator who should be:

- Trained in estimating.
- Familiar with work study techniques.
- Knowledgable about the jobs for which he is estimating.

Activity sampling

This method provides for a large number of instantaneous observations to be made over a period of time of a group of machines, processes or workers. Each observation records what is happening at that time and the percentage of observations recorded for a particular activity or delay is a measure of the percentage of time during which that activity or delay occurs. This is a statistical method which is based upon the same theory which underlies market research and opinion polls. This theory is that random observations can produce results whose accuracy depends on the number of observations made. This technique is used both in method study and in work measurement and can also be used to quantify safety elements within a work unit.

Time study

Of the five techniques of work measurement discussed above, it is advisable to examine time study in a little more detail for two reasons. First, because it is still the most used technique in practice and second, because it contains some fundamental problems such as elements and rating. Time study procedure divides naturally into three stages which have been called:

1. The preparatory stage;
2. The study; and
3. The concluding stage.

The preparatory stage

- Obtain the supervisor's confirmation that the job is ready for study.
- Speak to the operator(s) to obtain co-operation or permission.
- Observe the job as it is carried out and become familiar with it.
- Check that safety regulations and standards are met.
- Check that quality of standard of output is within specifications.
- Check that job specifications are being adhered to and that method of doing the job is identical with agreements in force.
- Check that materials being used conform to specifications.
- Record the operator's name and other relevant information.
- Sketch out details of any special aspects of the job.
- Decide upon a suitable unit of production (this may be decided by company policy).
- Break the job down into elements.

It is important to break down the job into elements because:

- A greater understanding of the job can be obtained if the job is analysed into elements.
- Element breakdown is necessary as a basis for synthesis.
- Rating accuracy is facilitated.
- Allowance allocation is made more accurate.

There are three basic principles used as a guide to element breakdown. The selection of elements is often dictated by technical considerations. For example, if the elements are to provide a basis for future synthesis as well as being the constituent parts of an individual job, the choice of elements could well be based on the similarity between one job and another.

Principle 1

An element should be made up of one type of work only. That is:

- Machine work should be separate from manual work.
- Constant type work should be separate from variable work.
- Work occurring in every work cycle should be separated from occasional work.
- Heavy work should be separated from light work.

Principle 2

The end of an element should coincide with the natural break point in the work. If this can be identified by audible indications then this will provide the observer with a relief from continuous observation.

Principle 3

The length of an element should be such that it aids accuracy in timing and rating. Opinions disagree as to the minimum length of elements but it is generally agreed that the shortest time in which an element can be rated and timed is about five seconds. The length of an element should be longer when:

- Several comparatively short elements occur successively.
- The work is of such a scale as to make short elements unworkable.

The study

During a time study, each observed element is timed using a stop-watch and recorded on the study sheet. Simultaneously, each element is rated and the rating recorded. There are various points that could be considered here, such as stop-watch techniques and study form design but by far the most important feature of the study is the rating. This is an assessment of the worker's rate relative to the observer's concept of the rate. This corresponds to the standard rating. The observer may take into account several factors necessary to do the job, such as the speed of movement, dexterity, effort, consistency. Safety should also be seen to be included. Rating is carried out when elements are timed since it is the assessment of the speed and effectiveness of the worker at that time. A work study observer must be conversant with the correct way of doing the job in order of reliability. Rating is probably the most important albeit the most controversial part of time study particularly where safety is concerned.

   A work study observer must have some standard of rating to which he can relate his observations. In the past, it was assumed that the basis for this standard would be the output of the worker on *time rate* (datal rate or basic rate) and that a normal worker at *incentive rate* would produce one-third more in the same time. Of the many numerical rating scales in use, the most popular was the 60/80 or Bedeaux scale. This assumes that a normal worker will produce at a speed of 60 when on a time rate and at a speed of 80 when on incentive rate. Other scales which are sometimes used are the 100/133 and 75/100 scale. More recently a 0/100 scale is used where the 100 corresponds with the 80 or 133 on the other scales but no lower point (60,100 on the other scales) is defined (see Figure 6.15). Which-

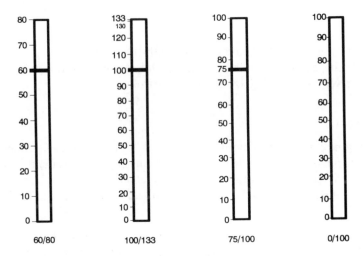

Figure 6.15

Rating scales

ever system is in use, it is necessary for safety practitioners to have an understanding of basic rating scales so that appropriate advice and input may be given.

The concluding stage

Information gathered before and during the study is used to obtain the work content and standard time for the job. Basic time, sometimes referred to as extended, converted or standardised time, is defined as the time for carrying out an element of work at standard rating. This can be expressed as:

$$\text{Basic Time} = \frac{\text{Observed time} \times \text{Observed rating}}{\text{Standard rating}} + 1\% \text{ for safety}$$

NB For a more precise method of allowing for the *safety factor*, see Chapter 8.

From the many observations of an element, a series of basic times are obtained. From these, the selected basic time for each element must be obtained. There are two basic methods of obtaining the selected basic time from a series of selected basic times:

1. The arithmetical mean method; and
2. The frequency distribution method.

These two methods are illustrated below.

Example 6.5

The basic times for an element, including a safety provision, are:

0.152	0.207	0.223	0.220
0.157	0.193	0.147	0.210
0.149	0.173	0.152	
0.161	0.182	0.153	
0.213	0.153	0.141	

The total of these times is 2.986 minutes and the number of observations is 17. Therefore the mean time is:

$$\frac{2.986}{17} = 0.1756 \text{ minutes}$$

This value is the selected basic time obtained by the arithmetic mean method. Alternatively, by the frequency distribution method for the same data set we have:

Interval	Occurrence
0.140 to 0.149	///
0.150 to 0.159	/////
0.160 to 0.169	/
0.170 to 0.179	/
0.180 to 0.189	/
0.190 to 0.199	/
0.200 to 0.209	/
0.210 to 0.219	//
0.220 to 0.229	//

In this case, more values fell within the 0.150 to 0.159 interval than any other group. The observer may regard these values as the most typical. The central value of this interval is usually taken to be the selected basic time, in this case 0.1545 minutes. When the basic time for each element has been obtained, certain allowances must be added, including any further safety allowances, in order to obtain the work content and the standard time.

Allowances

There are several allowances which may be applied to the basic time, depending on the circumstances. The main one is the relaxation allowance which is provided to allow a worker the opportunity to recover from the physiological and psychological effects of carrying out specified work under specified conditions and to cater for attention to personal needs. The amount of allowance depends upon the nature of the job. Other allowances can be made for:

- Learner allowances.
- Introductory allowances.
- Contingency allowances.
- Unusual conditions allowances.
- Unoccupied time allowances.
- Interference or synchronisation allowances.

Economic rates of return

This is sometimes referred to as cost benefit analysis or risk analysis. For our purposes, cost benefit analysis can be regarded as a procedure devised to work out how much would be saved in financial terms by implementing a scheme. As the need to be more accountable in financial terms for our actions increases, so does the need for value for money (vfm). Criteria which help the safety practitioner's decisions are:

- The statistical significance of accident data.
- Expected effectiveness of the remedial action.
- A discounted economic rate of return on expenditure.
- Resource availability.

The first two considerations are based upon an analysis of past accident records and the results of previous remedial measures undertaken.

The costing of human life is always very difficult but several attempts have been made in recent years. Most consider the loss of working ability for society and in terms of emotional loss to a family. Whereas the first of these can be estimated, given age, sex and social status of the person, the second has proved more difficult. When figures are given for the cost of an accident, there is usually a notional amount added for the emotional effects but whether this is realistic can be debated. Whether someone dies in a road accident or in the workplace, the figures can be argued to be the same. Because of the severity of the road accident problems experienced by all nations, attempts have been made to cost such events. It is argued here that these costs are similar whether they take place outside the factory gate on a public highway or inside the factory compound. The same factors need to be considered in costing fatal, injury and non-injury accidents. Dangerous occurrences would need to be considered separately for each type of industry. In calculating the cost of accidents the United Kingdom consider the following which is based upon the cost of the number of elements averaged for each type of injury:

- The loss of output due to death or injury (loss of earnings plus non-wage payments).
- Ambulance costs and the costs of medical treatment.
- The cost of pain, grief and suffering to the casualty, relatives and friends. Although considered to be important, the evaluation of these costs is difficult therefore a notional figure is used in the estimated costs.
- Cost of damage to property and equipment.
- Cost of 'policing', administration and accident insurance costs.

Cost elements are re-estimated from time to time and in periods where no re-estimation is undertaken then costs are updated from those of the previous year using an index which reflects inflation and economic growth. This is carried out by multiplying the old cost by a factor equal to:

$$\frac{(1 + \% \text{ increase in prices})}{100} \times \frac{(1 + \% \text{ increase in GDP})}{100}$$

Although each industry (or organisation) can calculate its own costs based upon its own data it is surprising that few actually do this. However, in the United States many attempts have been made to cost accidents and to advise on appropriate benefits. For example, Figure 6.16 shows a risk-benefit analysis for comparing the cost of two methods of controlling asbestos pollution. The analysis shows there would be a national cost of $10 million per life saved if filters were installed. Substitute brake materials would produce a cost of $100 million per life saved. From this work, it was concluded that neither alternative comes close to the $300,000 value that workers in hazardous occupations implicitly give to their own lives. In the United Kingdom it is estimated that a life is worth some £555,000 and an injury approximately £10,645. The average cost of an injury accident approximately, is £15,000. Damage-only type accidents are estimated to be approximately £650 (average) but this can vary from industry to industry.

When calculating the discounted economic rate of return of a scheme, there are two factors to be considered:

1. The capital cost of the scheme; and
2. The benefits obtained over the life of the scheme computed at current value.

The capital cost will be a once only payment whereas the benefits may take several years to accrue. When a scheme is chosen and capital invested in it, other schemes cannot be implemented so there is a resultant loss of potential benefit from them. This loss of benefit reduces that actually gained from the chosen scheme. The rate of loss due to not spending the capital in another manner is called the *discount rate*. Because prices may

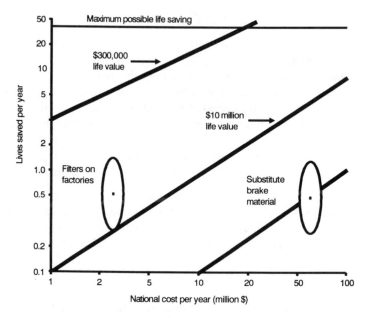

From the American Industrial Hygiene Journal 4-77 "Risk-Benefit Analysis for Industrial and Social Needs" by Moll and Tihansky

Figure 6.16

Risk-benefit analysis

increase in the future, this rate is adjusted and is then referred to as the *net discount rate*. It is the latter rate that is always used in the calculations.

Benefits which cover the life of the scheme can be calculated if the likely first year saving or benefit (FYB) is known. The FYB (B) is multiplied by the factor (V) from the net discount tables (see Appendix 7) to provide the expected total benefits. For example, if the benefit in the first year is £2,000 and the life of the scheme is five years and the net discount rate is 7% then the total benefit over five years will be:

£2000 × 4.100 = £8200 (where 4.1 is the multiplier taken from Appendix 7)

This is usually written as BV and is the benefit receivable over the full life of the scheme. The FYB (B) must take into account the net value of accident savings as well as any changes in maintenance costs and work times which are brought about by the scheme. So if:

A = accident savings
M = difference in maintenance costs
W = difference in work times

then $B = A + M + W$
and $BV = (A + M + W)V$

However, once the capital has been spent, it cannot be spent again so the capital cost (C) must be subtracted from the benefits received to produce a net benefit over the life of the scheme expressed as a percentage of the original cost. The discounted economic rate of return is thus:

$$\frac{BV - C}{C} \times 100\%$$

Placing (B) a different way into the above formula then the discounted economic rate of return is given by the following:

$$\frac{(A + M + W)V - C}{C} \times 100\%$$

This is regarded as the basic formula for calculating cost-benefit analysis for the comparison of options.

Calculating local accident costs

In many cases, the proportion of accidents which are fatal and those which cause injury may differ significantly from those industry *averages* which are published from time to time. For example, the petroleum industry may publish figures as follows:

	Land based %	Off-shore %	Total %
Fatal accidents	36	64	100
Injury accidents	45	55	100
Dangerous occurrences	27	73	100

It is common for a particular organisation to experience small numbers of accidents and in the absence of any other information it is better to use the average severity partition. However, if the number of accidents is sufficiently large to suggest a real divergence from average severity proportions then the use of the average figures could lead to a serious under/over valuation of likely accident savings. An indication as to whether this is appropriate can be obtained by calculating a range of values for estimated accident costs at the various in-house locations, so that if the range for the estimate based upon the severity proportions of accidents recorded lies outside the range using the average severity partition then there is a case for using the actual severity proportions. The following is a procedure used in the United Kingdom for estimating such ranges but it must be acknowledged that this is not statistically rigorous but rather a convenient way to show whether there is a case for using local rather than group severity patterns. Using the average severity partition, a central estimate of total accident costs (T) is calculated thus:

$$T = C \times A$$

where

> C = average cost per accident
> A = number of accidents

The range of values for total costs is $T - s$ (Lower limit) and $T + s$ (Upper limit) where $s = C \times A$.

A similar procedure is used to calculate a range of values for costs based upon the actual severity partition. The central figure for total cost is given as:

$$T = Cf \times Af + Ci \times Ai + Co \times Ao$$

and the value for s is given as:

$$s = Cf^2 \times Af + Ci^2 \times Ai + Co^2$$

where

> Cf = average cost of a fatal accident
> Ci = average cost of an injury accident
> Co = average cost of a dangerous occurrence (where damage
>   occurred)

Research estimates that there are some 5.2 dangerous occurrences per injury accident but these figures are based upon known occurrences and does not account for those which go unreported.

As before, the values of T range from $T - s$ to $T + s$.

Example 6.6

Petrol Company A have a worldwide off-shore accident situation as follows:

Fatal accidents	30	(42%)
Injury accidents	40	(58%)
Total injury accidents	70	(100%)
Dangerous occurrences	320	

The proportion of fatal injury accidents is higher than the average for land based accidents given above. In calculating total costs based on the average cost per injury accident we have a central estimate of:

£282,800 × 70 = £19.8 millions

and a range either side of this central figure of:

+ £282,800 × 70 = + £2.4 millions

This then gives a range from:

£17.4 millions to £22.2 millions

Using the actual severity partition, total costs (T) are estimated by:

$T = £(555,000 \times 30 + 10,645 \times 40 + 650 \times 320)$
    $= £17.28$ millions

the range of values is obtained from:

$+ £555,000^2 \times 30 + £10,645^2 \times 40 + 650^2 \times 320 = + £1.25$ millions

so the total costs range from:

£16.03 to £18.53

Calculating time element

In addition to accident savings, remedial measures may produce changes in operating procedures either in a positive or negative way. This in turn will alter work timings. Although the purpose of remedial measures is the reduction of accidents, other effects can influence the rest of the work community and these costs should be regarded as part of the cost of the remedial action and the current value of benefits adjusted accordingly. In practice for most schemes alterations can be revalued as outlined above on page 240.

Break-even analysis

It is usually desirable for management to be aware of the break-even point. This is the point at which benefits just cover the fixed and variable costs of a scheme as this illustrates the minimum level at which activity must be held. The break-even point may be calculated as follows:

Contribution = benefit costs − variable costs
per unit   per unit   per unit

the break-even point then (in the number of units) $= \dfrac{\text{fixed costs}}{\text{contribution/unit}}$

For example, suppose an organisation produced a remedial scheme which altered unit to £1.25 per tonne of goods produced and the variable costs are 0.75p per tonne and the factory fixed costs were £40,000 annually then the contribution per tonne under the revised safety scheme is:

$$£1.25 - 0.75 = 0.50p$$

$$\text{Break-even point} = \frac{£40,000}{50} = 80,000 \text{ tonnes}$$

It must be remembered that fixed costs are only fixed in the short term. For example, if the organisation above were to expand production beyond 100,000 tonnes then extra plant might be required costing, say, £20,000. This shows that over different ranges of output and different safety schemes, an organisation will have different break-even points. For the higher production level discussed above, the break-even point is now:

$$\frac{£60,000}{50} = 120,000 \text{ tonnes}$$

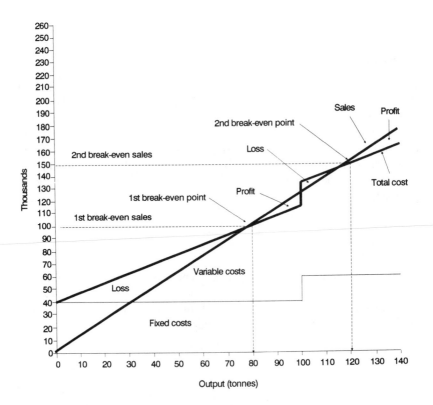

Figure 6.17
A Break-even chart

It is common in competitive businesses to find that the margin between the benefit and the variable cost is small (i.e. a low contribution) and as a result, any increases in fixed expenses cause a large change in the level of output required to reach the break-even point. An organisation which has a high level of fixed costs (e.g. in a capital intensive industry) will have a break-even point at a higher level of output than a business with low fixed costs. A capital intensive industry is therefore always under pressure to maintain turnover. Break-even analysis can be shown diagrammatically as illustrated in Figure 6.17. This uses the example discussed above.

The break-even chart is a useful device for presenting a more simplified picture of cost-volume-profit relationships but as a means of profit forecasting, it has several limitations. These are due to the many assumptions that have been made in order to construct such a chart. It must be regarded as a rough estimation and the normal assumptions made are:

- That costs fall neatly into categories of *fixed* and *variable*.
- That volume is the only factor affecting costs and assumes that all other factors remain constant.
- The selling or benefit price per unit is constant.

Normally, the relationship will be valid only within a limited range of activity above and below the level of capacity from which the data was computed. It would be more realistic if the cost and revenue lines were drawn on the chart as wide bands suggesting a break-even area rather than a point.

Further reading

Beecham, B J (1988) *Monetary Economics* (Pitman Publishing)

Bradshaw, J (1989) *Economics: A Students Guide* (Pitman Publishing)

Donaldson, P (1975) *Economics of the Real World* (Pelican Books)

Druker, P F (1973) *Management Tasks, Responsibilities and Practices* (Harper Row)

Glautier, M W and Underdown, B (1986) *Accounting Theory and Practice* (Pitman Publishing)

Liversey, F (1983) *Economics for Business Decisions* (Pitman Publishing)

Sizer, J (1974) *An Insight into Management Accounting* (Pelican Books)

Wood, F (1989) *Business Accounting 1 and 2* (Pitman Publishing)

7

Human resources management

'The most valuable asset an organisation can possess are the people within it.'
Field Marshal Viscount Montgomery of Alamein

Introduction

It is required that safety managers understand the human resource function within an organisation and how to use it effectively. Human resources management is difficult to define but generally comes in two parts. First, that which is described as theory, and second, the practice. This division has influenced the way in which the subject has been written about and more important, the way in which it is taught to students. What this means is that a subject such as *motivation* can be taught as a subject in itself without necessarily relating the theory to the management of people or relating it to, for example, the introduction of an appraisal system or a change in the way in which employees might be paid. A management decision to introduce such changes is influenced by our ideas on what actually motivates people to work. A safety manager should be able to apply his knowledge of people in the workplace if he is to manage the human resource effectively. People are rarely thought of in the same way as, say, equipment, time, cash, etc possibly because people are flexible, different, creative and are able to learn from their own behaviour. In addition, it is human resources which create, organise, control and co-ordinate all other resources in order to meet organisational aims and objectives.

Human resources form the basis of organisational activity and as such it is important for safety managers to learn and understand all they can about factors which affect the way people behave when at work. The study of behaviour is an organisational context referred to as behaviourial science and is covered later in Chapter 8. Such disciplines involve the study of psychology, sociology, economics, politics and anthropology. These disciplines combine to provide a collection of findings, ideas, methods and approaches to the development of knowledge as to why people behave as they do and to be aware of what implications this has for management. It is important to remember that an aspect of theory may affect one or more practical situations or that a practical problem may draw upon many theoretical inputs. Although motivation is followed by remuneration and appraisal, questions of manpower, planning, organisational structure and training also draw upon motivational theory.

The study of systems theory has had a major impact on the way people have approached the study of organisational behaviour. In the beginning, the study of organisational behaviour centred on individual behaviour but as research developed, psychologists and sociologists came to realise that an organisation was a complex social system which required it to be studied as a total system if individual behaviour within it was to be understood. It is a traditional human failing to assume that any event (like the accident) stems from a single cause. There is always a tendency to simplify cause and effect relationships. This can be illustrated by the development of scientific management approaches to the installation of new technology which tend to focus on ultimate efficiency at the expense of the human and social aspects of the work situation. From this, human relations theory stressed that informal work groups are important as is the need for management to communicate with the workforce. This theory neglected the technological aspects of organisations generally and both approaches failed to consider the effects of the environment and cultural norms upon organisational behaviour. In order to assist the safety manager to operate more effectively, there is a need to look at what determines the behaviour and responses of individuals within organisations and how they can become more effective in achieving their aims and objectives. In order to do this, it is necessary to move away from thinking that events have single causes and approach organisational behaviour from the concept of systems theory. This has as its basis the notion that all events are determined by multiple contributory factors (like the accident) and are interdependent.

Systems theory – applied to organisations

Systems theory is derived from several disciplines which include biology, cybernetics, physics, psychology and sociology. It can be compared to a way of thinking rather than a specific technique as it involves the process of attempting to define and utilise all variables that produce a particular event or situation. Such a theory is an holistic approach to looking at a complex organisation in order to attempt to develop a complete picture of all events and their respective inter-relationships. The easiest way of viewing an organisational structure as a system is to see it as consisting of an input, a change process, and finally an output. This is shown in Figure 7.1.

Systems theory

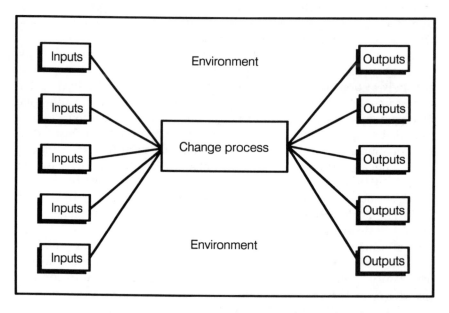

Figure 7.1   A model of the change processes

Figure 7.1 is a very simple model and it implies that an organisation interfaces with the environment both at the input and the output stages. This can be described as an *open system* because of its relationship, rather than being a *closed system* which is self contained. From this it is necessary to consider a number of major *sub-systems* which go to make up the total *organisational system*. These are summarised below as:

- Sensor sub-systems.
- Information processing.
- Decision-making.
- Processing.
- Control sub-systems.
- Memory (or information) sub-systems.

These are now discussed in more detail.

Sensor sub-systems

Those parts of an organisation which are designed to monitor changes within the organisation itself or in the environment within which it operates. A safety department or unit can be described as a sensor sub-system as it is required to seek out areas of risk and take appropriate action.

Information processing sub-systems

All organisations tend to amass amounts of data or information which needs to be coded and/or classified if it is to be of any use. In the same way that people cannot deal with large amounts of data without breaking it down, organisations also need to process internal and external data if effective decisions are to be made. A good example of a processing sub-system in an organisation would be the accident investigation and analysis unit or the accounts department.

Decision-making sub-systems

A decision-making sub-system can be regarded as a central part of the organisation as it is decisions which guide the organisation. Fundamentally, decision-makers take in information as an input and emit planning messages which are followed by one or more sub-systems within the organisation. In the widest sense, management is responsible for decision-making though this multiple function can be carried out to a greater or lesser degree by all levels within an organisation.

Processing sub-systems

These systems will vary according to what the organisation does. In manufacturing situations where raw materials are converted into saleable items, people turn inputs into outputs. For example, in a car factory, the processing sub-systems will allow the technology and the people to come together in such a way as to convert the inputs of steel, plastic and rubber into finished cars. Service orientated organisations will similarly involve technology and people to convert inputs into outputs. It is at the processing stage that the interface between the social and technical sub-systems is important if an organisation is to be effective. This sub-system utilises energy, information and materials to accomplish tasks.

Control sub-systems

It is important for an organisation to know if its processing is in accordance with its aims and objectives or whether it is deviating in any significant way. If it is then remedial action can be taken. There are several control sub-systems within an organisation such as the safety, budgeting, quality control units and to be effective, these sub-systems must be able to highlight deviances so that decisions can be taken to allow corrective action to be taken.

Information storage sub-systems

Organisations must store information so that appropriate decisions can be taken. The storage of information usually takes the form of records or filing systems, computer systems, procedures, practices, manuals etc.

There are a number of features which are common to all organisations because it is a *system*. These are:

- Equilibrium.
- Negative entropy.
- Equafinality.
- Integration.
- Fluidity.

These are discussed briefly below.

Equilibrium

Organisations tend to dislike change and will resist it wherever possible but they need to change in order to survive. Some organisations do not adapt and as a result they continue to exist in a state of limbo. To cope with this dichotomy, organisations develop adaptive systems and maintenance systems which need to be kept in balance if the organisation is to remain effective. In the same way that human systems adapt to change in temperatures, for example, the body will stop sweating when normal temperatures are reached. Similarly, organisations need to adopt change processes.

Negative entropy

An organisation, unlike other systems, can import new energy when required and can for example, recruit new staff. In this way it can re-adjust and survive.

Equafinality

There are many routes to the same objective and organisations become involved in complex decision-making processes because of this.

Integration

This is sometimes referred to as *differentiation* and refers to when organisations attempt to carry out complex tasks and therefore need to specialise but also need to integrate these specialisations if they are to operate in a unified goal-centred way. Large organisations often have problems trying to integrate their various specialist functions particularly with hired staff relationships.

Fluidity

All organisations have some movement through the system and this is characterised by the input, process, and output model shown in Figure 7.1. Most organisations have a prime process system which is backed up by facilitating systems which are designed to aid and develop an effective flow of energy, materials or information.

Use of systems theory

The use of a *systems approach* to organisational behaviour means that decisions can be made more realistically as a total view rather than a narrow specialist view. Organisations can be thought of as having four major inputs. These are:

1. Human inputs;
2. Technical inputs;
3. Organisational inputs; and
4. Social structure and norms.

These inputs need to be viewed as a whole in order to understand what effects a change in one input will have upon the others. For example, if it is considered necessary to change the technology employed in a working environment, what effect will this have on the way the organisation needs to be structured, the basic working groups and on the individuals involved? These four inputs are all interrelated with each other and with the environment in which the organisation operates. One aspect may be considered ideal in isolation but when related to the other remaining inputs is found to be wanting. Organisations have often concentrated on one particular input such as designing a complex formal organisational structure but neglecting the need to be aware of changes in the environment or the fact that the organisation is only functioning because of the informal systems that have developed. The easiest way to illustrate the use of systems theory is to give an example and work through all the sub-systems that are affected.

Example 7.1

Following an accident investigation study an organisation is to change from a PBR system to a measured daywork system as part of an overall accident reduction programme. This change will affect or be affected by a number of systems within the organisation.

The human system

- Will the new method of payment increase or decrease motivation?
- How will individuals react to the change?
- Will the change lead to an increase/decrease in absenteeism?
- Will it increase/decrease turnover?
- Will it reduce accidents?

The technical systems

- Is the method of work suitable for the payment system?
- Is quality important?
- Are the machines expensive to repair?
- Will the technical systems need to be altered?

The social systems

- Will work groups form their own agreed output?
- Will the revised method of payment need the separating of work groups?

The organisational system

- Will workers need less or more supervision?
- Will a new department be required to administer the system?

The control system

- Will this need to be altered to accommodate the new payment method?
- Will budgeting control be made more or less easy?
- Will quality control be made more or less easy?
- Will safety monitoring be made more or less difficult?

The environment

- Will the organisation be more or less able to attract labour?

These are just some of the questions which may be asked when deciding whether or not to change a payment system. This approach can be applied to all decisions that are to be made in organisations and should enable management to make realistic changes within the organisation based on more complete data.

Some problems using a systems approach

- Is it possible to take into account all the subsystems and factors when making safety management decisions?
- Does the attempt to include all important factors lead to a superficial analysis?
- Where are the boundaries to be drawn?
- Systems theory enables organisational analysis to be more realistically carried out but does it provide answers?
- Is it possible to use a systems approach in the analysis of behaviour at the group or individual level?

The individual

It is not possible within the context of this chapter to explain and describe the nature of the individual in some absolute sense. Neither is it possible to examine here all the aspects connected with personality, motivation and learning or cognitive factors such as intelligence although these areas are considered later in Chapters 8 and 10. As far as human resources management is concerned with safety, two areas of study have been selected relating to the individual which appear to be important in the understanding of behaviour at work. The first of these is motivation and the second is perception and how the individual views the environment about him. These are dealt with in Chapter 8. However, there are two questions about human behaviour that are important to the safety manager.

In what way can we regard people as being the same?

From an examination of current notions about human behaviour, it can be seen that three basic concepts are supported by most psychologists. These are:

1. *Causality:* human behaviour is *caused* by heredity or by environmental factors acting on an individual;
2. *Directedness:* the notion that people desire things in such a way that their behaviour is directed towards some goal.
3. *Motivation:* is goal orientated behaviour which has an element of

intensity behind it usually indicated by words such as *want, need* or *drive*.

These three ideas can be linked together as a closed system in order to form a simple model for understanding human behaviours. Such a model is given in Figure 7.2.

The individual

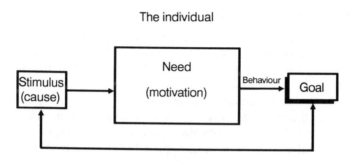

Figure 7.2
A model for understanding human behaviours

An individual receives some form of stimulus, for example, a headache. When this stimulus becomes severe enough, motivation is raised to a level whereby some form of action is pursued which will enable the goal of relief. Two aspirin tablets are swallowed thus achieving the goal and in so doing removing the stimulus and so this particular piece of behaviour stops. In such a case there are a number of issues that are raised by the adoption of this particular model:

- What about the notion of free will?
- Why take aspirin rather than paracetamol?
- Some goals do not seem to be achieved totally (the stimulus is not removed completely). What about goals such as ambition and status?

People are the same in that their behaviour is *caused, goal directed* and *motivated* and that they have roughly the same sort of physical features to operate with.

In what way should people be regarded as being different?

People can be regarded as being different in the way that they approach and operate the model illustrated in Figure 7.2. Any individual will develop or possess particular *personality* characteristics. Here, personality is defined as the pattern of relatively stable states and characteristics that will influence an individual's behaviour in the achievement of goals. Personality is made up of many components and it can be recognised in the importance of individual differences in:

- The *abilities* and *aptitudes* an individual has or develops.
- The *attitudes* possessed or developed.
- The pattern of need or motives maintained by the individual.

Developing individual needs

From the above, it can be seen that an individual can be classified into two broad areas:

1. Physical; and
2. Psychological.

In terms of the physical needs, these are essential to the survival of the animal and include food, water, warmth, sleep and so on. They are easily identifiable and are universal in that everyone has them. Psychological needs, however, tend to be much less easily definable and are much more individualistic. Needs such as prestige, status or ambition seem to exist in some people and not in others. There are also those needs used to make judgments about people. '*He is ambitious*' is much more likely to be used than '*he is hungry*'. What follows is an attempt to explain how it is that some people have particular patterns of need. Although this is presented in a simple form, it does illustrate the importance of the environment within which individuals exist, operate and learn to behave in certain ways. It is also important to remember that this explanation describes only one approach to the problem.

It is assumed that a new born baby starts life with:

- His body and physical capabilities which will develop.
- His physical needs.

A characteristic of the human infant is that it is unable to satisfy these physical needs by itself. It is dependent upon others, principally parents, for the satisfaction of its needs. Although the human infant has been described as the perfect example of minority rule, it is the dependency relationship that accounts for the development of the particular pattern of psychological need. To the extent that this dependency produces satisfaction of existing physical needs, feelings are likely to be positive, affectionate and protective. From this it is likely that strong social needs are developed. To the extent that the dependency relationship does not satisfy but rather frustrates existing needs, then to that extent a person is likely to develop feelings of anger and hostility, to wish more strongly for independence and autonomy, and to develop egotistic needs.

The way in which parents are able to meet the dependency needs of their child will depend to a large extent on the general pattern of personality development for that individual child. Teachers, friends, employers, etc, will carry this on in later life.

Abilities

The most obvious way in which people can display that they are different is in what they are able to do. Psychologists have studied differences in the areas of:

- *Mechanical ability:* the understanding of mechanical relationships and the ability to visualise how parts fit together into a whole.
- *Mental ability:* the intelligence, logical reasoning, verbal and numerical abilities, etc.
- *Creative ability:* the aesthetic judgment, musical ability, artistic talents and the like.

The issue as to whether abilities are inherited or learned is still being studied. More recent approaches take the view that abilities lie on a continuum. At one end are the responses that are geared to physiological capabilities such as dexterity, reaction times, etc, and at the other, those where genetic or physical factors are not the restricting factor such as interpersonal skills.

Attitudes

These are learned predispositions to behave towards or to respond to stimuli in particular and predictable ways. For example *'all Jews are good businessmen'*, *'all Scotsmen are mean'*, *'all Poles living in America are stupid'* or *'wearing safety gear is cissy'*! Attitudes can serve a number of purposes:

- They can give order to the way an individual views events and thus help make sense of the constant and varied bombardment of stimuli affecting him.
- Attitudes and values can help a person deal with his or her psychological problems and conflicts.
- They contribute to a person's identity.

There are many attitudes existing in the workplace. Good examples are the two opposing attitudes to work that are held by employees:

1. Work is a means to an end. Whilst it is often unpleasant, it is a necessary evil in order to satisfy other needs;

2. Work is an end in itself. A person gains satisfaction and self-fulfilment through work.

An understanding of attitudes prevailing amongst those being managed will enable the prediction of likely outcomes of alternative safety management strategies. For example, if work is seen as a means to an end, then the effectiveness of safety programmes could be limited.

The group

Having considered the individual, behavioural scientists have increasingly come to regard the study of groups within organisations as a profitable and important area. They have attempted to answer:

- What constitutes a group?
- How important are group processes in determining organisational effectiveness?

The answers to these questions are based on an understanding of the dynamics or processes that go on within groups. For example, the interactions of behaviour between people, status, authority and leadership patterns, the relationship between physical behaviour and the emotional climate or feelings that exist within the group. It is felt that an understanding of group dynamics is best obtained in a practical rather than theoretical manner. However, some basic concepts which should be understood are discussed below. These include an understanding of the relationship between a work group and its organisational environment and the notion of behavioural norms.

Behavioural scientists define a group as any number of people who:

- Interact with one another.
- Are psychologically aware of one another.
- Perceive themselves to be a group.

The second and third concepts are important in that they give a means of distinguishing between potentially similar situations. For example, which of the following fits the above definition in all respects?

- The staff in the safety department.
- A football team.
- The passengers on a hijacked aircraft.
- A church congregation.
- A fan club.

The definition also focuses attention on some of the areas concerned with working group effectiveness. For example, the way members interact, the psychological and emotional processes within the group and the group's feelings of cohesion and unity. The following model is useful in understanding groups.

Conceptual model

Group tasks can be split into two types. These are:

1. *Content needs:* what the group has to do. This will require certain types of resource;
2. *Process needs:* how is the group to operate? What process will it go through in order to meet its objectives? Process needs can be further split into the following:

   (a) *Task process:* doing things that are primarily concerned with solving the problems in an effective and constructive way; and
   (b) *Maintenance process:* are those activities which are concerned with producing feelings of cohesion and morale amongst group members almost irrespective of the particular task being undertaken.

These needs are illustrated in Figure 7.3, and some examples of the task process and maintenance process activities are given.

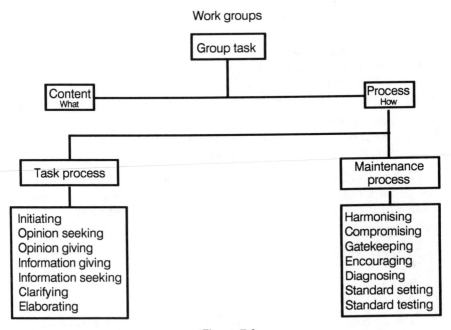

Figure 7.3

Conceptual model of the work group

It will be noted that the examples of process behaviour given in Figure 7.3 are all positive in that type of behaviour which is felt to contribute towards effective group working. Risk is listed amongst those negative factors which can hinder a group's behaviourial effectiveness. The same piece of behaviour can and often does meet content and process needs at the same time. For example, a good idea to reduce accidents expressed at an appropriate moment might shift the group on towards its objective and generate feelings of intense satisfaction amongst group members at the same time.

Effective working group

The model suggests that an effective working group can be viewed as one where both content and process needs are identified and met as appropriate rather than where too much emphasis is placed on either content or process orientated behaviour. This requires a flexible role structure similar to that shown in Figure 7.4.

An effective working group is seen as one which is characterised by:

- Higher quality decisions.
- More appropriate leadership.
- Distribution of authority according to task needs.
- High level of trust and openness leading to co-operation rather than competition between group members.

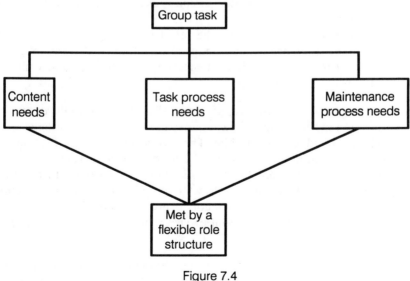

Figure 7.4

Flexible role structure

Some aspects of group behaviour

Solidarity is a key issue within a group context and without it, the group would cease to exist. Other issues are:

- *Similarity:* the more the group members have in common, the greater the solidarity. If everything else is equal there will be greater solidarity within single sex or single race groups rather than mixed ones.
- *Pressure for conformity:* the more willing a group is to exclude or punish a member the stronger become the bonds that keep them together thus the more intolerant the group becomes, the greater its power.
- *Equality:* the greater the equality between members, the greater the solidarity. This means that a social group can be weakened if someone deliberately sets out to make members unequal for example using awards or medals to neutralise informal opposition.
- *Safety issue:* the bigger the issue is perceived to be, the greater the solidarity induced. This is where opinion leaders are crucial in building up the significance of safety issues.
- *Membership changes:* no social groups can survive large and frequent changes in membership and continue to be effective.
- *Participation:* the opinion leader who makes judgments without consulting his group helps to destroy its solidarity.
- *Dependence:* the more the members depend upon each other, the greater the solidarity. In such circumstances a threat to one becomes a threat to all.
- *Interaction:* the more often the members of a group interact with each other (i.e. meet, chat, signal and share), the higher the solidarity is likely to be. Interactions create common attitudes and common responses.

Within groups, there are two types of leader. The *informal leaders* owe their position in the group to image power in that the group recognises his competence and identifies with him. The *formal leader's* identification and competence are important but so is the *legitimacy* of his role and this is not decided by the group, but by the organisation as a whole. In a formal group people know when they are leaders but in informal situations people are never certain what their role status really is at any given time.

From the safety manager's point of view, some possible roles in groups might be:

- *The professional:* normally less militant than the activist except when his job is threatened. Can suffer complacency and delusions of invulnerability with time.

- *The activist:* does it for love! This person has to be prepared to take their own decisions, own punishments and own personal satisfaction in what is done. If not, this person could become a professional.
- *The playing member:* if too much is asked of this person he may become a non-playing member or leave if pushed too far.
- *The non-playing member:* usually takes the benefits provided and justification for the action. In some safety committee situations he has to pay his dues in which case he has the option of being a licensed critic as well (it is the outsider who is the unlicensed critic).
- *The outsider:* keeps himself indignant and fascinated with issues under discussion. The unlicensed critic lives through the experience of others. Tolerance, dignity and humour are usually the best responses to outsiders.
- *The spectator:* here the main preoccupation is keeping amused and concentrating on variety, excitement and changes; lively people with flitting minds.

The group and its environment

The complexity and nature of work organisations means that employees often find themselves members of teams or groups. Few people work entirely on their own and their behaviour is as a result influenced by the nature of the groups of which they are members. Experience tells us that when people work together, they develop ways of thinking and behaving which are characteristic and not strictly needed in order to perform the task for which the group came together. Following on from this is a description of a particular conceptual model or *systems* model which has proved useful in understanding how various elements come together to generate the behaviour that is characteristic of a particular working group.

This model is concerned to recognise the difference and the relationship between two types behaviour:

- The behaviour with which the group begins. Some behaviour is expected by external factors in the organisational environment such as the task the group is given or communication channels to be used. This is referred to as the *required* behaviour. Some behaviour is determined by the nature of the members of the group such as skills possessed or work habits learned previously. This is referred to as *given* behaviour; and
- Behaviour which develops internally, which is greater than that required or given such as the way in which some groups fix themselves higher output levels than others. This is referred to as *emergent* behaviour.

The relationship between the *prescribed* and the *emergent* aspects of a work group's behaviour is considered to be an important element in understanding the functioning of organisations. The model uses three categories of elements of behaviour:

1. *Activities:* what people do such as running, walking, talking, sleeping, eating, operating machinery, etc;
2. *Interactions:* communications or contacts between people so as to relate the activity of one person to the activity of another such as a conversation or one person handing something to another; and
3. *Sentiments:* an idea, feeling or belief about the work or about the others involved such as making cars is a good thing.

These three elements are combined with the notions of *required, given* and *emergent* behaviour and are used in a manner illustrated in Figure 7.5.

Background factors or the organisational environment of the group under study will determine the nature of the required and given behaviour. This might be thought of as the starting point in behaviourial terms for that group. As a consequence of the group being in existence, it will develop its own characteristic emergent behaviour, in addition to that which is formally prescribed. The total pattern of behaviour will have consequences in terms of productivity, satisfaction and individual development. These will in turn feed back and cause modifications in the required behaviour for that group.

Issues in work group behaviour and norms

The following are considered the important background factors in determining how a work group should develop:

- Is emergent behaviour good for the organisation?
- Can effective teams be built?
- How important are group norms in determining effectiveness?

One of the most frequently observed characteristics of the work group is the way in which it quickly develops a culture of its own. A particular work group or team is thought of as having an identity of its own and that the behaviour of the members is predictable. The major feature of this group culture is the development of *norms* which are standards or codes of behaviour to which members of that group conform. Safety practitioners might develop norms about conduct, dress, language or perhaps who does what, how, when, etc.

The kind of norms mentioned might be thought of as trivial, but the desire to conform seems to extend to areas that are more important from the work organisation's standpoint. For example, early experiments have shown that group members were very often willing to modify their judgments in order to conform to what they thought other members of the

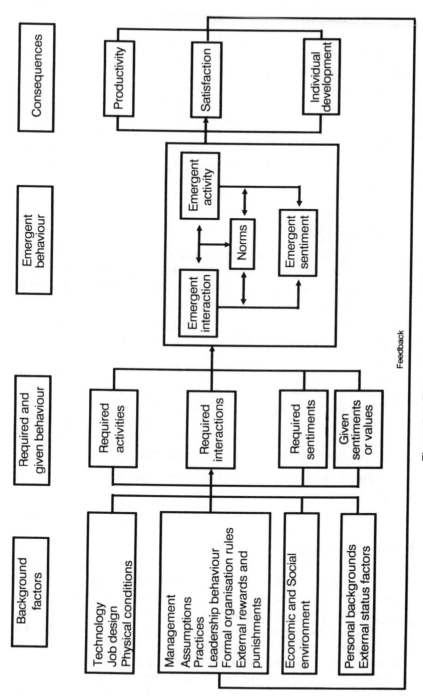

Figure 7.5 Elements of group behaviour

group might accept. Researchers attributed this phenomenon to an *attitude of social conformity* that people adopt in social situations. If such conformity is widespread, then it will have implications for team building and exploiting the creativity of individuals within a work group. Another example of the operation of norms is when output amongst members of a production team is restricted and becomes broadly similar, even when the members work independently or on individual incentive schemes. This phenomenon was first examined in some studies referred to as the Hawthorne studies conducted in the 1920s but would appear to have ruffled work study officers ever since! Norms do not only affect lesser issues like language and dress but also factors such as output, creativity, resistance to change and so on.

The three propositions

The group is a powerful instrument for influencing or controlling its members, but it is clear that groups differ markedly in the extent of such influence. In order to understand the problems of conformity of members within groups, three propositions are offered:

1. The more attractive a group is to its members, the more likely members are to change their views to conform with those of others in the group;
2. If an individual fails to conform, the group is likely to reject him; and the more attractive the group is to its members then the more decisively they will reject this individual; and
3. Members are more likely to be rejected for deviancy on an issue that is important to a group than on an issue that is unimportant in that non-conformity on peripheral issues is tolerated.

Other aspects of behavioural and psychological issues are discussed further in Chapter 8.

Industrial relations

Industrial relations is a multi-disciplinary subject which concerns both the individual and groups and is a subject which should be understood by safety practitioners. It can be regarded as a systematic approach to the analysis of social systems in which workers, trade unions, employers, the state and its agencies interact with one another. These are in turn influenced by economic, technological, social, political, ideological and historical factors in the environment. From the systematic analysis of these factors, an attempt is made to discover the rules and rule-making processes by which they regulate their behaviour and to define what they are all trying to do. Figures 7.6, 7.7 and 7.8 illustrate three ways of expressing approaches to the study of industrial relations.

Within this broad framework, it does not necessarily follow that all the participants share a common view of the purpose of their work or the solutions to the industrial relations problems with this in mind. Some tackle the problem from a different perspective. For example, some see it as the development of relations between management, workers, trade unions and employers. Although such groups are usually hard headed, pragmatic and unsentimental, they involve the use of language complete with normative and moralistic content. The most common application of normative vocabulary in industrial relations involves the concept of *fairness*; fair wages, fair comparisons, unfair dismissals, unfair industrial practices and a fair day's pay for a fair day's work are common terms in industrial relations.

The formation of attitudes towards fairness has been conducted within two perspectives:

1. This approach makes use of the *reference group theory* which is interpreted within a social psychological frame of reference. This perspective has raised important questions of not only how workers compare their own employment with those of individuals and groups but also why particular orbits of comparison are selected; and
2. This method makes use of the industrial relations' institutionalists who refer to the notion of an industrial relations system. Here it is likely that questions regarding social structure (the context of collective bargaining) are overlooked, but also this process can fail to recognise the complex interrelationship between the structure of inequality and occupational worth. Any explanation which excludes consideration of these factors amongst the determinants of pay and attitudes to pay can be regarded as incomplete.

In bringing these two approaches together, industrial relations may be seen as a constant process of change where new experiences and the results of empirical research will steer the safety manager away from the opposing assumption that industrial relations and safety management is a static subject. Having said that, the issues of industrial relations arise out of:

Who does what?
Who gets what?
Is it fair?

These questions usually relate to income, treatment and time, and these issues provide potential for the emergence of conflict and hence the problem of resolution and cause about which management needs to be aware.

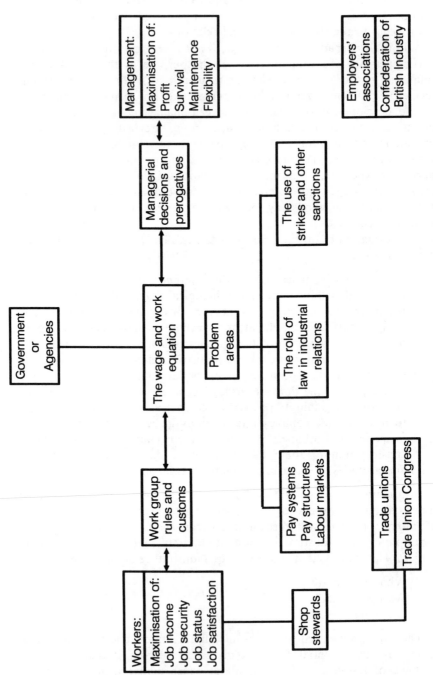

Figure 7.6 An approach to the analysis of industrial relations systems

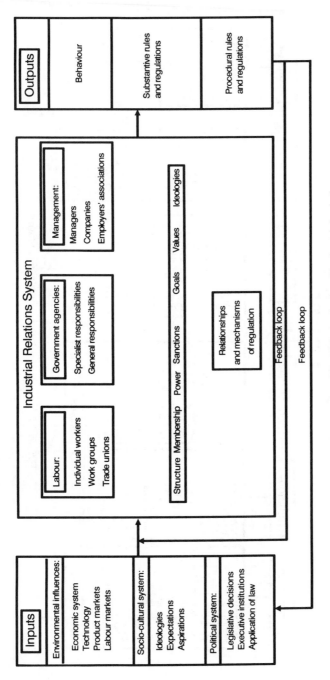

Figure 7.7 An approach to the analysis of industrial relations

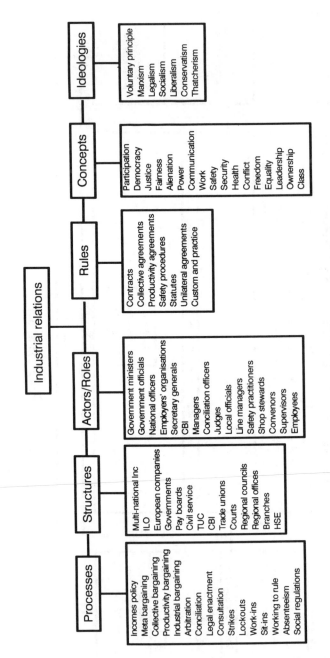

Figure 7.8 Industrial relations-goals and values

Income. Aspects regarded as unfair:

- Between the low paid and the rest.
- Between *earned* and *unearned* income.
- Between wage earnings and staff salaries and fringe benefits.
- Between occupations.
- Between grades and internal differentials.
- Between public and private sectors.
- Between jobs in different regions.
- Does the incomes and wages system reflect the changing aspirations of the participants?
- Does it accommodate technical change?
- Does it enable changes in output?

Time.

- Is overtime necessary?
- Shift work and the conflict between man and machine.
- Is *flexi-time* a possibility?

Treatment. Are the needs and expectations being catered for:

- Fringe benefits, staff status, etc.
- Management needs organisation; do workers respond as individuals or as informal working groups?
- Management must initiate change whilst the worker may be interested in security.
- The worker and manager are both employees but may also be members of external organisations such as professional associations or trade unions.

The study of industrial relations

It has been said above that the study of industrial relations can be regarded as the study of rules and rule-making processes which regulate the employment relationship. The purpose of rules, both *formal* and *informal,* is to establish *rights* and *obligations* which together outline spheres of *authority* and define *status* and thus establish *norms* of expected and appropriate behaviour. The main rules and rule-making processes are:

- Legislation.
- Collective bargaining.
- Unilateral management decisions.
- Unilateral trade union regulations.
- The individual contract of employment.
- Custom and practice.
- Arbitration awards both voluntary and statutory.
- Social conventions.

Thus, apart from the problems of *fairness* mentioned earlier as a means of providing potential conflict, aspects of the rule-making processes are also areas of possible controversy:

- Who should make the rules and how?
- What is the right process?
- What issues should the rules cover?
- How should the rules be administered?
- How should the rules be enforced?
- How should the rules be changed?
- How should the rules be legitimised by those affected?
- What effects will the new rules have on existing managerial prerogatives?

The safety manager is concerned with two types of rules which are referred to as *substantive* and *procedural* rules.

Substantive rules

1. Those rules governing compensation in all its forms;
2. Rules regulating duties and performance expected from employees, including rules of discipline for breaches of rules or standards; and
3. Those rules defining the rights and duties of employees which will include new or laid off workers, to particular positions or jobs.

Procedural rules

These are concerned with defining procedures for the establishment and administration of substantive rules above. In essence, substantive rules define jobs, whilst procedural ones regulate the defining process.

In order to get agreement on fairness it may be necessary to use job evaluation and analysis exercises concerning:

- Skill and training.
- Social worth.
- Risk and safety.
- Physical effort.
- Experience.
- Responsibility.

But other factors are also relevant such as:

- Ability and age.
- Expected working life of the job.
- Productivity.
- Persistence, reliability and honesty.

- Scarcity value.
- Social needs and traditions.

It is important to establish what effect each factor will have. Although job evaluation over an industry may overcome unfairness among people in the workplace and cater for unfairness arising from regional differences, can this method be extended to cover the other sources of unfairness which have been discussed so far? In terms of collective bargaining, fairness is felt only by the parties to the bargain and it tends to preserve an unfair status quo. In many ways, it can be said that the role of a trade union here is to act as a pressure group in defence of such differentials. It is not the intention within this chapter to discuss collective bargaining in depth and those wishing to learn more of this procedure should read other books on this subject some of which are given at the end of the chapter.

From a safety management point of view, a company's industrial relations policy should form an integral part of the total strategy with which it pursues its business objectives. There are five advantages to this in that it provides an ideal atmosphere for:

- Consistency;
- Orderly and equitable conduct;
- Planning;
- Anticipation of events; and
- Retaining the initiative in changing situations.

Being aware of relevant industrial relations objectives and the establishing of principles and guidelines for management, the areas of important activities to be covered by a framework of objectives and principles are:

- Company responsibilities, management prerogatives and union rights.
- Union recognition and facilities.
- Attitudes towards collective bargaining.
- Bargaining structures.
- Dispute settlement procedures.
- Payment systems.
- Security of employment.
- Communications.
- Employee involvement.
- Disclosure of information.
- Health and safety.

Outline for a typical company industrial relations policy

The objectives of a company's industrial relations policy will be different from organisation to organisation and from the type of industry it operates within. Some companies will express their objectives in quantitative terms as far as possible relating industrial relations objectives to corporate objectives. They would not wish to omit references to behavioural implications. Thus, senior management may consider such possible objectives as the:

- Development of an atmosphere of mutual trust and co-operation at the workplace.
- Prevention of problems and disputes wherever possible.
- Provision of solutions to problems and disputes which arise through agreed procedures.
- Encouragement of opportunities for employee motivation, development of skills and productivity among all categories of employee.
- Reduction or stabilisation of labour costs.
- Strengthening of managerial control over the work situation.
- Reduction or prevention of accidents, and health promotion.

A framework for the viable management of industrial relations should contain four essential features. These are:

1. *Management accountability.* Full acceptance by management for industrial relations in exactly the same way as for product quality or for marketing strategy.
2. *Management initiative.* Taking the initiative in collective bargaining and other facets of industrial relations.
3. *Management distinction.* This is based on the concept of accountability between the legitimate function of trade union and management.
4. *Management practice.* Where policy is a statement of objectives and commitment to principles issued by senior management and its application in practice.

To be effective, an organisation must have an industrial relations policy which conforms to certain standards such as:

- The policy statement must be applicable universally.
- It should be in writing.
- It should be flexible to meet varying local conditions.
- It should be justifiable on an assessment of profit forecasts or other criteria.
- It should be approved and authorised by the company chairman, chief executive or president.
- It must be regarded as inviolate as far as is possible.

It is necessary for employees, line managers, senior managers and personnel/industrial relations specialists to be aware of organisational policy, and they should have a basic understanding and knowledge of those details illustrated in Figure 7.9.

Line managers

* Knowledge of local IR policies
* Knowledge of local IR agreements
* Knowledge of local IR practices
* Knowledge of IR negotiating machinery
* Knowledge of pay system
* Knowledge of trade union structures
* Knowledge of role of trade union officials
* Knowledge of role of management
* Knowledge of his own role
* Understanding the limits of his authority
* Basic skills of communicating
* Skills in human relations
* Skills in negotiations
* Skills in handling grievances

Personnel and industrial relations specialists

* Knowledge of IR policies and agreements
* Knowledge of practices and negotiating machinery
* Understanding of payments system
* Knowledge of trade union structures
* Understanding of the role of shop stewards
* Up to date knowledge of latest IR practices
* Understanding of relevant legislation
* Knowledge of management structures and IR roles
* Knowledge of his role in disputes, grievance procedures
* Knowledge of consultative and negotiating machinery
* Knowledge of the limits of his authority

Senior managers

* Knowledge of IR policies and practices
* Knowledge of agreements
* Knowledge of negotiating machinery
* Knowledge of pay systems in use
* Knowledge of trade union structures
* Knowledge of local IR arrangements
* Understanding of trade union role
* Knowledge of other managers' roles
* Understanding of his own role in IR
* Understanding of local health and safety policy
* Possess good skills in communication
* Possess good skills in human relations
* Possess good skills in negotiation

Employees generally

* Knowledge of the first step in the grievance procedure
* Understanding of how grievances are dealt with
* Knowledge of disciplinary procedures
* Knowledge of trade union organisation
* Knowledge of trade union membership
* Knowledge of substantive agreements on pay and hours
* Knowledge of substantive agreements on working conditions
* Knowledge of substantive agreements on health and safety policy and practice
* Knowledge of fringe benefits applicable

Figure 7.9 Industrial relations-information and knowledge

The role of government in industrial relations

Unlike many European countries, the United Kingdom has traditionally adopted a non-intervention policy in respect of industrial relations. This is sometimes referred to as *voluntarism* and usually means that parties directly involved in a dispute should be left to settle their differences without government intervention. The main features of this process are:

- Self-government and lack of state interference.
- Freedom to bargain and manoeuvre.
- Flexible and dogma-free.
- Provides for agreement and compromise.

Traditionally, government has interfered in industrial relations when:

- Society was deemed socially unstable.
- When threatened with economic collapse.
- At war.

There are a number of pieces of legislation which affect industrial relations in the United Kingdom, most notably the Employment Protection Act 1975 and the Employment Protection (Consolidation) Act 1978. Other Acts of Parliament which are relevant include the Conciliation Act 1896, the Industrial Court Act 1919, the Health and Safety at Work Act 1974 and other pieces of legislation covering race relations (1968), sex discrimination (1975), disabled persons (1944/58) and so on. It is not possible to discuss the implications of these acts within the context of the safety management process, and the HASAWA is fully discussed in Chapter 1.

Recruitment and selection

Organisations are constantly involved in the process of attempting to select and recruit appropriate people for the right job. This process has become sophisticated and involves a great amount of time and effort particularly if effective recruitment and selection techniques are to be developed. A basic outline of the recruitment and selection process is discussed below but it must be stressed that each organisation will need to develop the process for its own ends. However, the fundamentals remain the same and the basic stages to consider in the recruitment and selection process are:

- *Job analysis or description:* have an understanding of the job to be filled.

- *Job specification:* understand the knowledge, skills and aptitudes required to do the job.
- *Recruitment media:* decide where suitable applicants are to be found.
- *Advertising:* decide how people can be persuaded to apply.
- *Job administration:* choose the means of finding whether the applicants have the required knowledge, skills and aptitudes. Consider methods of application such as application forms, interviews, references, selection tests, etc.
- *Rating schemes:* make a choice of which method to use for *scoring* applicants.
- *Induction:* introduce the successful candidate to the job and to the organisation.
- *Evaluation:* assess the recruitment and selection process.

The features of the recruitment and selection process outlined above are now discussed in more detail.

Job description

This process examines a job in order to establish component parts and to identify the circumstances in which it is performed. It should also answer the very basic question as to whether the job is really needed or not. Methods used for carrying out job analysis are as follows:

- Via a process of interviews or group discussion information should be gathered to ascertain what the job holder states that his job is.
- Via a similar process ascertain what the job holder's manager thinks the job is.
- Using activity diaries, activity sampling techniques, films, critical incidents and/or exit interviews find out what the job holder's job actually is.
- Conduct interviews with the job holder, manager and independent adviser (where appropriate), using company information to decide what the job should be.

It is important to develop a list of actual duties and what the job holder actually does rather than amass a list of general responsibilities such as a statement like 'he is responsible for 35 men'. The job description will result from the job analysis and it usually includes a broad outline statement of the purpose and scope of the job, together with a more detailed list of the activities and responsibilities involved.

A possible framework for a job description is given in Figure 7.10.

An example of a completed job description is given in Figure 7.11 and illustrates those features necessary for a secretary employed in the safety department.

Job title
Job information - Company
                - Department or section
                - Responsible to
                - Responsible for

Outline of duties - What are the main activities?
                  - What are the important parts?

Function and purpose - What is the purpose of the job?

Working conditions   - What are the hours, pay, holidays,
                        pension agreements, etc?

Physical conditions   - Where is the job and what is the environment?

Social factor - Is the job isolated?
              - Is the job working with other people?
              - Who are the other people?

Figure 7.10

A possible framework for a job description

Job specification

The job specification results from identifying the skills, knowledge and aptitudes required by a person to carry out their duties as described in the job description. It is a detailed statement of the physical and mental abilities required for the job and when relevant, social and physical environmental aspects of the job. When developing a job specification, it is important to remember that it is used as the basis of assessing a candidate, and should therefore be developed in such a way that the skills and knowledge lend themselves to being measured. It is an attempt to identify those human characteristics which are directly related to important aspects of job performance. The job specification is usually based on Rodger's 7-point plan or Munro Frazer's 5-point plan. Whichever plan a particular organisation uses it will normally consist of the following general headings:

- *Attainment:* School, further education, professional qualifications and experience.

- *Physical:* Health, appearance, manner, eyesight, fitness, etc.
- *Intelligence:* Judgment, problem solving, IQ, etc.
- *Special aptitudes:* Manual, written, verbal, language, etc.
- *Interests*: Temperament, adjustment, etc.
- *Circumstances:* Domestic, travelling, etc.

Job title: Safety Manager

Department: Health and Safety

Reports to: Chairman

Purpose: To plan, implement, monitor and evaluate the health
and safety programme within the company

Duties: * To initiate an efficient and effective accident and
dangerous occurrence reporting procedure
* Systematically to collect accident data for analysis
* To reduce accidents and dangerous occurrences
* To implement efficient and effective education,
training and publicity programmes designed to reduce
or prevent accidents from happening
* To monitor and evaluate current procedures and practices
* To advise the company on current legislation
* To advise the Chairman on all Health and Safety matters

Occasional tasks: To service appropriate committees
To look after visitors
To attend seminars and conferences as required

Salary: Never enough, paid monthly

Hours of work: 0830 hours to 12 noon
1300 hours to 1630 hours

A 5 Day Week is in operation

Holidays: Too many days per year plus public holidays

Job changes in the future: Greater emphasis on new technology

---

Figure 7.11 A brief example of a job description

Job Title: Safety Manager   *Department:* Health and Safety

Part 1. Physical:

Age: 35 to 50 yrs (desirable)
Height: Not important
Weight: Not important
Health: Must be able to satisfy company
             pension scheme requirements

Part 2. Attainments:

Examinations passed: Must possess the CNAA Post-graduate
                          Diploma in Safety Management
                          or their MSc in Safety Management

                          Preferred also to be a corporate member
                          of either the Royal Society of Health or
                          the Institution of Occupational Safety and
                          Health

Experience: At least two years' post-graduate experience

Part 3. General intelligence:

Should be able to demonstrate at interview an understanding
of the Health and Safety requirements of the industry whilst being
able to demonstrate a knowledge of the tasks that would be
performed

Part 4. Special skills and aptitude:

Should posses leadership qualities and be a good and effective
communicator

Part 5. Circumstances:

It is desirable that candidates do not have children below school
age because of the unsocial hours worked.

Figure 7.12 A brief example of a job specification

Not all the headings may be relevant to any one job, as a study of the job will usually decide on the importance and relevance of each feature. For example, fitness and physical strength is more important than educational qualifications for the employment of unskilled labouring jobs. It is also important to have some system of rating individuals against the criteria which are considered necessary so that comparisons can be drawn. An example of a job specification is given in Figure 7.12.

Recruitment

This is the process by which organisations attract people to apply for job vacancies. The objective of any recruitment activity should be to attract a compact field of suitable candidates and to achieve an optimum balance between coverage and cost. There are various sources of potential candidates and these need to be considered if a sensible recruitment policy is to be developed. These are illustrated in Figure 7.13.

Possible recruitment media method	Uses and advantages
Internal:	
Promotion of existing staff or transfer	All levels: Develops employees and is economical
Introduce known people	Economical
External:	
Newspaper advertisements daily	Wide coverage; quick but expensive
Sunday	Necessary for an important post
Local evening/daily	Local coverage, cheaper and quick
Local weekly	Slower
Trade magazine	
Professional	Wide coverage but expensive
General	
Job centre	Wide coverage, free service
Employment agency	Expensive but good coverage
Specialist management consultants	Pay for results only
Radio and TV	Strong impact, wide coverage but expensive
Cinema advertising	Wide or local coverage but expensive
Notices and posters	Wide coverage and economical
Leaflet distribution	Specific coverage and economical
Record of previous applicants	Economical, all levels of post
Professional bodies and trade unions	Specific coverage, economical

Figure 7.13 Some recruitment media methods

Some problems associated with recruitment are:

- Choosing the right media.
- Obtaining the optimum number of candidates.
- The wording of the advertisement.
- The need to take account of the company image.
- The need to attract candidates and impel them to apply.

The advertisement

The first priority is to decide where to place the advertisement. The correct selection of media is a sophisticated business and is therefore often contracted out by organisations to outside agencies. The job advertisement has four roles. These are:

1. To attract a compact field of applicants who are capable of doing the job.
2. To inform suitable candidates about the job, the organisation and what is required.
3. To impress suitable candidates; and
4. To impel candidates to apply.

Most job adverts feature the following information:

- Title of vacant post.
- Grade or salary.
- Name of the organisation.
- Details of the job.
- The type of person required.
- Information about the organisation.
- Benefits.
- Action to be taken to apply.
- Closing dates for applications.

Selection

Those stages involved in selection are very similar for any job but the actual methods and level of sophistication needed will obviously depend on the specific vacancy in question. At a general level, there are two important parameters:

1. The number of candidates per vacancy; and
2. The possible costs involved should unsuitable candidates be recruited.

These parameters can be represented diagrammatically as shown in Figure 7.14.

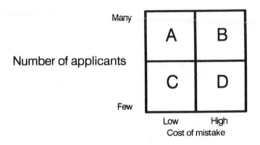

Notes:

Position A:	Many applicants and low selection error cost Short and easily administered selection process
Position B:	Many applicants and high selection error costs Sophisticated selection technique, use of tests, etc
Position C:	Few applicants and low selection error cost Very simple selection process
Position D:	Few applicants and high selection cost error Selection process requires careful planning and could involve much cost as an expensive investment decision is being made

Figure 7.14 A method of using selection parameters

Screening devices

The selection decision normally involves a number of screening activities whereby unsuitable candidates are eliminated. The first of these is the _Application form_ which serves three main purposes:

1. To provide a picture of the candidate;
2. To enable the organisation to compare one candidate with another; and
3. To assist the organisation to carry out an interview.

In addition, the application form of a successful candidate is the source document for the person's future personnel and training records. Application forms need to be designed to elicit information which demonstrates if the candidate meets the essential requirements of the job. The example in Figure 7.15 is suggested as a suitable list of main headings and topics to be considered for inclusion in an application form.

Bloggs plc

Application for Employment

Position [   ]   **Post Number** [   ]

Surname*

First names*

Maiden name

Married/Single/Divorced

Number of children

Other dependants

Next of kin

Relatives employed by Bloggs plc

Name of parent or guardian

Father's occupation

Doctor's name and address

Important items

Age*

Date of birth*

Place of birth*

Nationality*

Home address*

Present address*

Telephone number*
Home
Work

National Ins No

Religious affiliation

Educational and other attainments:

Secondary:

Schools attended (since the age of 11 years) with dates. Best subjects. Examinations passed (State subjects) standards reached and age on leaving school.

Further and Higher Education:

Schools, Colleges or University attended with dates. State full-time, part-time or evening. Courses and/or subjects taken. Degrees, certificates, diplomas awarded. Research experience and publications.

Non - Academic:

Professional qualifications held, including trade apprenticeships, articles, membership of professional bodies; academic or scientific societies, trade unions etc.

Special qualifications:

Include languages and driving licence particulars etc.

Previous experience: employment history
Include all jobs since leaving school

Dates (From - To)   **Name and address of employer**
Nature of business   **Position held**
Reasons for leaving   **Description of main duties**
                              Salary details

Figure 7.15 Typical application form

Please provide details of any previous employment with Bloggs plc

---

Military service:

Dates (From - To)
Training courses taken

Particulars of service
Rank on discharge
Awards and decorations

Medical history:

Height, weight and details of any serious accidents, illnesses, operations or disabilities, including colour blindness. Also, liability to any particular form of sickness or allergy which might prove a hazard or disqualification for the type of work applied for. Details of any compensation received under the Industrial Injuries Act.

Leisure interests and hobbies:

Athletic and social activities such as games played, teams played for etc. Include membership of clubs and societies with particulars of positions held. Activities at school (where appropriate) and details of any positions of responsibility held. Membership of youth organisations, religious activities, church membership and other interests and activities.

Ambition:

Not included in every case. Where appropriate, outline career envisaged and plans for the future.

Personal circumstances:

Freedom of travel, availability to work shifts, nights, overtime, etc.

Other information:

Which the applicant would like to add such as further details of particularly relevant qualifications and/or experience or reasons for wanting the job. Leave adequate space of the application form or ask for the information to be written on a separate sheet.

Date free to commence employment:

Or give notice required.

References or testimonials:

Names and addresses of two or three referees, with qualifications. It is usual for one of these to be a previous employer. Note whether references are to be taken up before or after the interview and with the permission of the candidate.

Signature and date:

General comments:

Choose those items from those given above
Lay out the questions clearly giving adequate space
Forms should conform to standard typewriter settings

Space for office use:

Date application received/acknowledged
Action to be taken on outcome
Shortlisted/rejected
Medical
Position offered
Accepted/rejected

In designing a suitable application form for a specific category of employment, a selection should be made of those items of information likely to be most relevant to the job, and the rest should be discarded. Thus, it will be necessary to have a number of standard application forms for different classes of employee. The layout of the form should set the essentials in clear relief, and leave plenty of space for the candidate (or interviewer) to write in. Psychologists recommend that there be at least twice to four times as much blank space as print. Two sides of A4 paper should be the minimum for all grades of employment below managerial level. Above foreman level and for posts requiring technical qualifications and experience, a form covering four sides of A4 is more likely to be required. All forms should fit standard typewriter spacings, and for ease of filing they should be of a standard size. Adequate instructions for filling in the forms should be clearly given including those parts to be completed by the interviewer.

The interview

This is the most common method used for assessing candidates. Though the interview is extremely popular, it has been criticised by researchers regarding its validity and reliability as a measuring device. The interview is simply a structured conversation which is designed to gain data from a candidate concerning his suitability for a particular job. It also allows candidates to gain information about the job and the organisation. The four basic aims of the interview selection process are:

1. To explore relevant information to be obtained from the candidate;
2. To give the candidate the relevant information about the job;
3. To judge the suitability of the candidate; and
4. To encourage the suitable applicant to accept the job.

In preparation, the interviewer should become familiar with the job description and the job specifications whilst at the same time reviewing the techniques to be used in the interview to avoid or weaken:

- Subjectivity.
- Limited time availability.
- Artificial nature of the situation.

Generally, it is better to concentrate on past work experience and attempt to ascertain:

- Exact nature of the various jobs held previously.
- How these were linked.
- How difficulties were identified and dealt with.
- Reasons why the job was originally taken.
- Reasons for leaving the job.

- Relevant experience for the new job.
- Overall career plans.

Following on from this it is important to establish the general level of education and training of the candidate. Here the interviewer will need to establish:

- The level and types of examinations passed.
- The level of attainment.
- Type of training courses attended.
- Reaction to these courses.
- The relevance of these for the new job.

Further insight can be gained by a discussion of the applicant's general interests, attempting to find out:

- Whether the candidate has any interests outside work.
- The depth of these interests.
- Time committed to these activities.
- The relevances of these activities to the new job.

From an examination of these areas, a reasonably broad factual picture can be obtained of the candidate concerning their personality, special aptitudes, intelligence and physical make-up. The aim throughout is to get the interviewee talking so it is important to ask *open-ended* questions thus avoiding '*yes*' and '*no*' answers. Examples of *open-ended* questions are:

- I see you were with company ABC. Tell me about your job there?
- What qualifications and experience do you have that will be useful to this job?
- Why do you want the job?

One may use a scoring system to allocate marks out ten for:

- First impression or circumstances.
- Qualifications and attainments.
- Abilities and personal qualities.
- Motivation and intelligence.
- Adjustment and temperament.
- Aptitude.
- Social interests.

Interviewing is a highly skilled process and requires much practice. Avoid stereotyping candidates. An example here concerns one of the authors on a recent consultancy assignment where a senior executive pointed out after some interviews were held to appoint a senior safety manager that he:

- Never employed a person who read a particular newspaper.
- Never employed a person who wore brown suede shoes.

Further enquiries lead the author to discover that readers of the offending newspapers could (according to the executive) tell all the points for and against some particular problem but were unable to make a decision! On the question of brown suede shoes the author was not able to obtain a satisfactory answer! How many good individuals may have been refused employment in this organisation because they either read the wrong newspaper or wore the wrong type of shoe?

There has been a tendency in recent years to use the group interview where a number of candidates are requested to undertake tasks together or to discuss certain topics. Other organisations also use command task exercises which have been specifically designed to test a candidate's ability to solve problems or to lead a group or team through a pre-set problem. Selection tests can be viewed under the following headings:

- Intelligence.
- Personality.
- Interest.
- Aptitude.
- Achievement.
- Managerial potential (coupled with leadership potential).

In order to compare one candidate with another some form of rating system should be used. There are several systems in use and it is not possible to describe them all here. The most effective is to score on each of those headings listed above a score out of five or 10 points rather like judges at a boxing match!

Induction

The introduction of a new employee to the organisation is a complex and difficult process. Not only must the new person assimilate the formal aspects of the new job but also the informal side of the organisation. Research shows that staff turnover is high within the first three months of a person's employment. This may be due to ineffective induction programmes. Induction should start before the new employee commences work and should be an integral part of the recruitment process from the time the application form is sent out. An induction training programme should include those people who will be directly involved with the new recruit in a formal work situation and must include the safety management team. The personnel department cannot be expected to staff an induction programme as it is the line relationship that is important. In outline, the following induction programme might include:

- Their place in the organisation.

- The relationship between work and the finished product.
- The relationship between the company, the industry and the world outside.
- Methods of raising matters with management.
- Introduction to procedures and practices.
- Meeting colleagues and visiting the workplace.

Performance appraisal

A task of the safety manager which is often overlooked is the appraisal of subordinates. An important part of every manager's job is to gather information on subordinates' work performance and to take action based on this information. There are two aspects of appraisal which are equally important:

1. The systematic evaluation of employees by their managers in order to develop an understanding of how efficient they are at their jobs; and
2. The more informal aspect where managers and subordinates discuss work problems and jointly seek methods to overcome these problems.

There are several reasons why a formal performance appraisal scheme can be of use to an organisation.

1. Training

In order to develop useful training programmes, it is necessary to identify the areas of knowledge, skill and attitude where improvement is needed. By the use of performance appraisal it is possible to identify training needs by highlighting individual areas of weakness and recognise individuals who may require further training in order to fit them for promotion. Finally, it must be used to evaluate the effectiveness of training in relation to improved job performance.

2. Promotion

Promotion decisions are often made on very sketchy and subjective data. The use of performance appraisal, where a more objective and complete view of an individual is taken, should provide more accurate data on which to base promotion decisions. Managers are very often involved in making promotion decisions, whether formally or informally and, as a person's career is concerned, it is as well to develop as much objective data as possible about all potential promotees.

3. Wage and salary administration

Within the limitations of any pay policies and job evaluation schemes which may be in existence, it is useful for organisations to be able to reward individuals on a merit basis. The use of performance appraisal schemes permits management to make merit awards based on agreed criteria and a more complete measure of performance, thus potentially eliminating the problems associated with informal and subjective pay increases.

4. Personnel changes

There is a need within organisations to balance organisation and individual needs. All too often, managers are very short of information concerning their subordinates' aspirations and needs. Performance appraisal can ensure that some dialogue takes place and subordinates are able to discuss their wishes regarding future careers. This information together with data on their ability allows a more reasoned decision to be made by management.

5. Selection

The development of effective selection procedures requires that recent entrants are evaluated in terms of how well they carry out their jobs. If there is no systematic method of measuring job performance, then there are no means by which an organisation can know if it is selecting the right sort of people. In order to improve the selection decisions made, information must be available regarding how well or otherwise recruits are doing.

6. Job performance

One of the aims of performance appraisal must be to improve individual job performance. By ensuring that managers and subordinates discuss job performance and thus highlight areas of weakness, it should be possible to devise a method to overcome these weaknesses which may or may not involve formal training.

All performance appraisal systems need some form of paperwork back-up although with the use of computers this can now be minimised. The first priority is to develop criteria for measuring job performance which are objective and in some way measurable in a realistic sense. Many appraisal schemes can be criticised for the very subjective criteria which they utilise such as attributes concerning loyalty, trustworthiness, honesty and application. The criteria are normally listed on a form which the manager or worker marks. The completed form is then shown to the subordinate and a discussion based on the return should take place. Many schemes now make use of computerised bar codes which represent various tasks which can be simply entered into a computer thus saving considerable time in form filling. The various types of appraisal systems are briefly discussed below.

Rating scales

This is the most common system and it provides for the rating of employees on each of a number of scales covering task requirements, performance and individual characteristics. Examples of some scales are given in Figure 7.16A to C.

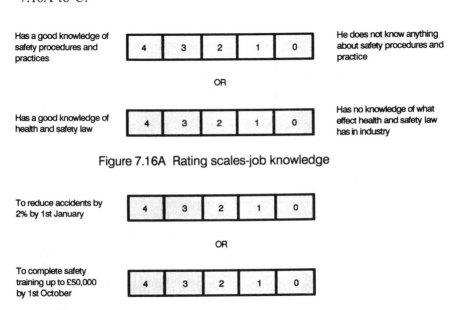

Figure 7.16A Rating scales-job knowledge

Figure 7.16B Rating scales-job performance

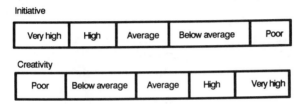

Figure 7.16C Rating scales-individual characteristics

Paired comparisons

Provides for rating employees in comparison with each other. All employees of a similar level are compared with each other on a number of traits. This method avoids the problem of standards since the rating of employees is relative to each other. However, it can be a time-consuming exercise depending upon the number of employees being appraised.

Ranking

Staff are merely ranked in order of merit from best to worse. To use this system, as with the paired comparison method, criteria for measuring job performance will need to be generated.

Results centred

This approach relies upon some form of management by objectives being in operation. At the beginning of a fixed time period, each subordinate with his manager agrees a number of performance targets that are to be met. The subordinate is then appraised by comparing his actual performance against the targets set.

Critical incident method

This system provides for a recording, by managers, of *critical behaviour* on the part of their subordinates. Whenever an employee does something note-worthy, it is recorded on the appraisal form. These behaviours are normally classified by categories and then used to assess job performance. Critical behaviour will vary from job to job but examples could include such things as 'his weekly report was one week late' or 'he came up with an idea which could reduce accidents by 2%'.

Forced choice

This system attempts to overcome the problem of the average rating by forcing the assessors to choose a statement which is most applicable to the particular individual being assessed. Groups of three or four statements are used such as:

- *Administration:*
  always keeps paperwork up to date;
  often leaves important letters to the last minute;
  filing is not very good.

There are other methods of appraisal and those mentioned are given merely as examples. One important point when designing an appraisal scheme is to avoid it becoming administratively cumbersome and something regarded as unimportant by subordinates. The method of implementation and design is important and it is essential that staff are aware of the reasons why the information is gathered and how it will help them. This will avoid next month's forms being filled in now!

The appraisal interview

The most difficult part of performance appraisal is the interview. It is often rushed and takes place in an embarrassed atmosphere which then results in little benefit being derived from the exercise. The object of the appraisal interview must be to:

- Let subordinates know where they stand.
- Recognise good work.
- Point out areas for improvement.
- Indicate areas for further development.
- Plan joint action for improvements.
- Increase subordinates' motivation.
- Improve management/staff relationships.

These objectives need to be borne in mind and fully understood by all parties to the interview if embarrassment is to be avoided. In order to improve the process, it is essential that the art of providing feedback is improved. Managers also need to appraise themselves and the art of good leadership is in not giving people jobs that they are not prepared to do themselves. Leadership is discussed in Chapter 8 and is an important aspect of the safety management process.

Further reading

Argyle, M (1974) *The Social Psychology of Work* (Pelican Books)

Bottomley, M H (1983) *Personnel Management* (Pitman Publishing)

Cooke, S and Slack, N (1984) *Making Management Decisions* (Prentice-Hall International)

Cuming, M (1977) *The Theory and Practice of Personnel Management* (Heinemann Press)

Graham, H T and Bennett, R (1989) *Human Resources Management* (Pitman Publishing)

Handy, C B (1977) *Understanding Organisations* (Penguin Books)

Livy, B (1988) *Corporate Personnel Management* (Pitman Publishing)

Mullins, L (1989) *Management and Organisational Behaviour* (Pitman Publishing)

Scheine, E H (1970) *Organisational Psychology* (Prentice-Hall Inc)

8

Psychological and behavioural issues in safety management

'Human error is a feature in over 95% of all accidents.'
Royal Society for the Prevention of Accidents

Perception

Some argue that this is a major mechanism by which human beings come to know the world outside of themselves. Perception *translates* the stimuli received by the senses and attaches meaning and significance. People learn through a series of inputs transmitted to the brain via the senses. Senses are information channels to the brain and everything experienced by people is passed through these channels. This process can be simply illustrated, see Figure 8.1. Senses can be described as colours, shapes, sounds, pains and pressures, etc. Something must be added to them before they have *meaning* and *significance* and their source identified. This mental process of giving meaning and significance to sensation is rather complex and is called *perception*. It is an internal process in the sense that whatever is external cannot be known about unless it is filtered through a human nervous system. Somewhere behind the eyes is a perception called *reality*. What is perceived is largely a function of:

- Previous experiences.
- Assumptions.
- Purposes and needs.

The perceiver decides what an object is, where and why it is, according to purpose and the assumptions made at any given time. There is a tendency to:

- Perceive what we want to.

- Perceive what we need to.
- Perceive what our past experience has led us to assume.

Perceptions are unlikely to be altered until and unless there is some frustration in attempts to do something based on them. If actions seem to allow purposes to be fulfilled then perceptions will not be changed no matter how often we are told that they are wrong. In this context, *wrong* means that a perception does not work for the perceiver. However, this does not mean that people automatically change their perceptions if they are frustrated in attempts to act upon them. It does imply that there is an alternative to changing perceptions. Hence the ability to learn can be seen as the ability to give up inappropriate perceptions and to develop new and more workable ones. Since perceptions come from individual and past experiences, it is clear that each person will perceive what is '*out there*' in a unique way. Thus, communication, in the sense of sharing meanings, is possible only to the extent that two perceivers have similar purposes, assumptions and experience. The process of becoming an effective social person is dependent upon seeing the other's point of view.

The meaning and significance of perception is ultimately how it causes people to respond and act. When it is raining, some people head for cover whilst others enjoy walking in it. Their perceptions of what is happening are different and are reflected in the fact that they do different things. The fact that both groups understand and agree with the statement 'it is raining' does not mean that they perceive the event in the same way.

Sociological analysis is possible only because people tend to act in similar ways when confronted by the same types of social situations, for example, safety managers in a classroom! Some sociologists view human behaviour as being mechanically determined by the social structure. Such terms as *role* or *social institution* are used by behavioural scientists to refer to the stable patterns of the relationships that they discover. There is a tendency to treat people as wholly passive in the face of social forces. Such assumptions are rejected by others who take an action frame of reference. Here people are seen as consciously interpreting the situations in which they find themselves and, in the light of these perceptions and interpretations, selecting their responses in accordance with the goals they wish to achieve. Whilst the behaviour of human beings is restricted by the objective characteristics of the situations, there is increasing evidence to suggest that individuals *construct* the reality we perceive, rather than passively *receive* or *reflect*. Society itself serves to define reality and objectivity. For example who says $2 \times 2 = 4$? Even the way individuals perceive themselves, their self-image, is affected by feedback obtained from others. The notion of *reality* is not important, what influences behaviour is what we perceive reality to be.

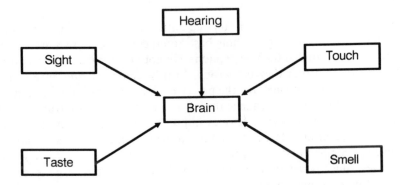

According to the Centre for British Audio Visual Communications these senses are in use when learning as follows:

Sense	%
Sight	75
Hearing	13
Touch	6
Taste	3
Smell	3

And from what we learn, remember and believe:

%	Mode
90	of what we SAY AS WE DO
80	of what we SAY
50	of what we SEE and HEAR
30	of what we SEE
20	of what we HEAR
10	of what we READ

Figure 8.1 The senses

Issues raised for safety management

In the management of people, differences in perception can be a source of difficulty, conflict and problems. For instance, perception has clear relevance in the study of industrial disagreements and how people *see* danger. Some contradictory safety management views of workers' behaviour are:

- They will risk anything for more money *v* They will always reject incentives and merit money in the name of safety and solidarity.
- What they need is discipline *v* What they need is motivation.
- They have no company loyalty *v* They will soon let you know when things go wrong.
- Most workers will obey safety procedures *v* They are out to do as little as possible as easily as possible despite the risks.

Thus there are many phenomena relevant to safety management, and industrial problems are evidently influenced by the participants of the situation. For example, the shop steward suffers a similar difference in perception. He is often described as a '*trouble maker*' yet trouble is thrust upon him. In circumstances like this, he may be striving to bring some order into a chaotic situation, and management may rely heavily on his efforts to do so. Thus, a shop steward is rarely an agitator pushing workers to unconstitutional action. For the most part, the shop steward is viewed by others and himself as an accepted reasonable, even moderating influence and seen as a lubricant rather than an irritant. The perception here then can be summarised as:

- A shop steward is a trouble maker *v* A shop steward is a moderator.

Whilst there is a pro- and anti-shop steward view, there are other areas where perceptual differences occur such as:

- The conflict and co-operation in industry.
- The managerial prerogative or the legitimacy of managerial authority.
- The meaning and significance of absenteeism.
- The meaning of hard work.

In the previous chapter it was seen that one of the main aims of human resources management is to attain a situation where the particular skills and abilities of the individual are matched in an appropriate way to the job required of him by an organisation. One, recruitment and selection, we have discussed already. The other important area concerns training and development and these issues are discussed in Chapter 11. An understanding of the development of individual differences and of the problems of perception is important in their sensible application. However, it must be remembered that the ideas and concepts outlined have other and wider applications for management.

A perception of danger and risk

Individuals vary as to what they see as dangerous and what they regard as acceptable risks. Some people will readily involve themselves in such activities as car racing and sky diving, whilst others adopt a more cautious approach. Because risk can be perceived so differently, safety managers must adopt a more formal approach to assessing levels of risk. In this way, everyone including the more adventurous worker can be included in the assessment. Safety researchers have shown that risk can be generally calculated as follows:

$$\text{Risk} = \frac{\text{Number of Accidents}}{\text{Exposure}}$$

These calculations may also include dangerous occurrence data where it is known but the results should only be used as a feature of the general decision-making process.

Early work in the area of accident *proneness* emphasised the statistical notion that a minority of individuals sustained a proportionally greater number of accidents than would be expected on a purely random basis. More recently, researchers argue that the high frequency of accidents incurred by a few individuals may be accounted for by reference to their abnormal personality characteristics such as guilt and temper. In general terms, it may be found that accidents occur as a result of normal behavioural situations such as loss of concentration or familiarity. Research can show that human error is a factor in over 95% of accidents which occur. Risk assessment, therefore, should be considered, particularly at the job assessment stage (see Chapter 6). The above formula is best used when using data published by the industry concerned. For example, the HSE publish accident figures by industry each year. By using these data and dividing it by the number of man hours (m/H) worked per individual then a general risk factor can be obtained.

Example 8.1

The John Bloggs Engineering Company in Woodshire has just won a large overseas contract to provide engine parts. To meet their obligations, the company are to operate three eight-hour shifts per day for the machinists. During the past three months, the mechanical engineering industry has had 6,193 reported injury accidents of varying degrees of severity. During the contract period, each operator completed 5.5 hours exposure (actually operating a lathe or other product producing tool). Assuming a five-day week then 27.5 m/H per week is worked which (allowing for statutory holidays and leave, etc) works out at 1,210 hours of exposure per operator per year (contract periods may also be used). The risk factor (R) can thus be calculated:

$$\text{Risk} = \frac{6193}{1210}$$

$$R = 5.12 \text{ per man}$$

These results therefore show a fairly high level of risk and care should be exercised when planning financial reward schemes and safety programmes. Careful monitoring of safety procedures and practices would be essential. At the same time, safety practitioners may wish to calculate their own respective accident performance and some common indices in current use are given in Appendix 6. If performance is below that expected then answers to the following may provide a solution:

● Are the present shift structures satisfactory?
● Are current safety clothing provisions satisfactory?
● Are current workshop procedures and practices meeting objectives?
● Is further safety training the answer?
● Is production supervision satisfactory?
● Are incentive schemes a contributory factor?
● Will a publicity campaign help?
● Are organisational rules clear and understood?
● Do the rules and regulations need improving?
● Are guards and other safety equipment of the approved type, are they serviceable and are they being used in accordance with instructions?

Although there are many ways of assessing risk it has been found that to quantify it is a helpful tool within the review process. Perception of risk differs widely between individuals and even organisations and there is always the danger of incompatibility between the two. This must be maintained at a minimum. There have been several models submitted by researchers to examine the link between a person's perception of risk and his behaviour. The current debate over these models is inconclusive. For example, Wilde, in 1982 argues that the accident rate is ultimately dependent on one factor only, the target level of risk in the population concerned which acts as a reference variable in a homeostatic process relating accident rate to human motivation. A figure illustrating this model is given in Figure 8.2.

The model in Figure 8.2, although simple in structure, suggests that people have risk control mechanisms which can be varied over a period of

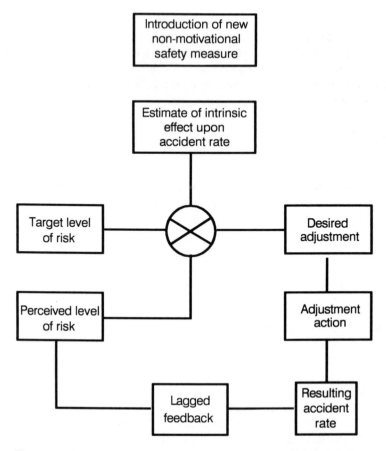

Figure 8.2 Wilde's risk homeostasis model (Source: Wilde 1982)

time by individuals. Typically, the control settings for young males would be set higher than that of the middle-aged female! The model also suggests that any non-motivational safety measure which is accurately perceived by a person may result in behavioural adjustments which re-establish the level of risk at which the person feels happy.

Although this model has been criticised (Evans 1984, McKenna 1982, 1984) and by those accepting the thesis of risk compensation, Evans summarises his position in a simple equation which he refers to as the human behaviour feedback model. This is:

Actual safety change $= (1 + f) \times$ engineering safety change

Where: The engineering safety change is a measure of the safety change which would result from engineering change (to equipment or working environment) in the absence of any behavioural response.

f is a parameter which measures the amount of behavioural response or feedback in the system. If there is no feedback then f will equal 0 and the engineering safety change will achieve its full and expected safety change. If compensation is complete, f will equal -1, and there will be no safety benefit. This represents risk homeostasis. McKenna raises objections to Wilde's risk homeostasis theory in the form of four questions:

1. Do workers have a straightforward representation of risk which directs their behaviour?
2. Do workers detect the presence of safety measures?
3. Do workers always completely compensate for a change in risk?
4. Is it the case that workers cannot be discouraged or prevented from compensating?

Robertson also questions the ability of workers to perceive and act upon minor changes in risk associated with safety measures such as improved safety legislation and asks:

'How many of us know the precise reduction of risk of injury that safety standards have provided.'

These questions can be organised around Wilde's risk homeostasis model illustrated in Figure 8.2 above.

Motivation

A large number of behavioural scientists who pay attention to the problem of motivation at work see industrial and human relations problems caused essentially by conflict between the organisation and the personality of the mature individual. Common to this is the idea that individuals have different levels of need. The satisfaction of different needs may well be involved in:

- Choosing whether to work at all.
- Deciding which job to choose.
- Deciding how hard to work.

A further idea is that individuals may behave in very different ways in the satisfaction of their needs. The organisation, on the other hand, is dominated by the concepts of economics and *scientific management*. The motivational assumptions are that the individual is fundamentally idle and will only work hard in return for financial reward whilst subjected to close supervision, direction and punishments. It is also assumed that individuals avoid responsibility and prefer direction.

The organisation is based on the principle of specialisation, i.e. the narrower the task, the higher the productivity. This applies to management and men and creates a large number of groups requiring a great deal of co-ordination and direction. From this grows the management chain of authority with its attendant principles of unity and span of control, etc. At the bottom of the pyramid are a large number of individuals performing minute tasks of little interest and no challenge, subject to direction from above, but unable to exert any influence upwards, all responsible decisions having been removed from them and concentrated in the hands of remote specialists. Thus, the mature adult is reduced to a state of dependency and passivity, like that of a child. It is also argued that while the motivational assumptions of scientific management may have had validity at an earlier stage of economic and social development, this is no longer the case. Higher wages, personnel programmes, social legislation, full employment and collective bargaining have led to relative satisfaction of both physiological and security needs.

Generally, the result of the conflict between organisations and individuals is either frustration or alienation expressed in either apathy or hostility to organisational goals. This reaction to the authoritarian organisation, its excessive division of labour and its false motivational assumptions, shows up in behaviour as restrictive practices, high absenteeism and staff turnover rates, with a high level of disputes and grievances. Senses of common purpose disappear!

Some theories of motivation

There are some basic theories concerned with the study of motivation, particularly those regarding work.

Elton Mayo (1880–1949) – The Hawthorn Studies

In 1926, Elton Mayo was appointed head of Industrial Research at Harvard University where his research concerned the social and psychological problems of industrial workers. Until the time of Mayo, most attempts to improve worker performance and increase output were based on the assumptions that:

- A worker could be regarded as a machine whose output could be increased by improving physical conditions.
- The elimination of wasteful movements and fatigue.

These assumptions were tested by Mayo as the result of the Hawthorn works of the Western Electric Company in the United States. Previous investigations of the low morale and dissatisfaction in this company involved attempts to improve physical conditions which had proved to be inconclusive. The results of one particular study involving lighting conditions indicated that every change introduced led to an increase in output and that the output of a control group, undergoing no changes, also increased. Mayo's colleagues began a test by studying the output of a small selected group of women whose co-operation had been agreed and who were consulted about each of a large number of changes introduced. Again, nearly every change led to an increase in output, and with one final return to the original conditions, output increased further. Such results led Mayo to conclude that since the changes observed could not be attributed to the changes and physical conditions they must be due to social factors and a change in the attitude of the workers. This could have been due to:

- The research study itself in that someone was taking an interest.
- The workers being made to feel important because they were being studied.

The need to take an interest was further demonstrated in a subsequent interview programme where it was found that most grievances raised were only a symptom of a general discontent, and that a chance to discuss them in the presence of a sympathetic listener often led to their disappearance. Furthermore, the interest demonstrated the need for their co-operation and the fact that they were consulted about changes had transformed a number of individuals into a group, whose members valued their membership, felt responsible to the group and to the company and were concerned with meeting group standards. According to Mayo, this discovery ended the long held view referred to as the *rabble hypothesis* characterised in industry by the assumption that the management must deal with a number of socially isolated individuals, each intent on pursuing his own ends. Despite the fact that financial incentives to produce more existed, production did not increase until the investigation had brought about the existence of a cohesive group making a co-operative effort to solve problems with the company.

The importance of belonging to a group was clearly demonstrated in another part of the Hawthorn studies within the bank wiring room. The men here had developed into a social group with a highly effective code of conduct, of production no more (or less) than a tacitly agreed amount per day – the group's interpretation of what constituted a 'fair day's work'. Mayo stressed that management must forget its old assumptions about workers, recognise the existence of the human and social factors and try to ensure that these factors operate in such a way as to benefit both workers and company. In order for this state to be achieved, it is important that the need to develop and use social skills, too long neglected in favour of technological skills, be recognised.

Abraham Maslow (1908–1970) – A hierarchy of needs

Professor of Psychology at Brandeis University and President of the

American Psychological Association, Maslow differed from many of his colleagues in that his interest focused on mature, healthy, self-actualising individuals rather than on the mentally ill. Maslow was a strong exponent of the view that man is not simply a product of his past experiences and learning but a forward-looking animal and self directed, capable of shaping life and behaviour. Maslow claimed that human needs can be hierarchically organised as follows:

The need for self-actualisation and realisation
The need to become everything that one is capable of becoming, covering self-fulfilment, self-expression and creativity.

The esteem needs
The need for self respect and the respect of others; for competence, independence, self confidence and prestige.

The social needs
The need to relate to other people, the need for friendship and affection, for belonging to a group.

The safety needs
Needs for physical and psychological safety and security, for shelter and freedom from attack both physically and mentally.

The physiological needs
Needs for food, water, air etc.

These are shown in hierarchical order in Figure 8.3.

Figure 8.3 Maslow's hierarchy of needs

According to Maslow, when a lower need has been satisfied, the next highest becomes dominant, and the individual's attention is turned to satisfying this higher need. At the higher level, the need for self-actualisation is destined to remain unsatisfied as new meanings and challenges arise. Maslow noted that only an unsatisfied need can motivate. However, there is not necessarily a straightforward progression from a lower to a higher need. Circumstances may force a person to direct energies toward fulfilling lower level needs which have for a long time been satisfied and to forget for a period those higher needs which have become dominant. For example, unemployed people might only be satisfied if they can get enough food. There are exceptions to the rigid hierarchy of needs. Some creative artists will forgo lower-order needs and become dominated by the higher need of self-actualisation.

Man, therefore, is seen as a wanting animal where the average member of society is most often partially satisfied and partially unsatisfied in all of his wants. The hierarchy principle is usually empirically observed in terms of increasing percentages of non-satisfaction as we proceed up the hierarchy. Some authors have noted that the principal lesson to be learned is that all needs must be considered in an attempt to motivate people to work. Any attempt to provide motivation by means of incentives relevant to needs of a level lower or higher than that which is dominant is likely to fail. In modern society, higher needs tend to dominate where physiological and safety needs in most individuals are at least reasonably satisfied. Since individuals and groups differ with regard to the needs that are dominant the same incentives cannot be expected to motivate everyone and attempts are made to recognise the dominant needs and to act appropriately.

Frederic Hertzberg (born 1923) – preventative and growth needs

Hertzberg became Professor of Psychology at Case University, America, in 1957 and considers that man has two sets of needs. These are described as *maintenance* needs and *motivational* needs. The first are concerned with avoiding pain and dissatisfaction whilst the second deal with activity seeking and achieving satisfaction and fulfilment. Maintenance needs are referred to as *hygiene* factors. This is because attention to them can only prevent or eliminate dissatisfaction without promoting satisfaction or happiness. Furthermore, maintenance needs are continuous and progressive and can never be permanently satisfied. In the work situation, maintenance factors are all contained in the total environment in which the employee works, including physical conditions, salary, security, social factors, interpersonal relationships, etc. The safety manager must constantly attend to these factors if the individual is not to be dissatisfied, but cannot expect this attention to lead to active satisfaction. An increase in salary may eliminate unhappiness (at least until the progressive nature of the maintenance needs produces a further sense of dissatisfaction in a corresponding desire for a further increase) but it will not make the employee happy and motivated.

The motivational needs which lead to positive happiness are the needs for growth, achievement, responsibility and recognition. These needs can be met only through what is actually done by the job itself. According to Hertzberg, the job can potentially provide a more powerful motivator than any extrinsic incentive. Employees can be actively satisfied only when the work done is perceived by the worker as meaningful and challenging and can thus fulfil his motivational needs. Failure on the part of management to recognise the distinction between hygiene and motivational factors can lead to a complete lack of understanding of worker problems. The worker, not satisfied by a job which is meaningless to him, will react to his work with apathy and detachment. Hertzberg recommends *job enrichment* as a solution to the problem of meeting motivational needs. Provided it is not so great or sudden as to arouse excessive fear or alarm, job enrichment makes it possible for the growth and achievement needs to be met through the worker's efforts on the job.

Motivators affect motivation in a positive direction and an analogy drawn from a familiar example of psychological growth in children may be useful. When a child learns to ride a bicycle, he/she is becoming more competent, increasing the repertory of his/her behaviour, expanding skills and growing psychologically. In the process of the child's learning to master a bicycle, the parents can safeguard the child from injury by providing the safest and most hygienic area in which to practise; they can offer all kinds of incentives and rewards and they can provide the most expert instructions, but the child will never learn to ride unless given a bicycle. The hygiene factors are not a valid contributor to psychological growth. The substance of the task is required to achieve growth goals.

The theory's usefulness lies in the clarity with which it focuses attention on the motivational distinction between task and environment intrinsic and extrinsic factors. Historically, managerial practice and company personnel policies in the light of this distinction, make clear that the whole trend of scientific management has been to engineer out of jobs (at nearly every level of the organisational hierarchy) much of the individual interest, challenge and responsibility which are the motivational source of job satisfaction. Attention to people has been confined to making would-be compensatory improvements in the environment; issues of pay and conditions, job security, supervision, communications, and joint consultative procedures have dominated personnel work. According to Hertzberg, no amount of environmental improvement can compensate for task impoverishment. If we are concerned to motivate people we must look again at the task they are asked to do. A diagram illustrating Hertzberg's theory is given in Figure 8.4.

Other researchers, notably Argyris, see each individual as having a potential which can be fully realised. Such self-realisation, or self-actualisation, benefits not only the individual but also those around him and the organisation in which he works. Regrettably, business and other organisations are usually run in a way which prevents such benefits. There are three prime factors involved with this problem:

1. Development of the individual towards personal and psychological maturity;
2. The degree of interpersonal competence in dealing with one another shown by work colleagues, and
3. The nature or the organisation worked for.

Job enrichment:

Opportunities for achievement
Recognition of achievements
Interesting and challenging work
Genuine responsibility (If wanted)
Scope for individual advancement
Scope for individual growth

Motivators:

These lead to
individual and
group satisfaction

The environment

**The task
itself**

The environment

The organisational policy
and administration
Technical supervision
Working conditions
Salary or wage
Human relationships
Health and safety

Hygiene factors:

Factors which can
help overcome
dissatisfaction at
work

Organisational efficiency and effectiveness

Figure 8.4 Hertzberg's theory of motivation

Basically, what an adult does at work can be understood by the extent to which he/she has matured. This progression from infancy to maturity may be said to consist of the following developments:

- From infant passivity towards adult activity.
- From dependence towards relative independence.
- From limited behaviours to many different behaviours.
- From erratic, shallow, brief interests to more stable and deeper interests.
- From short-time perspective to longer-time perspective.
- From a subordinate social position to an equal or superior social position.
- From lack of self-awareness to self-awareness and self-control.

The typical approach to management of organisations can cause problems in that the lack of interpersonal competence prevents people becoming mature in outlook and fails to arouse full psychological energy. People too often remain short sighted in their actions on the job, concerned with present advantage and unable to see future consequences, they shirk responsibility and are uninterested in opportunities; their approach to work is apathetic. But the fault is not theirs individually. A real and lasting cure, claims Argyris, can be effected only by changing attitudes and values of upper and middle levels of management. He believes that management is by and large opposed to any show of emotion and to the expression of any idea of sentiment which might supply a need to take risks or to change the status quo. This leads to ineffective communication due to deliberate filtering and selection of information passed on, and inadequate feedback, resulting in the making of ineffective decisions by managers who have not been given all the relevant facts. For the effective organisation, the values have to be changed in order that the emphasis is on individuality rather than conformity, and discussions can be completely open with nobody being afraid to contribute. Unless this is achieved, people will not be honest, there will be lack of trust and there will be no commitment to the job.

Argyris feels that this atmosphere is common in organisations which are not *axiologically good*. He describes an axiologically good organisation as one where all the parts are well co-ordinated and integrated to further the overall objectives, and one which is able to respond to internal and external needs for change. Informal *rational* organisations are based on reducing tasks to minimal specialisation routines. In such organisations, the individual cannot progress from infantile behaviours. In his/her limited routine tasks, he/she looks forward to the end of the day's work, but is unable to foresee the success or failure of the whole organisation over a period of time. To superiors, his/her inability to see beyond the end of their nose is inexplicable.

Where there is a lack of response, even amongst lower management or specialists, executives are liable to become autocratic and directive. The increased use of management controls deprives employees of any opportunity to participate in important decision-making which affects their working life. This can lead to feelings of psychological failure. It is not only the workers themselves, but the control systems which define, inspect and evaluate the quality and quantity of performance. As subordinates begin to care less about what is happening, less effort is put into the job. The first step towards increasing organisational health is to increase the interpersonal competence of senior management. Senior managers must not be afraid to show feelings to those above and below them.

Tasks can be enlarged to include more operations and to expand the use of the individual's intellectual and interpersonal abilities. Each employee can have more control over what is done in his/her own sphere of activities and greater participation in decisions about them. The organisation will change and may be able to adapt rapidly to the point where they have different structures for different purposes. Each structure will have a different blend of characteristics. The authoritarian approach should not be abandoned as it may be appropriate when time is short and decisions need to be taken quickly. The important point is that human costs of using it must be recognised. Conversely, when time exists for discussion and consideration a maximum personal responsibility is needed, and thus the organic strategy can be used.

Douglas McClelland feels that *achievement motive* is an important factor and describes this phenomenon as a tendency of a person who is not being required to think about anything in particular (i.e. when free to relax with an idle mind) to think about ways to accomplish something difficult and significant. This tendency is measurable by means of special psychological techniques. Another characteristic of achievement motive reveals its importance to management. Although only around 10% of the people in the population at large have a strong achievement motive, the percentage in certain occupations is likely to be much higher. This is true for sales and marketing positions, general management positions and for independent businessmen. A person with a strong achievement motive is likely to surpass the accomplishments of an equally able but less strongly motivated person especially in one of these occupations. McClelland identifies three major characteristics of the self-motivated achiever:

1. Strategies

An achiever will follow a strategy throughout life which will begin at a very early age. They help to explain why the person is likely to be successful and they also indicate why supervisory tactics which may be appropriate for other kinds of worker are often inappropriate when applied to a person with a strong achievement motive. These people will set their own goals and are nearly always trying to achieve *something*. They are seldom content to drift aimlessly and do not let life happen for them. Also, they are particular about which goals they commit themselves to and for this reason are considered unlikely to accept goals set for them if they do not like them. They rarely seek advice or help except from experts or people who can provide required skills or information. The achiever prefers to be fully responsible for the attainment of his goals as much as possible. If achievers win they like the credit, but losers readily accept the blame;

2. Analyses

Achievers tend to avoid the extremes of difficulty in selecting goals. They prefer moderate goals that are neither too easy to obtain nor so difficult that to reach them would be regarded as luck. They gauge what is possible and then select a goal that is as tough as possible in order to provide the hardest feasible challenge. This attitude will constantly keep an achiever at their limits of ability in order to satisfy the need to win;

3. Performance appraisal

An achiever prefers tasks which provide immediate feedback or measurements of progression towards the goal. This may be one reason why achievers often decide upon a career in sales.

McClelland points out that the effect of monetary incentive on an achiever is rather complex. On the one hand, achievers have a high opinion of their worth and tend to place a high price on them. They are unlikely to remain for a long period of time if an organisation does not pay them well. Conversely, it is questionable whether incentive payments actually increase output since achievers are usually operating at peak efficiency anyway. Monetary incentives are more effective with people whose achievement drives are weak as this group need some sort of external reward to increase effort levels. It must be emphasised that the achievement motive is not the only source of high achievement. Other drives can also lead to high levels of attainment in other occupations. In the business world, achievers are at an advantage. This raises the question of whether the level of achievement motivation could be increased in people whose achievement drives are not usually strong. McClelland believes that this may be possible as he has found reserves of latent, untapped achievement motivation in most organisations. The key, he feels, is to build more achievement characteristics into more jobs; personal responsibility, individual participation in the selection of productivity targets, moderate goals and fast clear-cut feedback on the results that each individual is attaining.

From the work of industrial psychologists, it is argued that management should increase motivation if productivity levels are to be improved. This might be obtained by making use of the following strategies:

- *Job enrichment:* An increase in satisfaction and responsibility attached to a job is achieved either by reducing the degree of supervision or by giving a worker a unit of work in which he has freedom to choose his method and sequence of operation provided safety and health is not sacrificed.
- *Job enlargement:* In this case, the worker is required to increase the number of operations provided the worker can cope with this safely.
- *Job rotation:* Here, the worker is required to undertake a wider variety of tasks particularly in jobs where repetitive or automated tasks are the norm.

Areas for potential participation are:

- *Personnel decisions:* Hiring, firing, promotions, transfers, deployment, redundancy, discipline and on-the-job training.
- *Social decisions:* Health and safety, welfare administration, pensions, regulation of hours, rest periods and vacation schedules.
- *Economic decisions:* Technical issues such as new methods of production, production planning and control, and business matters such as production times, sales, expansion or contraction, rationalisation, investment, distribution and use of profits, changes in plant organisation, mergers, revised health and safety procedures.

The aim is to reduce authoritarian type management and replace it by a more participative style. The participative leader is one who plans work and then consults subordinates as to the best course of action. This person is skilled in selecting and training people for jobs and in reconciling conflicts in order to achieve group cohesion and group effectiveness. Also, such a person would be interested in individual employees and their problems. The authoritarian, however, uses rewards and punishments of the traditional sort, exercises close supervision and is more interested in those above than below. What should be noted from this is that such leadership skills may ignore conflicting interests of power, a combination which makes a bargaining approach more likely. Inequities in wage and salary levels may reduce the level of effort and create conflict. This introduces a cultural element into an argument so far conducted in psychological terms. Unlike the psychologist, the sociologist sees needs not as psychological constants but as cultural variables. The individual in a given work situation may adopt a pattern of needs in accordance with their own wider set of objectives and this pattern need not follow the same order as that of the Maslow hierarchy. For example, the individual may elect to satisfy higher needs outside the work situation, in hobbies, in family, community affairs, etc.

Leadership

This is a behavioural issue that managers often feel ought to be of particular importance and significance to them in their jobs. Leadership is a major contributory factor in the dynamics of a working group. Managers are said to be leaders and this includes those safety practitioners in management positions. It is necessary to consider the effect of different styles of leadership and how it can affect the morale and performance of the people being managed. Leadership can emerge under many different conditions and be exercised in several ways. Some leaders are elected, some come into prominence suddenly (some might say by accident) whilst others are appointed to positions of authority. The latter situation is the one which relates to the manager. This is an important factor because it will have several implications for what the manager can or cannot do as a leader. A person appointed to a position of authority and responsibility cannot avoid exercising it, nor can it be delegated or given away. The boss, whether popular or not, is the boss. Although managers cannot often choose whether or not to exercise authority they can quite often choose how they exercise it. Leadership is a much researched subject and a number of behavioural scientists have been concerned with identifying and describing various leadership styles and examining their appropriateness to the work situation.

Early studies on leadership involved the study of the effects of differing leadership styles on the performance of groups. It was concluded that an autocratic style of leadership seemed to be the most effective in terms of the level of productivity or work effort, but that a more democratic style led to a better quality of work done. Subsequent research also examined a third leadership style referred to as *laissez-faire* or passive leadership, interacting with members of the work group only on their initiative. Here it was found that the groups tended to be more productive in the absence of a leader!

One criticism of this work frequently made is that the styles examined are extremes, and in practice the behaviour of managers lies somewhere in between these points. It has been suggested by Tannenbaum and Schmidt in 1958 that leadership behaviour varies along a continuum according to the amount of subordinate participation and involvement in the decision-making process. A simplified version of this continuum, together with possible conditions under which each style might be effective, is illustrated in Figure 8.5.

Tannenbaum and Schmidt suggest that the kind of leadership represented by the extreme democratic end of the continuum is rarely found in formal organisations. This might be because organisational pressures make

Autocratic (tells)	Persuasive (sells)	Consultative (consults)	Democratic (consent)
Style:	Style:	Style:	Style:
Leader takes decisions alone and expects subordinates to carry them out without question.	Leader takes decisions alone but believes that people are better motivated if they think the decisions are correct. Time is spent persuading subordinates that decisions are right.	Leader confers with subordinates before taking decisions. Takes into account group's advice and feelings when making decisions.	Leader puts problems in front of subordinates and allows a decision to emerge through the process of group discussion.
Appropriateness:	Appropriateness:	Appropriateness:	Appropriateness:
In emergencies and where time is critical.	Where the leader has all the information but requires enthusiasm and commitment from subordinates.	Where information needed to make the decision is spread amongst subordinates.	Similar to the consultative style but used where a high degree of commitment and involvement is needed particularly where results are the responsibility of the group.

Figure 8.5 Leadership style and decision making

it impossible for a manager to give up his responsibility for making a decision (i.e. the boss must be boss).

Another aspect from which leadership can be studied concerns the way a person operates, particularly in respect of the amount of enthusiasm shown for completing a task and concern for satisfying the needs of subordinates. A suggestion for measuring the degree of a manager's concern for production and concern for people, their health and safety on a nine by nine matrix is referred to as a managerial grid. The matrix and representative positions on it are shown in Figure 8.6.

It is suggested by researchers that the five by five position represents the way in which most managers lead their groups but that the nine by nine is felt to be the ideal situation to be aimed for. The nine by nine approach involves the utilisation of people's needs (including health and safety) in the interests of production, and, through the use of team work, achieving both high production and high morale. Other researchers have adopted an approach to the notion of a concern for the task and a concern for relation-

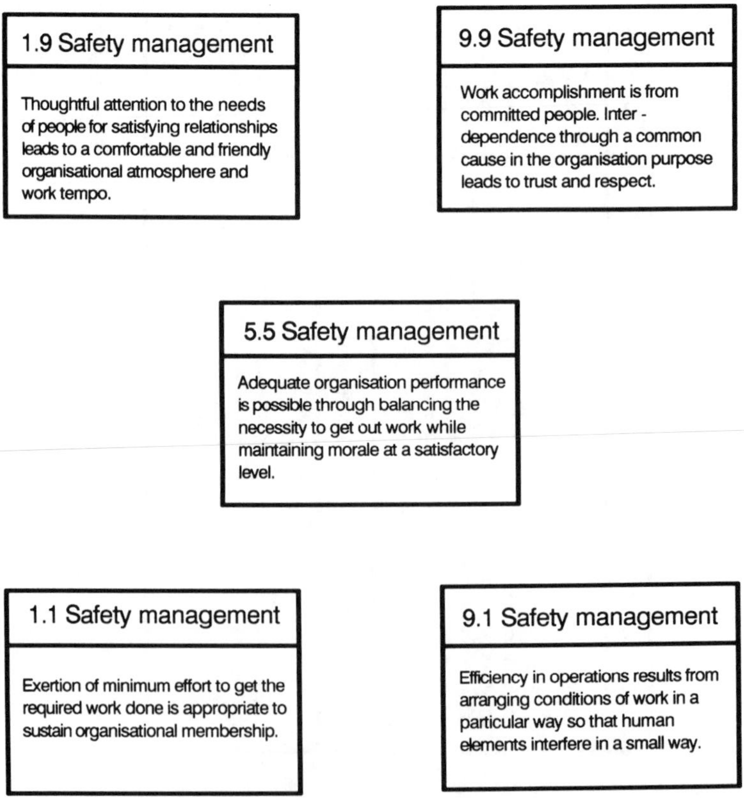

1.9 Safety management

Thoughtful attention to the needs of people for satisfying relationships leads to a comfortable and friendly organisational atmosphere and work tempo.

9.9 Safety management

Work accomplishment is from committed people. Inter - dependence through a common cause in the organisation purpose leads to trust and respect.

5.5 Safety management

Adequate organisation performance is possible through balancing the necessity to get out work while maintaining morale at a satisfactory level.

1.1 Safety management

Exertion of minimum effort to get the required work done is appropriate to sustain organisational membership.

9.1 Safety management

Efficiency in operations results from arranging conditions of work in a particular way so that human elements interfere in a small way.

Figure 8.6 The managerial grid.

ships with people and from this have produced a basic categorisation of four latent styles as illustrated in Figure 8.7.

There is no suggestion that one particular style is better than another as this is dependent on the task being undertaken. Each of the four styles may be carried out effectively or ineffectively. By adding the dimension of effectiveness to the matrix this approach is given the popular name of 3-D management style. This is illustrated in Figure 8.8.

Latent styles

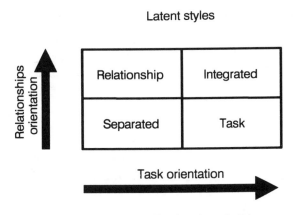

Figure 8.7 The four latent styles

A brief description of the four ineffective and four effective styles is given in Figure 8.9.

There has been an attempt to develop an approach which takes account of three sets of needs within a leadership situation. These are:

1. The needs of the task to be undertaken;
2. The needs of the individual in the work group; and
3. The needs of the work group to be maintained as a cohesive social entity.

The interaction of these needs can be shown in Figure 8.10.

In order for these needs to be met in any group or organisation, certain functions have to be performed. In this integrated theory, it is said that these functions are the responsibility of the leadership, but that this does not necessarily mean that the leader will perform all of them personally. Adair suggests the following as typical leadership functions:

- Planning.
- Initiating.
- Controlling.
- Supporting.

- Informing.
- Evaluating.

A general concept of a leader is a person with certain qualities of personality and character, which are appropriate to the general situation and supported by a degree of relevant technical knowledge and experience, who is able to provide the necessary functions to guide a group towards the further realisation of its purpose, whilst maintaining and building its unity as a team − doing all these things in the right ratio or proportion with contributions from other members of the team.

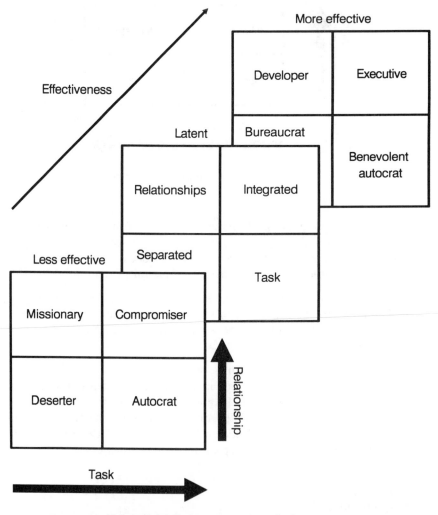

Figure 8.8 3-D management style theory

Ineffective styles:	
Deserter:	A manager who has no interest in either the task or his subordinates. This type of manager often has a depressing effect on the work of those left to get on with the job.
Missionary:	A manager who places harmony and good relationships as a high priority. Such a manager has difficulty facing unpopular task demands.
Autocrat:	A manager who places the immediate task above other considerations all of the time. Subordinates tend not to feel close to such a manager and are motivated to work only when direct pressure is brought to bear.
Compromiser:	The manager who realises the advantages of being concerned with both task and people but who is unable to carry out this role effectively. This type of manager will tend to respond to the most recent or heaviest pressure.

Effective styles:	
Bureaucrat:	The manager who follows the rules and who is not particularly task or relationship orientated. This sort of manager is effective and is seen by subordinates as fair.
Developer:	This manager tends to work on the basis of trust. This type sees the prime task as being to develop the talents of others and to motivate them in order to produce their best work potential. This tends to be successful but may cause problems in the short term particularly where task issues are primary.
Benevolent autocrat:	This type of manager is primarily concerned with the task but has sufficient skills to deal with people and to get what needs to be done without creating undue resentment or opposition.
Executive:	A manager who sees his task as maximising the efforts of others in relation to the jobs in both the short and long term. This manager is effective because his commitment to both task and people are apparent. He is a motivator.

Figure 8.9 Styles of management

Figure 8.10 Interaction of needs

Some views on leadership held by leaders

Harry Truman in his memoirs defines leadership as the ability to get other people to do what they don't want to do, and like it! This may be too brief to describe a complex matter such as leadership. Montgomery in his memoirs describes leadership as:

'The capacity and the will to rally men and women to a common purpose, and the character which inspires confidence.'

He goes on to say that capacity is not enough; the leader must be willing to use it. Leadership then is based on truth and character; there must be truth in the purpose and will power in the character. A leader must exercise an effective influence, and the degree to which this can be done will depend on the personality of the leader − the *incandescence* of which the leader is capable, the flame which burns within, the magnetism which will draw the hearts of the workforce are all things people will want to know. A leader should always:

- Know where he/she is going.
- Commit him/herself fully to the task or tasks.
- Be decisive.

A leader should also possess the talents and resources, including knowledge, experience and courage. He/she must take decisions and accept full responsibility for them. A leader should delegate and decentralise, having first created an organisational structure in which there are definite focal points of decisions so that the *master plan* can be implemented efficiently and effectively. A leader must know what is wanted and must be able to see objectives clearly and be able to strive to attain these goals. Everyone must know what these goals are and be aware of the basic elements of the policy. The leader must give firm guidance and a clear lead. It is necessary to create an atmosphere where subordinates will work. Some senior managers consider that once they have made their plans and passed them on to others for implementation, there is no need for further contact except to influence a programme by the use of extra resources. This is a major mistake. A leader should be involved in the programme from start to finish so that balance and cohesion is maintained. Being in control does not mean interference nor cramping the initiative of subordinates. It is to do with seeing the plan through to its natural conclusion. Keeping in close touch with subordinates means visiting the factory floor. A good leader will hold meetings to give guidance and instructions and to seek opinions. These should never be kept back by the leader; the leader should always go to meet the subordinates. Then nobody need look over their shoulder. A meeting of subordinates to collect ideas is the resort of a weak manger. Sir Winston Churchill wrote of Marlborough:

'The success of a leader does not arise from following rules or models. It consists of an absolutely new comprehension of the dominant facts of the situation at the time, and all the forces at work. What is required is a profound appreciation of the actual event. There is no surer road to disaster than to imitate the plans of bygone leaders and heros and fit them to novel situations.'

An organisation is not merely a collection of individuals and equipment and its strength is not the sum total of these. On the contrary, the real strength of an organisation must also include its morale, spirit and mutual confidence in its leaders and many other spiritual qualities. Maintaining organisational morale is important to its success. This does not necessarily mean surrounding the workforce with canteens and other social benefits but should include keeping them informed about how well the organisation is doing and showing an interest in workforce members and their families. Field Marshal Montgomery was able to approach any of his soldiers and he would always know a great deal about the people he spoke to and of their families. He would show great interest in what they had to say. To do this effectively requires preparation and a good adjutant but is extremely beneficial for everyone's morale. How many leaders in industry today know all the names of their managers let alone their staff?

Some famous leaders (Wellington, Nelson, Montgomery) have been reported as saying that every person has their *ceiling* and must not be allowed to rise above it or be expected to perform beyond it. Managers, if they are to be effective leaders, must be carefully recruited and they must also be trained to recognise each person's operating ceiling. Some people end up in jobs beyond their capabilities and this can have disastrous results for an organisation and, for some, can even be dangerous.

Leadership is a complex subject and there is only time here briefly to cover some of the more general issues relating to this aspect of management. Some works used in this section have been produced by behavioural scientists through their research whilst others have been obtained from leaders who practised the art and have discussed the subject within the framework of their memoirs. It is a fascinating subject worthy of further reading – some examples of which are given at the end of this chapter.

Organisations

Attempts to define the nature of organisations have reached a broad level of agreement, and differences seem confined to the use of language. There are four functional problems that any organisation must solve in order to remain in existence:

1. *Goal Attainment:* The achievement of desired objectives. This generates problems such as the adoption of means appropriate to ends and the allocation of resources to various goals;
2. *Adaption:* This involves coming to terms with the external situation or environment and the ensuing adjustment of internal processes;
3. *Integration:* This concerns the maintenance of internal relations and the balance between the units within systems such as between the safety and the production departments; and
4. *Pattern Maintenance:* The development and conservation of appropriate motivational and value systems within the organisation.

Researchers look at similar issues when defining organisations. Schein states that an organisation is:

'The rational co-ordination of the activities of a number of people for the achievement of some common explicit purpose or goal, through the division of labour and function and through a hierarchy of authority and responsibility.'

The essence of organisation is regular, standardised and recurrent behaviour. The regularities are structured into the behaviour by norms. The basis of social relationships within such a structure comes from the relation of dependence – in which one person is dependent on the other for the security or the continued availability of something that is valued. It should be considered as to what extent any organisation – a family, a work organisation, a national state – meets with the same functional problems and can be managed in the same way. The scheme outlined above, for example, is meant to apply to any social system.

Some researchers have concentrated on the individual within an organisation and have discussed why people do as they are told. Webber, for example, makes the distinction between *power* (the ability to make people obey regardless of resistance) and *authority* (the right to expect obedience where orders are obeyed voluntarily). He distinguished between organisational types according to the way authority is legitimised. There are three main types:

1. *Charismatic authority:* derived from the influence of one person on the organisation (personality);
2. *Traditional authority:* based on precedent and usage; and
3. *Rational (Legal) authority:* authority based by means of rules and procedures applicable to any office.

An exploration of the notion of rational–legal authority which is regarded as the proper form of organisational authority has led to the concept of bureaucracy as the ideal organisation, with the following characteristics:

1. Official business is conducted continuously in accordance with stipulated rules;
2. Each official's work is delimited in terms of imperial criteria;
3. Authority is delegated to the extent necessary to carry out the precise work of each position;
4. The official in any position has only limited means of compulsion;
5. Each official's responsibilities and authority are part of a hierarchy authority;
6. No official has property rights in his job;
7. Official business is conducted on the basis of written documents; and
8. Health and safety requirements form part of the hierarchical authority.

Some characteristics of the bureaucrat are that:

- He is personally free and appointed to his position on the basis of contract.
- He exercises authority in the organisation.
- He is faithfully involved in the organisation.
- He is appointed and placed in his job on the basis of technical qualifications.
- He has a full-time involvement in administrative work.
- His career rewards largely consist of regular salary and prospects of regular advancement.

Some attributes of a bureaucracy can be summarised as:

- It is technically superior because of its precision, speed, lack of equivocation, continuity, uniformity of operation and calculability.
- It concentrates the means of administration.
- It tends to level socio-economic differences.
- It produces an indestructible system of authority under the Rule of Law.

A fully developed bureaucratic organisation can be regarded as technically superior to other forms of organisation in terms of its precision, speed, unambiguity, knowledge of files, continuity, discretion, unity, strict subordination, induction of friction and of material and personal costs. Most studies of the formal and structural characteristics of organisations start from this base. The most frequent criticism of bureaucracies concern their *dysfunctional* aspects such as:

- They exert strong pressures to conformity, resulting in some people taking the rules and administrative procedures as ends in themselves.
- That work will expend to fill the time available resulting in an expansion of management and officers.

Early work into the study of organisations did not consider the problems that arise when an organisation's *rule promulgators* are trying to establish legitimacy of their authority in the face of opposition and a refusal to consent on the part of the governed. Gouldner made a close study of such a situation in an American gypsum mine, where he describes the effects of the introduction of bureaucratic organisation in the face of opposition and a previous management system on the *indulgency pattern*. The rules were ignored or applied very leniently and there was a relaxed atmosphere and a favourable attitude of the workers towards the company. Into this situation came the new mine manager who set about seeing that the rules were enforced, that the authority structure functioned effectively and, in general, that an efficient rational-legal organisation was operated. But this also resulted in a great drop in morale and increased management-worker conflict which included a *wildcat* strike. In this analysis, Gouldner was able to distinguish three patterns of bureaucratic behaviour. These he described as *mock*, *representative* and *punishment-centred* where each had its characteristic values and conflicts.

Mock bureaucracy

This is where the rules are imposed on the group by some outside agency such as an insurance company forbidding smoking in a factory because of its danger. In this situation, neither sub- nor superordinates identify themselves with the rules which were often ignored. This was looked upon as redtape bureaucracy but Gouldner points out that morale may be very high since the informal values and attitudes of all participants are bolstered by the joint violation or evasion of the rules in order to get on with the real job. Here the safety manager would need to ensure that outside rules are identified by the workforce.

Representative bureaucracy

These are rules promulgated by *experts* whose authority is acceptable.

In such a situation there may be tension among those who obey the rules but there is little overt conflict. As the values are held in common by all, deviations are explained by carelessness or ignorance. The joint support for the rules is buttressed by feelings of solidarity and participation in a joint enterprise where authority is based not on position but on accepted knowledge and expertise.

Punishment-centred bureaucracy

This occurs where rules arise in response to the pressures either of management or workers. The attempt is made to coerce the other side into compliance, for example where management introduce stricter control of safety procedures, clocking in or fines. The solidarity of the subordinates can impose rules on management such as demarcation rules, overtime bans and the like. Deviation from the rules is not explained away as described above in the representative bureaucracy characteristic but is regarded as wilful disobedience. Such a situation clearly entails much conflict and tension.

The patterns of behaviour characteristic of these three types of bureaucracy may co-exist in different degrees in any organisation. The punishment-centred type is intended to produce an efficient organisation which conforms to rationally designed rules and procedures. These rules, however, are general and impersonal and decrease the emphasis on the personal power of those in authority. Gouldner also considered the differences between *manifest functions* (those that are intended and recognised) and *latent functions* (dysfunctions or those which are unintended or unrecognised). There are unanticipated consequences of bureaucratic functioning which earlier researchers had omitted. General and impersonal rules by their nature define what is not allowed and this increases people's knowledge of what is the minimum acceptable behaviour. This lowers efficiency and, in a punishment-centred bureaucracy, leads to increasing closeness of supervision which can result in greater tension and conflict. This can only be countered by the continued issue of formal impersonal rules and so the cycle begins again.

It is also important to distinguish between the different outlooks of administrators, and show the effects these have upon their attitudes to their jobs, their employers, their professions and colleagues. Gouldner suggests that there is an inherent contradiction in bureaucracy between a system of authority based on the appointment of experts and authority based on hierarchy and discipline. In the first case, authority is legitimised because of superior knowledge whilst in the second, it arises from the office held. This represents a particular incompatibility in organisations which employ large numbers of professionals who may have more technical knowledge than their hierarchical superiors. Gouldner distinguishes two main categories of administrator:

1. Cosmopolitans; and
2. Locals.

Cosmopolitan administrators are ones with little loyalty to the organisation but who are committed to their specialised skills. They have a completely professional outlook. Locals are administrators with great loyalty to the organisation but with little commitment to specialised skills. They think of themselves as company men. Although organisations wish to retain the loyalty of their personnel (and therefore e.g., promote from internal staff), they also have a basic rational orientation towards efficiency (which requires appointments to be made by skill and competence). This built-in dilemma is another prime cause of concern with regard to tension in organisations.

Burns and Stalker distinguish two systems which they refer to as *mechanistic* and *organic*.

1. Mechanistic systems

These are characterised by the breaking down of the tasks of the organisation into distinct jobs, pursued by the individual as ends rather than means. A fairly rigid hierarchy prevails, each level of the hierarchy being responsible for the integration of the functions performed at the level immediately below it, and responsible to the level immediately above. Every individual's role has attached to it clearly defined rights and privileges. Interaction is generally vertical in that it travels between superior and subordinate rather than laterally, and each individual's behaviour tends to be determined by instructions issued by superiors. The head of the organisation is the ultimate centre of control and communication at all times. Loyalty and obedience are regarded as essential conditions of employment. This system they perceive as appropriate to companies operating in stable conditions, in which new responsibilities and unforeseen difficulties are unlikely to be constantly arising. This system is economical of individual effort in that each person knows exactly what is required of them, what their responsibilities are and the extent of their desired loyalty to the organisation.

2. Organic systems

Such systems are more appropriate to conditions of rapid change. They are characterised by their lack of definition of individual jobs. As conditions change, boundaries of individual responsibility are constantly changing and are never properly defined. The individual's tasks are *realistic* and seen as directly related to the goals of the company, to which the individual contributes any special knowledge or abilities at his disposal. Responsibilities are distributed to whoever is best qualified, by knowledge and skill rather than by position, to deal with them. Control, authority and communication are distributed in a network structure where individual responsibility is to organisation goals rather than to superiors. Communication takes the form of information rather than of command, and is lateral as well as vertical. Commitment rather than loyalty is required of its members.

This system is appropriate to conditions of change because the deliberate non-definition of roles eliminates the need to create new posts and divisions as new problems arise. A consequence of the flexibility of the organic system is the sense of insecurity expressed by members who can never be entirely certain of what is expected of them and of where their responsibilities start and finish. They claim that many yearn for a clearer structure and a more precise definition of roles and expectations.

Burns and Stalker offer explanations for the failure of organisations to adjust to changing conditions. Rapid change brings with it confusion and insecurity, and a number of threats to individual and group interests. In these circumstances, there is a need for the clarity that used to prevail and people are likely to appeal to tradition and past practice to justify reinforcement of the mechanistic system. They note that the working organisation does not exist as an entity on its own, but co-exists with two other systems of commitments described as the status structure and the political system, representing hierarchies of rank and privilege and of power and control respectively. People at work seek to further their own ends in these systems as well as those of the organisation, and moves from mechanistic to organic systems may be seen as a threat to status and power which will be met by counter moves designed to preserve the status quo.

The concept of organisations

There is a need for safety managers to have a greater conceptual clarity in understanding organisations, their structure and the social systems which operate within them. To help with this researchers have used four concepts of organisational analysis:

1. *The manifest organisation:* This is described in organisational charts illustrating the formal hierarchy;
2. *The assumed organisation:* That which is perceived by the people involved;
3. *The extent of the organisation:* The real structure as revealed by systematic analysis such as the structure which an outside firm of consultants might draw up following a detailed investigation; and
4. *The requisite organisation:* That required to meet the realities of the environment.

In an ideal organisation, these four descriptions should correspond exactly with each other. According to Brown, organisations must grow if they are to survive. Growth means change and adaptation, and Brown emphasises the need for planned rather than haphazard adaptation to change. Where the organisational structure is not fully understood, changes and adaptations are likely to lead to uncontrolled changes in the work loads of different roles. This will result in anxieties and pressures which are not understood and cannot be effectively met. In dynamic changing situations, frequent analysis is necessary to reveal the extent of the situation to enable management to recognise and then deal with real problems existing at any time. Brown distinguishes between the executive, representative and legal systems, all of which exist in any organisation and stresses the need to be aware of which system one is operating in at any one time.

The executive system

He describes the executive system as the network of roles occupied by people in an organisation, their roles being those occupied when people are engaged in doing the work of the organisation. Brown describes the analysis of work into its prescribed and discretionary components, the latter concerning the decisions which a safety manager must make. Jaques' work lead Brown to introduce a system of ranking executive roles according to the time span of discretion. This is explained as the length of time before which a decision is made in a role which may come under review. He found a lack of clarity in the boundaries of authority and responsibility which gave rise to restrictions in executive freedom to act. So-called freedom to decide causes confusion about which decisions the executive may legitimately make and about who is responsible for the outcomes. Brown devoted much attention to this problem, to defining the prescribed and discretionary components of roles and to clarifying lines of authority in such a way that responsibility for decisions is known and fully understood by everyone concerned.

Brown argues that written policy by virtue of its explicitness and general accessibility is more flexible than unwritten and was responsible for organisations drawing up detailed policy documents which must be the subject of continuous review and modification.

The representative system

This is an electoral system for communication and negotiation and has properties quite different from those of the executive system. For example, responsibility for actions taken in an executive capacity rests legitimately with one person, whilst responsibility for actions taken in a representative capacity rests with the whole of the electorate. In the representative system, every level of employee and manager is involved, and in this system representatives speak for their constituents and not as individuals. It is in the executive system that individual initiative is seen but this initiative is constrained by the interaction of the executive with the representative system.

The legislative system

The third system described by Brown is the legislative system which comprise of four bodies:

1. The executive system;
2. The representative system;
3. Shareholders; and
4. Customers.

Each of these has the power to resist change and whose support and consent to proposed changes are required.

Another psychologist, Likert, conceptualised management based on the classification of organisational characteristics as essentially autocratic/bureaucratic through to the democratic/organic system. Likert's research indicates that most managers place their preferred organisational system to the 'right' of the way in which they actually run their own departments. The discrepancy between the actual and preferred system is often considerable. However, if managers prefer a system more to the right of the one in operation, then why are there not more examples of change to the right? Likert's answer is that managers are generally reluctant to deviate from the managerial style of their superiors. Superiors expect subordinates to follow their own managerial concept, rewarding those who do and putting pressure on those who do not.

Within the organisation, Likert describes three types of variable:

1. *Causal variables:* These are independent variables which can be changed by the organisation, determining the course of developments such as management policy or skills and behaviour;
2. *Intervening variables:* These reflect the internal state of health of the organisation such as loyalty, attitudes and motivation of company employees; and
3. *End result variables:* These are dependent variables reflecting organisational achievements such as productivity, profit and safety record.

Likert's idea is that two systems exist:

1. *System 1.* Management inputs cause a short-term improvement in the required end result variables at the cost of a reduction in the relevant

intervening variables. This eventually causes a tailing off of the end result variables.

2. *System 2.* Management inputs cause a fairly long-term build up of relevant intervening variables at the cost of low or even reduced performance as measured against end result criteria. However, the build up in intervening variables results in a long-term increase in end result performance.

The three principles for System 2 management are as follows:

Principle of supportive relationships

A general principle which members of an organisation can use to guide their relationships with one another. This principle has a critical dependence on the superior/subordinate relationship and should be ego-building and supportive. It is the subordinate's perception of the situation which determines whether the relationship is supportive or not. Experiences must be seen to contribute to personal needs and increase sense of significance and worth.

Principle of group decision making and supervision

A rigid organisational structure of man-to-man interaction at every hierarchical level. System 2 uses an overlapping group form of structure with each work group linked to the rest of the organisation by means of people who are members of more than one group as illustrated in Figure 8.11.

Interaction and decision making relies on group processes. At each hierarchical level, all subordinates in a work group who are affected by a decision are involved in making that decision. However, a group

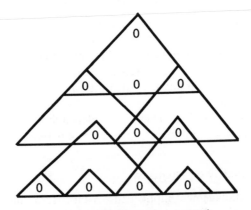

Figure 8.11 Linking pin concept

decision does not dissipate the superior's responsibility. The group method holds a superior fully responsible for the quality of decisions and for their implementation.

The principle of high performance aspirations

Many studies show that employees generally want stable employment, job security, opportunities for promotion and satisfactory compensation in financial terms. They also want to have pride in company performance and accomplishments. High performance goals should be set for the organisation, for departments and for individuals. Under System 2, it is not sufficient only for superiors to have high performance goals. Such goals should be agreed for all the members of the organisation. Agreed goal setting is allowed for in group decision making and overlapping group structures. Ideally, System 2 objectives should be expanded to integrate the needs of members of the organisation, its shareholders, its clients, suppliers and customers.

Peer group loyalty

Likert's research shows that the higher the commitment and loyalty to a group, the higher will be the motivation to achieve and therefore, the greater the probability of achieving the goals of that group. One of the more important aspects of the manager's job is to develop high group loyalty and to assist it in setting its own maximum achievable goals. Many studies have shown that informal leadership is often the cause of costly reductions in organisational performance. Likert claims that peer leadership can contribute substantially to high performance and should be used positively for this purpose rather than being allowed to restrict performance. Similarly, competition has been shown to have a detrimental effect on performance, whereas group co-operation will replace group competition and work groups will set their own superordinate standards such as beating last year's safety record.

The importance of time as a variable

Research into the relationship between such variables as the type of management system, leadership style, employee attitudes and end result variables like productivity, have produced conflicting results. This problem has led to consideration of another important variable and that is time. Changes in the causal variables apparently need an appreciable period of time before the impact of the change is fully manifested in corresponding improvements in the end result variables. Time patterns in a shift to a system using a management edict for cost reduction, productivity, timekeeping and so on (System 1) differ from those illustrated by System 2. That is, in System 1, a larger time interval than is generally recognised in management accounting is needed before the adverse effects of the managerial strategy begin to take effect. An example of possible consequences would be that improvements in productivity and/or costing caused by such factors as automation and technological change tend to hide for a time, any unfavourable trends brought about by managerial edicts aimed at reducing costs. Differing time patterns relating to cause and result variables serve to confuse the diagnosis. Unless there is an analysis of the effect of each causal variable, accounting data will indicate only the overall result and not whether any unfavourable developments are being masked by more favourable ones. Likert maintains that these conflicting results of research findings on such variables as leadership style (causal), subordinate attitudes (intervening) and individual or organisational productivity (end result) are caused by the observations being made at different points in the time scale.

Management systems

These must be internally consistent. Statistical analysis of Likert's data from management questionnaires indicates clearly that a component part of System 1 is compatible with all of its constituent parts. From this it was concluded that the management system of an organisation must have compatible parts in order to function effectively. Experiments in organisations should involve internally consistent changes such as a test of the upward communication processes. Likert suggests that a further concept of his approach to management is that of including estimates of the current value of the human organisation and of such factors as customer goodwill in the organisation's balance sheet. This might yield useful insights into organisational health.

The problems of co-ordination within an organisation have four preconditions:

1. The organisation must provide high levels of co-operative behaviour between superiors and subordinates and between peers. Attitudes of confidence and trust are needed amongst its members;
2. The organisation must have the structure and the skills required in interacting to solve differences and conflicts and to attain creative solutions;
3. It must possess the capacity to exert influence and to create motivation and co-operation without traditional forms of line authority; and
4. Its decision making processes and superior and subordinate relationships must be such as to enable a person to perform their duties well without hazard and risk when reporting to two or more superiors.

For Amatai Etzioni, there is no one right way for organisations to be managed. It depends on historical circumstances, the purpose of the organisation and the actual fit between management's assumption about people and the actual characteristics of the organisation members. According to Etzioni, management and workers interact in organisations on the basis of a psychological contract. Both parties to the contract are guided by assumptions of what is fair and equitable. Etzioni analyses organisations by examining the relationship between two characteristics. These are illustrated in Figure 8.12.

The organisational types which fall along a diagonal line (see Figure 8.13) have just and workable psychological contracts with their members, and management needs to avoid violating the psychological contract by expecting too much.

Types of power and authority used	Types of involvement
* Coercive * Rational - Legal (utilitarian) * Normative	* Alienation * Calculative * Moral

Examples of the above might be:
* Concentration groups   - coercive authority and alienated members * Business and industry - utilitarian authority and calculative authority * Religious organisation - normative and moral involvement

Figure 8.12 The psychological contract relationship
between organisations

	Coercive	Utilitarian	Normative
Alienation	X		
Calculative		X	
Moral			X

Figure 8.13 The psychological contract matrix

Fit 1	Between individual needs, expectations and aspirations in work and the individual's work experience = *Job satisfaction.*
Fit 2	Between organisational needs translated into role requirements from staff and the ability and motivation of the employee to meet these needs = *Effective relationships.*
Fit 3	Between environmental demands and the ability of the organisation to respond to these = *Organisational flexibility.*
Fit 4	Between the amount and kind of required adaption and to the availability of resources within the organisation to enable it to adapt successfully in the short and long term = *Organisational development.*

Figure 8.14 Organisational health in terms of fit

However, work carried out by the Manchester Business School has extended the notion of just and workable contracts to other variables other than simply a psychological contract. The work led by Enid Mumford examined the concept of job satisfaction and organisational health in terms of the degree of fit (see Figure 8.14) between organisational needs and individual needs expressed in a series of contracts, both being affected by technological innovation, labour market and product market pressures.

For Mumford, the healthy organisation requires job satisfaction, effective relationships, organisational flexibility and a capacity for organisational development. These are summarised in Figures 8.15 and 8.16.

From a safety management point of view, it is important to understand the individual and group characteristics which are necessary for the effective implementation of appropriate safety-related strategies. This complex subject has been widely written about and a further reading guide is provided at the end of this chapter.

Safety problem analysis

'One of the major problems that safety managers and groups meet when trying to solve a safety problem is that there is no such thing!'

What is meant by this rather bizarre and apparently silly statement? Well, the problem is that all safety problems, even the simplest, consist in fact of a series of problems. If we fail to realise this we can be met by three kinds of difficulty:

1. We tackle only part of the safety problem;
2. We try to tackle different parts of the safety problem in the same (and therefore inappropriate) way; and
3. We tackle the different parts of the safety problem in the wrong order (or in no order at all).

	The company	The employee
The knowledge contract	Requires a certain level of skill and knowledge in its employees if it is to function efficiently.	Requires the skills and knowledge the employee brings with him to be used and developed.
The psychological contract	Needs motivated employees.	Needs factors which will motivate, provide for achievement, interest, responsibility and status.
The efficiency contract	Needs to achieve a set output and quality standards.	Needs an equitable effort reward bargain and needs controls including supervisory ones which are seen as acceptable.
The ethical contract	Needs employees who will accept the company's ethics and values.	Needs to work for an employer whose values do not contravene his own.
The task structure contract	Needs employees who will accept any technical constraints associated with their jobs.	Needs a set of tasks which meet his requirements for variety, interest, targets, autonomy, safety and feedback task identity.

Figure 8.15 Contract states between company and employee

	Both sets of needs met	Organisational needs met but not those of the individual	Individual needs met but not those of the organisation
Knowledge contract	Effective utilisation of skills and knowledge	Individual frustration due to recruiting of competent staff	Organisational dissatisfaction with competence due to recruiting staff who are not fully qualified
Psychological contract	Psychological health	Conformity to organisational goals with low morale	Individuals identifying with sub group goals rather than organisational goals
Efficiency contract	Good work performance	Productivity and quality together with low morale	High morale and deteriorating product
Ethical contract	Organisation and individual values seen as legitimate	Conformity to organisational but little identity with these values	Identification with peer group values, little support for organisational values
Task structure contract	Task structure fits technological constraints and individual needs	Technological determination, boredom or stress	Job interest and high production costs

Figure 8.16 Interaction of organisational and individual needs

The first step therefore, in improving our ability to solve safety problems is to identify the stages which are generally involved in solving problems, and to use this model to guide our approach to safety problems.

A large number of different analyses of the stages of problem solving have been put forward by various researchers. Despite their detailed differences, all of them seem to suggest that problems can be thought of as having six major stages as illustrated Figure 8.17.

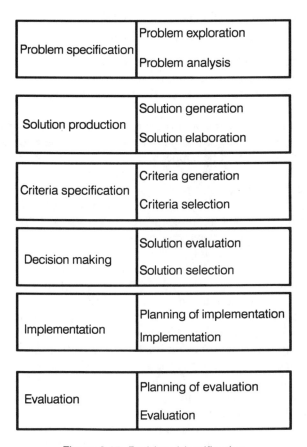

Problem specification	Problem exploration
	Problem analysis

Solution production	Solution generation
	Solution elaboration

Criteria specification	Criteria generation
	Criteria selection

Decision making	Solution evaluation
	Solution selection

Implementation	Planning of implementation
	Implementation

Evaluation	Planning of evaluation
	Evaluation

Figure 8.17 Problem identification

Each of these stages makes different demands on the safety manager and on his team. The skills and abilities which are appropriate for each stage are quite different, and people who are good at one stage may be very poor at another stage, and the kind of tools that are useful for tackling one stage may be inappropriate when tackling another.

Like other skills we have examined, it can be seen that it is possible to improve our problem-solving ability by improving our ability to perform each of the component stages, and also by improving our ability to tackle the problem in a systematic and appropriate order. This section, and the following three sections will examine the first three stages. These are:

1. Problem identification;
2. Exploration;
3. Analysis.

Which safety practitioner was it that said:

'Never mind the answer, what's the question?'

A key stage in problem solving is the realisation that there is a problem to be solved. Equally important is the exploration of that problem by gathering information, and the specification of that problem in a way that allows productive and elegant solutions.

Safety managers, acting as problem solvers, are (or should be) constantly comparing what is actually happening in the area under their control with what should be happening. If there is a difference between the two (i.e. there is some discrepancy) then a problem exists. This discrepancy is the problem for which a cause, or causes, must be found. The cause (or causes) must not only be found but the relationship of that cause to the problem must be verified. Finding and verifying cause requires a systematic approach and a structured method of analysis.

An almost universal failing of problem solvers, once a discrepancy has been recognised, is immediately (and often erroneously) to leap to conclusions about the underlying cause. Effective problem solvers discipline themselves from speculating about cause until they have properly specified the discrepancy and identified all of the factors relevant to a complete understanding of the situation. This first, and very significant, stage in the problem solving process is one that is all too frequently short-circuited. The method outlined below sets out some guidelines which can help to structure the analytical thinking required to identify and verify the cause(s) underlying any given discrepancy.

In the method of problem analysis described here the problem solver, by making use of a set of key questions, attempts to specify the dimensions of the problem in as precise a manner as possible. The key to this process is to ask not only what the problem is, but also *what it is not*. Problem solvers in general tend to ignore such 'negative' information, whereas in practice it is information about what the problem is not which is often the most informative. The strategy of asking what the problem is not, as well as asking what it is enables the problem solver to clarify the circumstances surrounding the problem and to look for changes in those circumstances which are likely to be the causes of the problem. The strategy then tests these possible causes against the specification of the problem. If the possible cause is reconcilable with the identified effects, it becomes a *probable* cause and it is then subjected to further verification tests to establish it as the real cause. It is only when the real cause has been identified that the further stages of problem solving should be undertaken.

The stages of problem identification, exploration and analysis

This can be represented in model form as shown in Figure 8.18.

What is a problem?

A problem is a deviation from a standard which has undesirable effects, and the cause (or causes) of which are unknown.

Problems do not automatically present themselves to us. Indeed, if they do, they are often at the point of being crises or disasters, rather than mere problems. The first stage in dealing with problems is to identify them.

Stage 1: Identifying the problem

What is the deviation from the standard? (NB. A standard may be an existing expectation ('the norm') or it may be a desired, but not yet attained ideal.)

Problems should be actively sought. If they are, they can be tackled before they have become serious, and they can be tackled in a planned way, exploiting the time and resources which early identification have provided. ('A stitch in time saves nine.')

Information about problems should be sought from a variety of sources:

- Customer complaints analysis.
- Customer perceptions.
- Employee perceptions.
- Department purpose analysis.
- Situation appraisal.
- Communication audits.
- Quality audits.
- System audit.
- Safety audit.
- Brainstorming.
- Individual ideas.

At this stage, some selection of problems to be tackled, and decisions about the order in which they should be tackled will probably be needed. From the list of problems identified, the most significant problem should be chosen on the basis of some assessment of the effects of each. Once the problem has been chosen, a simple statement should be prepared identifying the problem as seen at this stage.

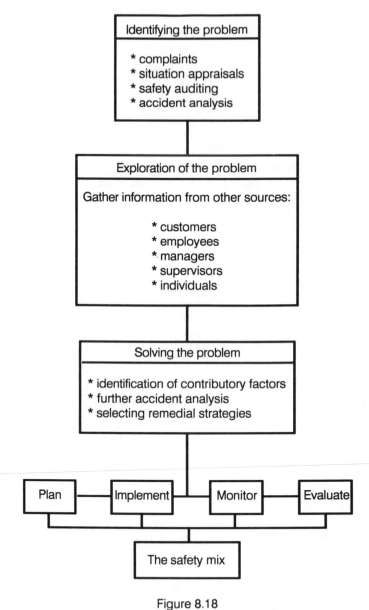

Figure 8.18

The stages of problem identification

Stage 2: Exploring the problem

The second stage is to gather all of the information available which could be of help when trying to identify the underlying cause(s). The information should be used to increase the precision with which the problem can be identified and described. This involves specifying items such as who, what, where, when, how and why.

Gathering data involves:

- Identifying the possible data requirements.
- Agreeing the data requirements.
- Collecting the data required.

The data required can be identified by using techniques such as:

- Cause and effect analysis.
- Situation appraisal.
- Problem analysis.
- Brainstorming.

Agreement about the data required can be obtained by using checklists, by seeking consensus, by using agreed decision-making procedures, which may involve balloting, or may be done on the basis of individual expertise.

The collection of data may involve:

- Surveys.
- Activity analysis.
- Process analysis.
- Sampling.

and the data collected may be collated and presented using:

- Tallysheets.
- Scatter diagrams.
- Charts/graphs.
- Flowcharts.
- Tables.

Stage 3: Analysing the problem

Once the data has been gathered, the potential causes of the problem can be identified. Analyses can then be performed to confirm which of these potential causes are actual (rather than illusory) causes. These analyses may show that there is a need for further data (because ambiguity remains about some of the possible causes) and it may be necessary to return to the previous stage. Once the probable causes have been found, the major factor(s) contributing to the problem can be selected, and tests performed to confirm that these are the root causes.

Problem analysis consists of:

- Identifying possible problem causes.
- Selecting the most probable causes.
- Selecting the most important causes.
- Identifying root causes by testing of probable and most important causes.

The output from these initial stages of the problem solving process should be a statement of the problem and of the root cause(s) of that problem.

A variety of techniques are available for assisting the process of problem analysis, such as:

- Pareto analysis.
- Cause and effect analysis.
- Controlled comparisons.
- Switch on/switch off analysis.

Distinctive feature analysis

One useful technique is to attempt to specify the distinctive features of the problem. Distinctive feature analysis attempts to specify what it is that distinguishes the problem from what it *is not*. These are the distinctive features of the problem.

The technique is useful because human problem solvers suffer from what is known as a *confirmatory bias*. That is, they are interested in the features that a given problem does possess, and tend to ignore those that it does not. The problem is that many of the features of a problem are essentially uninteresting, at least with respect to identifying potential causes, whilst many of the features that the problem does not have are extremely informative, if only because they allow us to eliminate some potential causes from consideration. Distinctive feature analysis attempts to overcome this confirmatory bias by directing attention to asking 'what the problem is not' (see Figure 8.19).

Step I: Draw distinctions

What is it that distinguishes what the problem *is* from what it *is not*? These are the distinctive features of the problem.

The identification of the distinctive features of a problem can be assisted

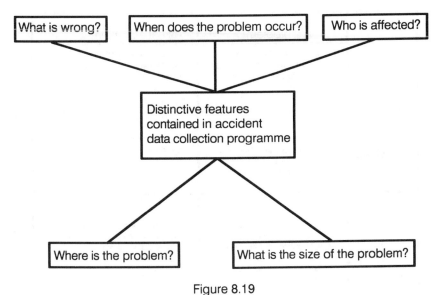

Figure 8.19

Distinctive feature analysis

by using a set of 'specification questions'. These provide a comprehensive and systematic scheme for the analysis of the problem:

1. *What* is wrong (what is the discrepancy)?
2. *What* is/are the object(s), processes, people affected?
3. *Where* is the discrepancy?
4. *When* in the lifecycle of the object/process does the discrepancy appear?
5. *How* big is the discrepancy? Is it continuing or stopping, static or increasing?

These specification questions should be applied to the identification of *both* the problem and the non-problem (see Figure 8.20).

Step 2: Identify possible causes

The cause of a problem is always a difference between the problem and what the problem is not, or a change that has taken place in some feature, mechanism or condition to produce undesirable effects.

The possible causes of the problem can be deduced from the relevant differences or changes found when analysing the problem in Step 1. How could this difference or change cause the problem? Alternatively, how could this difference or change plus another distinguishing feature cause the problem?

	Is a problem	Is not a problem
What	What is wrong? What is not as I expected it to be? Who is not as they should be? What is the complaint?	What is the closest thing to the problem which is not affected? What is OK?
Where	Where is it in the works? Where is it in the Department? Where is it found or discovered? Where does it happen?	Are there any similar places where this does not happen?
When	When did it happen (clock or calendar time?) When did it start? How long did it last? Has the identical situation arisen before? How long did it last then?	When was the situation OK? Were there times since the situation arose that we did not have it?
Size/Extent	How many (or how much) are affected? Has it been increasing or decreasing in size or number?	How many are OK? How much should it normally happen?

Figure 8.20 The problem identification sequence

Step 3: Test possible causes critically against the specification of the problem

The most likely cause of the deviation is one that exactly explains *all* the facts in the specification of the problem, that is, both the is and the is not. Thus, you should eliminate as possible causes those causes which, whilst producing the effects you have observed, would also have produced additional effects which you have identified as *not* occurring.

A set of test questions can be used to assist the process of identifying probable causes (see Figure 8.21).

Step 4: Verify possible cause(s)

This is normally an additional stage in which explicit procedures are followed in order to ensure that the possible cause(s) is in fact the real cause of the problem.

This normally involves some specification of what evidence and what

The organisation:
Are current safety policies adequate? Are safety procedures up to date? Is safety practice meeting needs? Are safety programmes effective?
The individual:
Does he receive appropriate safety training? Does he receive safety training regularly? Is he adequately protected? Is he sufficiently informed?
The equipment:
Is it regularly checked? Is maintenance regular? Are safety features adequate?
The environment:
Is the work area well lit? Is the work area properly ventilated/heated? Is the work area free from litter?

Figure 8.21

A sample of some typical test questions

procedures would be necessary in order to provide such verification. It is important at this stage to recognise and make explicit the assumptions that have been made when identifying the likely cause, and to test these assumptions.

The most important idea to get across during the presentation of this stage of the overall problem-solving procedure is the importance of examining the 'not' aspects of the problem. The importance of these aspects is demonstrated by both psychological and philosophical studies of problem solving. Most human problem solvers have a confirmatory bias, and this analysis is designed to counteract this bias.

Safety problem solving: creativity

In solving safety problems, it is important first, to establish criteria and generate solutions. The next stages in the problem solving model concern the generation of possible solutions and the development of criteria for evaluating those solutions.

Solution criteria must be generated because they will be used to select one of the possible solutions from the many possible solutions that can be generated. Criteria are often divided into categories, such as 'must haves' and 'would like'. A number of different procedures are available for developing a set of criteria, and for applying those criteria. These include brainstorming and cause and effect analysis, and they can be implemented using rating sheets and informal decision analysis.

The exact timing of the stage during which criteria are specified is optional. It can be seen as following on from the problem analysis stage, and preceding the solution generation stage, or it can be seen as following on from the solution generation stage, and preceding the solution selection stage. The model used by schemes such as BS 5475 Total Quality Management (TQM) programme uses the former, but in practice the process of specifying criteria and the process of selecting the solution are often integrated, and that is the approach that has been taken here.

Generating solutions: an introduction to the role of creativity

One of the major difficulties faced by problem solvers is that they are too solution oriented. That is, the predicaments and pressures created by the problem mean that as soon as a solution has been found, there is enormous pressure to put it into practice as soon as possible. This means that solutions may be adopted which, although they work, do not work as well as an alternative solution that was simply never considered, or even generated. It was not considered because the perceived pressure to get a solution meant that time to consider alternative ideas was seen as an expensive luxury.

One of the fundamental propositions about problem solving is that the greater the number of possible solutions generated (and considered), the better the eventual solution is likely to be. Thus, if we are going to improve our problem solving ability, one area to work on is our ability to produce a large number, and a large range, of solutions. The most fundamental way of doing this is simply to recognise that we need to do so, and to allow ourselves the time to do so.

However, even given this recognition, we will be aware that some people seem to be better able to generate a range of different, and novel, solutions than others. Commonly, we refer to these people as creative, and we refer to their ability as creativity. It is the case, however, that although we ourselves may not be amazingly creative, we all have some creative ability. Perhaps the most important question which then follows is whether or not it is possible to improve the ability we do have.

What is creativity? There are a number of analyses of what is meant by the term creativity. Although no single scheme of analysis is accepted as definitive, there is enough commonality between the various schemes to enable a consensus view to emerge.

It is important to distinguish early in our analysis between three different aspects of creativity. They are:

1. *Creativity* as a characteristic of a product;
2. *Creativity* as a characteristic of a person; and
3. *Creativity* as a characteristic of a process.

Let us look in more detail at each of these aspects of creativity.

Creativity as a product

Four features seem to characterise products which are referred to as creative.

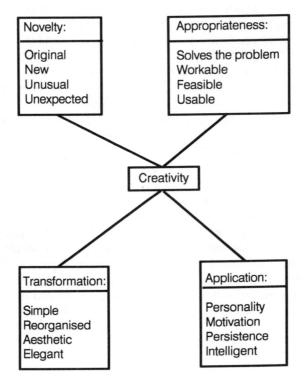

Figure 8.22

Some characteristics of creativity

1. Novelty

Perhaps the most obvious characteristic of the creative idea or product is that it is novel. Items which are creative generally demonstrate originality. They are unusual, unexpected and novel.

However, ideas can be original, but they are not therefore automatically creative. They may just be trivial. They must therefore have additional characteristics.

2. Appropriateness

In order to be truly creative, an idea or product also has to be appropriate. Put most simply, it must work, i.e. it must provide a viable solution to a problem. The history of man-powered flight, for instance, is full of wonderfully original solutions to the problem, the majority of which were completely inappropriate. One of the problems for the creative person is that their wholly appropriate idea may not be recognised as such by their contemporaries and peers. In a recent aid project to a developing country in Africa designed to reduce industrial accidents leading to amputation, a highly sophisticated computer system designed to log accident details was installed without proper training and without convincing the staff involved of its relevance. A more *appropriate* low-tech solution would have been to invest the money on machine guards and remote sensor switches which only allowed the machine to work when the guard was in place.

A second problem is that the appropriateness of the highly original idea may not be recognised for a considerable time. In a sense, they are solutions waiting to happen. Teflon is an example of this. The material and the process by which it can be produced was discovered, by accident, in the 1930s. The chemist concerned was creative in that he recognised that this was an appropriate solution; his problem was that he could not find a suitable problem. Not until some 30 years later, with the advent of the space programme, was a use found for the material, and then, as a spin-off from that programme, its most common use, as a coating for saucepans. A more recent example is the discovery of a form of rubber which has the ability to absorb enormous quantities of water without changing its own volume. Despite considerable effort by the company which developed this material, no appropriate use could be found for it. That is, until disposable ultra-nappies....!

3. Transformation

A third quality of the creative idea is that it involves a transformation. The use of the original materials or concepts are transformed. They are simplified, elaborated, combined, condensed or in some other way reorganised. There is a qualitative element here; the value of the transformation is generally a judgment of aptness, simplicity, and of feasibility. This applies as much to the design for a product, such as a new piece of furniture or household equipment (the Anglepoise lamp was originally designed as a way of absorbing the over-production of seating springs) or a new scientific concept or mathematical theorem.

4. Application

It is a common observation that 'genius is 1% inspiration and 99% perspiration'. More scientifically, it has been demonstrated that whilst creative people generally possess the above cognitive abilities, not all people who possess such abilities are recognised as creative. The fourth dimension appears to be a personality or motivational characteristic, and might best be described as persistence. The initial idea has to be elaborated, prototyped, tested, modified, produced, marketed, etc. The difference between 'bright ideas' and 'creative products' amounts to hard work.

Creativity as a person

The preceding analysis has concentrated on the characteristics of creative products and ideas. Other analyses have focused on the characteristics of creative people. In particular, they have tried to identify the cognitive abilities that underlie creative thinking. Four factors seem to have been identified which together constitute creative thinking (see Figure 8.23).

I. Fluency

Fluency of thinking is the ease with which we can use stored information. It is often equated with productivity, and is reflected in the amount of material that a person can produce, e.g. knowledge of risk in a process.

2. Flexibility

Flexibility, or freedom from rigidity, is a measure of the variation in the material that a person produces. The more flexible a person is, the more distinctly different ideas they will produce to solve a safety problem.

3. Originality

Originality is closely related to flexibility, and describes the absolute variation in the material produced. That is, the less frequently the item appears in the material produced by all of the people generating ideas, the more original it is. The extreme instance of this is when the idea is unique, and no one else has produced that idea, e.g. introducing a shut-off valve.

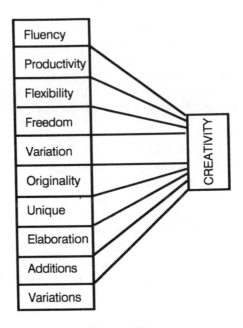

Figure 8.23

Creativity as a person

4. Elaboration

The ability to elaborate is the ability to create a large number of additions and variations around the basic material, e.g. developing a safety audit.

Creativity as a process

The final analysis of creativity has attempted to understand the process of thinking which characterises creativity. Three stages have commonly been identified.

1. Familiarisation

Most creative ideas do not appear easily. They are preceded by a lengthy period of effort in which the investigator thoroughly immerses themselves in every aspect of the problem. It normally involves a lengthy period in which possible, but unsuccessful solutions are produced and tested, and in the process of testing, further unsuspected aspects of the problem are re vealed. This period can be time-consuming, exhausting, and demoralising.

2. Incubation

A common characteristic of creative ideas is that they have been produced after the problem has been abandoned as insoluble, or where it has been placed on one side because of exhaustion or disillusion. The process underlying this is that the human brain operates at a variety of different levels, and even though we may not be consciously aware of it, processing of ideas and information can continue. This is what is known as the period of incubation. It appears to be necessary because, when solutions cannot be generated by well-tried, rational routines (algorithms) we are forced to rely on other approaches to problem solving, and our sub-conscious minds are sometimes able to operate in ways which are rather different to the ways we have trained our conscious minds to follow.

3. Inspiration or synthesis

As a result of the period of incubation, we are often presented with a *brain-wave*. This is the *eureka* phenomenon. The different elements of the problem have been put together in a particular way by our sub-conscious minds, and when a successful solution or resolution has been achieved, this is recognised by our conscious minds in the event we know as insight, and which is often associated with a massive release of emotional energy (elation), e.g. ways of avoiding handling toxic chemicals.

This analysis identifies three of the important stages in the creative process, but it omits an important fourth stage, that of application. This is the 99% perspiration that is a feature of the successful exploitation of original ideas.

Blocks to creativity

Two of the most common observations about creativity are that: 'children are naturally creative' and that 'genius and madness are closely linked'. As we have seen, consideration of our definition and discussion of creativity shows that neither of these statements is in fact correct, but both of them contain a kernel of truth. That kernel concerns the notion of inhibitions. One of the things that children and the mentally ill make us aware of is that our own lives are full of rules, of boundaries, and of taboos which constrain our behaviour. By breaking these rules, children and the mentally ill make us aware that they are there. These rules make it possible for an ordered society to exist and to function efficiently, but they also constrain our behaviour. They constrain what we do, what we say, and what we think. They therefore constrain our ability to think creatively. James Adams, in his text *Conceptual Blockbusting*, provides an excellent description of the blocks to creativity which most of us experience. He identifies four categories of conceptual blocks:

1. Perceptual blocks;
2. Emotional blocks;
3. Cultural and environmental blocks; and
4. Intellectual and expressive blocks.

Perceptual blocks

Stereotyping

Seeing what you expect to see, and not being able to see what you don't expect. Similar perceptual problems constrain our ability to think creatively about problems: often the key to the solution lies in seeing the problem in another, unfamiliar way.

Example

Psychologists have shown that most of us are *conservative* when it comes to making management decisions in that we prefer the *status quo* and under pressure we will revert to standard solutions that we feel are tried and trusted e.g. 'we have always had a centrally positioned fire response team in this refinery and we have never had any problems ... we can get to anywhere in no more than 10 minutes!' One has to question on what assumptions that continuing policy is based. The refinery has grown, and high risk activities such as column rectification of flammable liquids are ten minutes drive from the central fire point. If the objective is to be able to control a fire as quickly as possible, then the right solution is to have some form of central coordination with fire fighting facilities at a local level to give a quick response. The objective of damage control and limitation was obscured through this stereotyped 'solution' which cost a Texan refinery $32 million through a disastrous fire.

The wide-angle lens problem

Difficulty in isolating the problem. When faced with complex problems, it is often difficult to isolate the key features. This is made more arduous because in many real life problems, many of the key features are interrelated, and so it is difficult to understand how each aspect of the problem is related to any of the others.

Example

Complex technological disasters are good, if rather frightening, examples of this problem. Post mortems which have been conducted on accidents at nuclear power plants such as Three Mile Island and Chernobyl show that their operators simply did not understand what was happening once these plants had deviated from their normal operating parameters, and did not understand what the effect would be of the actions they were taking in an attempt to regain control of the situation. In the majority of these cases the operators were simply overwhelmed with the quantity of information that they were receiving.

The telephoto lens problem

This is the opposite problem. It is the tendency to delimit the problem too tightly.

Inability to see the problem from various points of view

With many human problems, much of the agony comes from the fact that other people do not see things, such as our actions, in the same way that we do.

Example
You install additional safety guards with automatic shut-offs on a industrial milling machine. Your objective is to reduce accident risk for workers. This additional safeguard slows production rates down by 5%. The workforce are resentful and perceive the new guards not as a safety measure, but as a way for management to reduce piece rate bonuses.

Habituation

Many aspects of a problem are difficult to see because they are so familiar. Human sensory systems might best be described as systems designed to exclude information. The vast majority of the sensory input which we receive is not consciously perceived. Our sensory system *filters out* much of the information we receive as of little or no interest, and it does this very often precisely because the feature is a common, constant one.

Example
Temperature sensors and associated warning sirens in a machine shop are triggered on a fairly regular basis when a blast of hot air is produced by a metal casting operation in an adjacent workshop. Thus both the workforce and safety staff are *habituated* into discounting the sirens as just another false alarm. Until one day there is a major fire in the machine shop and time is wasted before evacuating the workforce and deploying a fire crew. We tend to ignore new information as long as possible unless we take deliberate steps to look out for risks. Habituation can lead to serious errors

until it is either too late or costly to rectify the problem. In the Chernobyl disaster warning signals were discounted for two hours.

Emotional blocks

One of the major problems in the area of creativity is that it is closely connected with notions of being trivial, of being wasteful, or of simply being an indecisive manager.

We live in a goal oriented, 'achievement' culture, where such behaviour is not admired or approved of. There are a number of emotional blocks which can be identified:

- The fear of making a mistake, of failing, of taking risks.
- The inability to tolerate ambiguity, disorder, uncertainty.
- The desire for security, for order; for control. (James Adams refers to our lack of an 'appetite for chaos'.)
- The inability to relax, to incubate, and to 'sleep on it'.

Example
A large water authority invested £500,000 in fencing off filter tanks that were inspected once a year. A cheaper solution was to have an inspector and an observer who could coordinate a rescue in the unlikely event that it was needed. When asked, the safety manager bluffed that is was a legal requirement. Do not be panicked into finding a 'quick fix' to a problem. Instant solutions rarely answer a complex question. You will lose much more face if the solution is a failure! Be prepared to admit that you have 'got it wrong' quickly. Don't continue to invest time and effort in failed solutions because of personal pride or worries about how you will be perceived. Don't promise safety solutions that you cannot deliver! Don't be forced into unrealistic time scales to solve a problem! Good problem-solving requires time to debug and reflect on the aptness of a solution.

Inappropriate motivation

Creativity demands that we are neither over-committed (a situation of stress, which tends to throw us back to old, familiar ways of behaving), nor that we are under-committed, so that we are simply not involved. Balancing this problem of a lack of challenge (because the problem fails to arouse our interest) versus excessive zeal (producing a desire to succeed quickly, and at all costs).

Example
Balancing between 'instant answers' and 'procrastination' is problematic; one solution is to identify an isolated period of time when you can ignore

the short-term, but urgent problems and concentrate on long-term important answers. Even at the height of the War, Churchill was able to create 'oases of calm' when strategy could be formulated and 'the really big decisions' could be made.

Judgmental bias

Perhaps all of these pressures are summarised in our preference for judging ideas rather than for generating them. The position of judging seems to be more powerful, and to have more status than being the provider of solutions. In some sense, we see the judge as the superior, whilst we see the originator as inferior.

Example

Most firms with less than 500 employees do not have a specialist safety officer, only a member of general management with a safety responsibility.

Cultural and environmental blocks:

Cultural blocks can best be described as a series of propositions, which are easily recognised once they have been stated:

- *Fantasy is escapism:* It is a waste of time, it suggests laziness, and may even suggest that you are a little bit crazy.
- *Playfulness is for children only:* Adults do not play, and if they do, they do so seriously, with rules, with the right equipment, and to win.
- *Problem solving is a serious business:* A serious problem is no place to fool around, and humour is definitely out of place.
- *Reason, logic, numbers, utility, practicality* are 'worthwhile', they are good. Feeling, intuition, qualitative judgments, pleasure are 'indulgences', and are bad.

Perhaps the most important environment for people is that of other people. Sartre noted that 'hell is other people', and in terms of blocks to behaviour, other people are probably the most powerful of all blocks.

Some of the blocks to creativity, which can operate in a variety of ways, are the following:

- Lack of co-operation and trust amongst colleagues.
- Autocratic management who value only their own ideas.
- Non-rewarding managerial culture, which punishes mistakes and ignores successes (and which does not give permission to occasionally fail).
- Lack of support to bring ideas into action.

Some blocks to creativity can simply be our physical environment. For instance, most working environments are a babble of noise and a constant succession of distractions: the telephone, coffee breaks, other tasks, gossip, etc.

Intellectual and expressive blocks

One of the problems with most of our education system is that it does not teach people to think. Rather, it teaches them about things, such as geography, or history, or English, and hopes that the thinking processes that underlie these abilities will somehow 'rub off'. Now clearly, if we are to learn how to use a set of tools, such as woodworking tools, or cookery equipment, it is useful to have the opportunity to use them to make something. But it is also the case that we normally start teaching such subjects by explaining how the tools work, and how they should properly and most usefully be used. We apply this principle to almost all areas of activity except thinking. The result is that we have problems in selecting and properly using thinking tools. We have difficulty because we have only learnt about the tools available by trial and error, if at all. We are an unusual person if we are able to articulate what the tools are, how they work, the principles that should govern their selection and use, their advantages and disadvantages, and so on.

The problem of trying to solve a problem using an inappropriate conceptual system (verbal, visual and mathematical)

The viability of particular kinds of conceptual tools, because we have been taught them, and the unavailability of others, because we have not been taught them, or have not practised them, is a considerable block to our ability to think creatively. We also have personal preferences for particular cognitive styles; some of us are verbalisers, some are mathematical, others are visualisers. And our culture teaches us that certain kinds of thinking strategies are more valued than others, for instance, the ability to use words effectively. The problem with each of these pressures is that they can lead us to try to solve a problem using an inappropriate conceptual system.

The problem of being inflexible, or of using inadequate intellectual problem-solving strategies

One of the greatest problems we face is that of being successful some of the time. The problem when we are successful some of the time is that it encourages us to use the strategy that was previously successful next time we meet an apparently similar problem. In most cases this is an extremely sensible strategy (a version of the 'win-stick, lose-change' principle of learning). The problem is when we persist in the use of an unsuccessful strategy when it should have been abandoned some time ago.

Examples of this abound, often at the level of whole cultures: perhaps the battles of the First World War are the most horrendous example of the pursuit of an unsuccessful strategy regardless of the evidence of its futility. They also illustrate the principle of 'too much invested to quit', which paradoxically locks us into a strategy which we ourselves may recognise as unsuccessful.

The problem of inadequate language skill to express and record ideas (where the language may be verbal, visual, mathematical, programming, etc.)

If we return to our analysis of creativity with which we started, we can see that creativity is in essence a social activity. The creative idea must (normally) be related to the outside world, either the objective world or the world of other people. This means that once you have had the idea, you need to be able to encode it in a way that other people can understand and appreciate. If you cannot do this, your creativity essentially will count for nothing.

Devices for increasing creativity

The problem with many of the blocks described above is that they are deeply ingrained within us. It is simply not good enough to point these blocks out to people and demand that they overcome them.

It is possible to change our habits, but we have to recognise that this is difficult, that we will need help, and that, initially at least, we may feel awkward and self-conscious. A number of techniques have been developed which are of assistance to us if, for a specific reason, we wish to increase our creativity when tackling a specific problem. The three techniques we will describe and practise here are known to be effective. They are also interesting because they are not odd. In fact, it may be difficult to accept that they are aids to creativity precisely because they appear to be highly simplistic and mechanistic. In a sense, they deny the notion that in order to be creative you must be unstructured, and therefore they challenge our common sense notions of what creativity is. However, they are extremely useful and effective precisely because they are simplistic and mechanistic.

Forced connections

One aspect of creativity is that it often involves the use of a familiar item in a novel way, or the modification of one aspect of an item to produce an improvement (which can be quite radical, and may in effect constitute a new item). Creativity of this kind might be described as evolutionary rather than revolutionary. It is, nonetheless, extremely valuable.

Evolutionary creativity can be assisted by the use of attribute listing. Attribute listing involves the production of a list of characteristics which together constitute a complete description of an item. For instance, the attributes of a Biro might be: cylindrical, plastic, hard, tube, ink and cap, e.g. its tubular qualities have seen it used for emergency tracheotomy.

A number of useful creativity techniques use the principle of listing and then modifying attributes to produce new ideas. Koberg and Bagnall, in their text *The Universal Traveller*, describe such a technique, which we will call 'forced connections'. The technique consists of the following procedure:

1. List the attributes of the item;
2. For each attribute, list as many alternatives as you can think of;
3. When you have done this for each attribute, run through the list of attributes, selecting a new value for each attribute at random. Each set of attributes-values becomes a possible new item. (This stage can be assisted by using a table of random numbers, a computer program, or wine glasses and bits of paper); and
4. Examine the list of new attributes-values for any items which seem promising, and are worth exploring further.

Evaluation of the set

Clearly, there is a high level of nonsense when using this technique because the majority of items (ie combinations of attributes) produced by the technique are going to be inappropriate (and maybe impractical or impossible). However, it is worthwhile because of the occasional appropriate and practical innovation which it can generate.

In addition to structuring the search for innovations, the technique also helps to overcome blocks at the perceptual and emotional levels. Because we are dealing with the attributes of the item, rather than the item itself, we are able to explore changes which we would find impossible to contemplate if we were dealing with the object itself. It does face its own blocks however, and those are our fear of waste, and our notion that creativity should be unaided.

Checklists

The recognition that creativity is not necessarily a magical quality of thinking, but is the result of the understandable and quite routine application of particular kinds of thinking has led to the development of a number of checklist approaches to aiding creativity. One such checklist was first proposed by Alex Osborn in his book *Applied Imagination*.

The checklist he proposed is as follows:

Checklist for new ideas

Put to other uses?
  New ways to use as is?
  Other uses if modified?

Adapt?
  What else is like this?
  What other idea does this suggest?
  Does the past offer a parallel?
  What could I copy?
  Whom could I emulate?

Modify?
  New twist?
  Change meaning, colour, motion, sound, odour, form, shape?
  Other changes?

Magnify?
  What to add?
  More time?
  Greater frequency?
  Stronger?
  Higher?
  Longer?
  Thicker?
  Extra value?
  Plus ingredient?
  Duplicate?
  Multiply?
  Exaggerate?

Minify?
  What to subtract?
  Smaller?
  Condensed?
  Miniature?
  Lower?
  Shorter?
  Lighter?
  Omit?
  Streamline?
  Split up?
  Understate?

Substitute?

Who else instead?
What else instead?
Other ingredient?
Other material?
Other process?
Other power?
Other place?
Other approach?
Other tone of voice?

Rearrange?

Interchange components?
Other pattern?
Other layout?
Other sequence?
Transpose cause and effect?
Change pace?
Change schedule?

Reverse?

Transpose positive and negative?
How about opposites?
Turn it backwards?
Turn it upside down?
Reverse roles?
Change shoes?
Turn tables?
Turn other cheek?

Combine?

How about a blend, an alloy, an assortment, an ensemble?
Combine units?
Combine purposes?
Combine appeals?
Combine ideas?

The checklist is used in quite a simple and routine manner. When faced with a problem, each question is asked in turn, and the possibilities suggested by that question are explored and noted. So, for instance, imagine that you work for a company producing cardboard boxes, and you have been asked to come up with ideas for new product lines. With the basic notion of *container* as the starting point, we start asking questions from the checklist. (Only a few questions that prompt interesting answers have been left in, many other ideas could have been generated in this way.)

Put to other uses?
New ways to use as is? (e.g. as an insulating material?, shred it?, corrugated layers?).

Adapt?
Does the past offer a parallel? (e.g. reproductions of old boxes).

Modify?
Change meaning, colour, motion, sound, odour, form, shape? (e.g. does cardboard box have to be brown?).

Magnify?
Stronger? (e.g. could we produce a range of reinforced boxes for some items?).

Minify?
Lighter? (e.g. is there a market for light boxes for airmail?).

and so on.

The list provided by Osborn can be extended by using 'manipulative verbs', that is, verbs which suggest ways of modifying the product:

- Multiply
- Divide
- Eliminate
- Subdue
- Invert
- Separate
- Transpose
- Unify
- Distort
- Rotate
- Flatten

and so on.

Clearly, the English language contains a vast number of such verbs, and exploring the possibilities suggested by each of them provides an enormous resource for creativity.

The ultimate checklist is in fact a dictionary. Ideas can be provoked simply by selecting words at random from the dictionary, and seeing whether, in conjunction with the problem, they spark any ideas for new or modified products. The dictionary technique creates a new checklist every time you use it, and also exploits the principle of forced connections.

Again note that there are two emotional reactions which tend to act as blocks to our use of the dictionary technique. One of them is that this is silly. It's not how intelligent people are supposed to try to solve problems (and the feeling that it is a form of cheating—note the instruction to copy contained in Osborn's list). The second is that it's a waste of time. You acknowledge before starting that most of the possible solutions generated will have to be abandoned. Clearly, there are emotional blocks to be overcome even when using these simplistic and mechanistic aids to creativity.

There are two major stages to finding 'good' safety solution. The first is to generate a large number of possible alternatives, which is why *creativity* is so important. The second is about how one evaluates these alternatives and makes a decision as to which one is the best!

Decision making

One of the most important rules for good decision making is that a decision should not be made until a number of alternative solutions have been generated. As we have argued above, the extension to this rule is that the more possible solutions there are to consider, the greater is the chance that one of them will be right. The converse of this is that possible solutions should not be rejected prematurely, that is, they should only be rejected as part of the formal process of evaluating alternatives.

If possible solutions are to be evaluated, it follows that criteria should be established against which evaluations can be made. Once these criteria have been established, it is possible to use a variety of methods to assess each possible solution and to then select the most attractive solution.

As noted earlier, the point in the problem-solving process at which criteria are specified is optional. It can precede the solution generation stage, and this is recommended in some models of problem solving. It can also precede, or form part of, the solution selection (or decision-making stage). It is this approach which will be used here.

At this point, it should be acknowledged that one of the problems with good decision making is deciding how to decide. It is possible to employ very sophisticated, and very expensive decision support systems to make a decision. Clearly, these are only appropriate if the decision being made is itself very sophisticated and expensive. It is also possible to use very simple and inexpensive decision support systems ('toss a coin') to make decisions. Again, it is fairly obvious that such techniques are only appropriate if the decision involved is simple and unimportant. In this regard we are not really concerned with either of these extremes. We are concerned with improving personal effectiveness, and as such are concerned here with those decisions which the safety manager is typically called upon to make on a day-by-day basis, and often with relatively short time scales. The problem with many of these decisions is that they are taken too lightly, and using decision making techniques at the 'tossing a coin' end of the spectrum of decision support systems. This may be because the importance of the decision is not realised. A typical example of such decisions is that taken in recruitment interviews. A fairly simple calculation shows that the decision to recruit, or not to recruit an entry level manager involves financial commitments of the order of £1 million in direct and indirect salary and support costs over the course of that person's career. And this does not include the financial consequences of the decisions that person is then going to make during their career. And yet, typically, such decisions are made in a very haphazard way, and without any awareness of the scale of the decision being made. Another reason that an appropriately structured and systematic decision making system is not employed is that the effort involved in mastering the complexities of the system do not seem to be justified, or even possible, in the circumstances. If we are to improve personal decision making we are therefore looking for a set of guidelines which are simple enough to remember and to use, even for ordinary decisions being taken in everyday conditions.

Informal decision analysis

Informal decision analysis suggests that each decision can be made in terms of a series of smaller decisions. These smaller decisions are the various outcomes that will follow from making the decision or implementing the proposed solution. For instance, outcomes are often closely related to the criteria that have previously been established for evaluating the decision. In the example given in Figure 8.24, the outcomes correspond to the following criteria: cost, practicality and effectiveness.

Informal decision analysis suggests that for each solution, for each of the component outcomes, three elements have to be determined:

1. The importance of that outcome/criterion;
2. The value of that outcome with respect to that criterion (i.e. how well does the outcome meet that criterion); and
3. The likelihood that that outcome can be achieved.

The significance of each component is determined by the product of these three elements, i.e. how good or bad an outcome is dependent on how important it is relative to other criteria, how well it meets those criteria, and what the chances are that it will be as expected.

Recent research on human decision making shows that managers are reasonably good at estimating the importance and value of outcomes, but are frequently not very good at estimating this last factor, that of the probability of that outcome being achieved. This is at least in part due to a tendency to over-estimate the likelihood of good outcomes occurring, and under-estimating the likelihood of bad outcomes occurring.

Managers also have difficulties in the case of complex decisions, and decisions made in stressful circumstances, because of the problem of

Informal Decision Analysis

The Problem: To reduce the number of accidents being experienced by the staff of a large road hauliers in the loading bays of their distribution depots nationally.

Alternative Solutions taken separately from the "Safety Mix"

Engineering: the introduction of mechanical lifting gear, and electric tail gates
on all transport vehicles over 2 tons.
Education: issue leaflets on how to lift properly, awareness campaign of the
need to wear appropriate protective footwear, safety officer visits.
Environment: construction of concrete ramps and incline steps in loading bays,
installation of air conditioning at access points, improved lighting.
Enforcement: Revision of company safety policy and disciplinary codes, penalties
for staff who have persistent record of absences from back problems

Score = Criterion evaluation x Weighting x Certainty

Criteria for Evaluation (rated from 0 poor to 10 excellent)

£50,000   £500,000   £5,000,000

Cost
(Weighting 3)   0   1   2   3   4   5   6   7   8   9   10
(Certainty 9)   Poor   Excellent

Unrealistic   Possible   Reasonable   Easy

Practicality
(Weighting 2)   0   1   2   3   4   5   6   7   8   9   10
(Certainty 6)   Poor   Excellent

No impact   Some effect   Desired outcome

Effectiveness
(Weighting 4)   0   1   2   3   4   5   6   7   8   9   10
(Certainty 5)   Poor   Excellent

Decision "Pay-off" Matrix

Solution / Criteria	Engineering	Education	Environment	Enforcement
Cost	4x3x9=108	8x3x9=216	6x3x9=162	9x3x9=243
Practicality	7x2x6=84	6x2x6=72	5x2x6=60	4x2x6=48
Effectiveness	8x4x5=160	7x4x5=140	6x4x5=120	3x4x5=60
TOTAL	352	428	342	351

On the basis of the alternative solutions and the relative judgments made on the three criteria employed, the best solution appears to be the Education strategy.

Figure 8.24   Informal Decision Analysis

combining the various components, and in comparing the overall value of one solution with that offered by other solutions (particularly when the alternatives do not differ by a large amount).

Informal decision analysis attempts to help managers improve their decision making by systematising the process of establishing the importance of different criteria, of determining the value of different outcomes, and of estimating their probability of occurrence. It also provides assistance by systematising the process of combining the various components, and of comparing the available solutions.

The logic underlying informal decision analysis is quite simple. It proposes that if a particular outcome is good to a certain degree, or bad to a certain degree, then greater weight should be given to those particular outcomes that are seen to be more important, and less weight should be given to those particular outcomes where there is a high degree of uncertainty.

Informal decision analysis begins by requiring that a list of these outcomes, or criteria is established.

Step 1. List the criteria or outcomes.

Step 2. Assign an importance rating to each of the criteria.

All ratings can be done on a 0-10 scale, where 0 represents the lowest rating and 10 the highest (e.g. 10 represents 'must have').

Because informal decision analysis involves a mathematical procedure, it is important that all criteria and outcomes are stated in the same direction, for example, that they are all stated as either positive criteria/outcomes or all are stated as negative criteria/outcomes. It is normal, and easiest, if they are stated as positive criteria/outcomes. This will sometimes involve reformulating the initial statement of the criteria/outcome. For instance, in the above example, the final criterion was initially stated in a positive form.

If we assign importance ratings to each of these criteria they might come out like this:

Step 3. Assign an evaluation rating to each component for each solution. All ratings can be done on a 0–10 scale, where 0 represents the lowest rating and 10 the highest (e.g. 0 represents 'the worst solution imaginable; does not meet this criterion at all', whereas 10 represents 'the best possible solution imaginable, meets the criterion in every respect').

Step 4. Assign a confidence rating to each outcome for each solution. For each of the outcomes that have been identified, the confidence with which each outcome can be predicted should be determined. All ratings can be done on a 0–10 scale, where 0 represents the lowest rating (no confidence that this will occur, i.e. complete confidence that it will not) through to 10 as the highest (10 represents complete confidence that this outcome will come to pass).

Step 5. Multiply and sum criteria scores for each possible solution (importance × evaluation × confidence).

The final stage of the process is to simply multiply out the three ratings for each criterion, and to add up the result for each possible solution. The most attractive solution is then the solution with the largest score.

If we then add up the values obtained, and compare the totals, we see that the comparison of the values achieved by the possibilities indicates when you would be happiest. ,

As noted earlier, the logic underlying informal decision analysis is quite simple. It proposes that if a particular outcome is good to a certain degree, or bad to a certain degree, then greater weight should be given to those particular outcomes which are seen to be more important, and less weight should be given to those outcomes which are uncertain. The procedure then consists of a systematic attempt to identify, evaluate and combine each of these elements.

The example that has been used here has generated a clear-cut, if quite close, result, and the decision-maker may be happy to act on this basis. There are a number of other possible outcomes however.

The first is that the outcome indicated by informal decision analysis is not the one that 'gut feelings' suggest it should be, and therefore it is difficult to accept this as the outcome. This can be one of the most useful outcomes of using the procedure. Such a disparity should cause you to return to your analysis and examine:

1. The criteria included: have any been omitted which your 'gut feeling' is including? Are your ratings of the importance of these criteria honest?;
2. The outcomes predicted; are these accurate?;
3. The confidence ratings given; are these accurate?

(Another possibility is that your arithmetic is inaccurate; it is often worth checking this as a possible explanation.)

Another possible outcome is that you will have a number of solutions/criteria where you are unable to make a decision. You are unable to make a decision because you have identified the criteria as important, but you are unable to assign sufficiently high confidence ratings to the outcomes from any of the possible solutions. If time allows, further elaboration of these solutions should take place until you are able to make a decision. In general, decisions concerning important criteria should be taken in the light of information of which you are confident. A figure of 80–90% confidence should be the minimum that you will accept for these criteria, and as a working guide, your confidence rating should in general be equal to or greater than your importance rating.

An alternative outcome is that there are no possible solutions; none of the solutions considered is sufficiently attractive, or none of them adequately meets your most important criteria. In this case, if you are in a position to defer a decision, you should return to an earlier stage in the problem solving process, and generate further possible solutions.

Informal decision analysis can be carried out using a piece of paper and mental arithmetic. It can be assisted by using a calculator (or your fingers), and if you want to, you can readily create a template on a spreadsheet to assist you with the analysis. The point should be, however, that the system is simple enough to use when making everyday decisions, even if you do not have access to a computer and particular software.

Further reading

Adair, J (1979) *Action Centred Leadership* (Gower Press)

Adams, J (1985) *Risk and Freedom* (Transport Publishing Projects)

Argyris, C (1964) *Integrating the Individual and the Organisation* (Wiley)

Blake, R R and Mouton, J S (1984) *The Managerial Grid* (Gulf Publishing)

Brown, W (1965) *Explorations in Management* (Pelican Books)

Burns, T and Stalker, G M (1966) *The Management Innovation* (Social Science Paperback, Tavistock)

Childs, J (ed) (1973) *Man and Organisations* (Allen and Unwin)

Churchill, W S (1947) *Marlborough: His Life and Times* (Harrap)

Gibb, G A (ed) (1966) *Leadership* (Penguin)

Gouldner, A W (1954) *Patterns of Industrial Bureaucracy* (Routledge and Kegan Paul)

Gouldner, A W (1955) *Wildcat Strike* (Routledge and Kegan Paul)

Koberg, D and Bagnall, J (1974) *The Universal Traveler: A Soft Systems Guide* (Kautmann)

Likert, R (1967) *The Human Organisation, Its Management and Value* (McGraw Hill)

McClelland, D C (1969) *Motivating Economic Achievement* (Collier McMillan)

McGreggor, D H (1987) *The Human Side of Enterprise* (Penguin)

McKenna, F P 'The human factor in driving accidents: an overview of approaches and problems' *Ergonomics* Vol 25(10) 1982, pp 867–877

McKenna, F P (1984) 'Do safety measures work? Comments on risk homeostasis theory' (MCR Applied Psychology Unit, 15 Chaucer Rd, Cambridge)

Maslow, A H (1987) *Motivation and Personality* (Harper and Row)

Montgomery, B L (1958) *Memoirs* (Collins)

Mumford, E (1972) *A Study of Computer Specialists and Job Satisfaction* (Longman)

Osborn, A (1963) *Applied Imagination* (Scribner)

Pugh, D S (ed) (1984) *Organisational Theory* (Penguin Modern Management)

Reddin, W J (1971) 'The 3-D Management Style Theory from *Personnel Management and Organisation Development*' by W L French and D Helriegel (Houghton Mifflin)

Robertson, L S (1983) *Injuries* (Lexington Books)

Sadler, P J (1968), 'Executive Leadership' from *Industrial Society* by D Pym (Pelican)

Wilde, G S (1976), 'The risk compensation theory of accident causation and its practical consequences for accident prevention' Paper presented to the Annual Meeting of the Österreichische Gesellschaft für Unfallchirurgie, Salzburg

Wilde, G S 'The theory of risk homeostasis: implications for safety and health' *Risk Analysis* 1982, pp 209-225 and 249–258

Woodward, J (1981) *Industrial Organisations – Theory and Practice* (Oxford University Press)

9

Communication skills for the safety manager

Introduction

Safety managers, management consultants and academic researchers, and all manner of other pundits have repeatedly stressed the importance of communication to the successful safety manager, and its central role in determining their personal effectiveness as managers. A safety department is an information and decision system and is complementary to that of the organisation as a whole. There have been several descriptions or definitions of communication and in general terms it may be described as:

'The exchange of information and the transmission of meaning – ... the very essence of an ... organisation.' Katz and Kahn (1966)

However, Simon (1958) defined an organisation as:

'The complex pattern of communications and other relations between human beings'

and also said that:

'Communication plays the central role in all administration. Administration is communication.'

Thayer (1961) posed the questions:

'What is the distinctive job of every safety manager, manager or supervisor?
What is the most important thing he has to do?'

None of the obvious answers gets to the heart of the safety manager's job. Nor does the usual breakdown into such activities as planning and assigning safe working procedures and practices, instructing subordinates, reviewing and appraising progress, and establishing and maintaining controls. No matter how varied the activities, or how special some of the skills involved, in the final analysis the job of every executive or supervisor is communication. Essentially, he must get work done through other people and to accomplish this he must communicate effectively with them.

Very simply, management is communication. If a revised safety procedure has to be implemented, everyone affected by it will have to be told about it.

One feature of the quotes cited above is that they are not particularly recent. The awareness that communication is both a core skill and a central problem for the safety manager, is not a new one. Why then does this message have to be repeated, and why is it that so little progress appears to have been made? The problem is that until recently the most common approach to improving safety communication in organisations has been simply to tell people that they should do it better. That is, a didactic approach of simply telling people that 'it is important', that 'they should improve' and that 'they must do it well', does not appear to have led to any noticeable improvement. Why is this?

By and large, it is not because people don't want to improve. Most people don't like being ineffective: being effective is easier and more rewarding than being ineffective. Why are good intentions simply not sufficient? The reason can be understood if we think about what safety communication is, and also, if we think about how we think about safety communication.

Safety communication is too commonplace

Evidence shows that people:

- Underestimate how often and for how long they talk to other people.
- Underestimate the importance of communication to the performance of other tasks.
- Underestimate how important good communication is to our psychological well-being and the achievement of goals.
- Habituate, i.e. show little reaction to repeated exposure to the same message.

Case study 9.1

In Iwasaquango Ltd the organisation gave each new worker a booklet which outlined safety policy and practice. The organisation was satisfied that as each member of the workforce had such a booklet the entire workforce was aware of its policy in terms of safety. The fact that the booklet had been written by a civil sevant in their particular brand of jargonese (the authors could not understand it either!), printed in very small print and was a third generation copy contributed to the fact that nobody seemed to know what was in the booklet when asked. The contents of the booklet had been enlarged and placed on notice boards but they had been there so long that other notices were pinned on top of them.

Safety communication is too massive

In general there is too much communication. Individuals only have a limited capacity for processing communication. If a safety message is to be thorough and be accepted, it has to compete with many other messages in the workplace and at home. Attendance at a safety conference provides pack upon pack of safety materials – too much even for the safety professional to take in all at once. Communication must form the fabric of our daily lives, and there is a problem in knowing where to start: if safety communication is a problem, which particular bit of it is the problem? If we do manage to isolate a particular feature as problematic, and change the way we deal with that problem, won't this have a 'knock-on' effect, throwing up new problems and demanding new solutions in all sorts of other areas?

The tactic of an individual is selectively to attend to certain messages or even certain parts of a message. Consequently, in trying to do something about safety communication, we may feel that we will be faced with enormous personal and/or organisational changes, and the prospect of such change is unnerving. Faced with the unknown, we are inclined to conclude that it is best not even to get started. Like traffic at a busy junction; leave it and it will sort itself out! It is true, a problem left alone can sort itself out, but at what cost? Experience shows that an intervention programme can be cost effective. At the junction, a police officer on point duty may be effective but a set of traffic lights is more cost effective.

Safety communication is too fast

Communication is made up of many small components – words, posters, leaflets, videos, gestures, expressions which tumble out of us, and which tumble over us in a fast-flowing stream.

When we try to look at, and do something about, communication we find that this stream simply flows too quickly for us:

'If only I'd said X'

or

'If only I hadn't said Y'

By the time we realise that something has gone wrong, and even more, by the time we've worked out why it has gone wrong (let alone worked out what to do about it) the moment has long passed, and we can only shrug our shoulders and press on. In order to take control one has to anticipate what is likely to happen: pre-planning prevents pathetically poor perform-ance (some will know this as P^6 theory)!

Case study 9.2

A local authority in the north of England decided that it should mount a publicity campaign for its highway maintenance staff. Leaflets and posters were ordered and the campaign was designed to coincide with the clocks reverting from BST to GMT. All appeared to be working until two weeks before the start of the exercise. The posters had not been ordered. The chief highway engineer thought that the safety department was running the whole programme whilst the safety manager thought that he had been con-sulted for his advice only. As a result the posters arrived too late and the aims of the campaign were not met. This was a classic P^6 exercise!

Safety communication is too intangible and nebulous

Like communication, conversation itself is a rich tapestry of words, ges-tures, facial expressions... often very brief, sometimes quite minimal in terms of physical movement or physical effect. For instance, the variations that exist on the production of the simple word 'safety'.

There is the *safety* signifying disapproval, a *safety* signalling puzzlement or uncertainty, there is the *safety* signifying acknowledgement, and there is the *safety* signifying interest and excitement.

We may know that these are different, and what the difference signifies, but saying precisely how each 'safety' is different is very difficult – it would seem that we can recognise the different effects, but we are unable to specify and describe the cause. It is difficult to change if you cannot say what it is that you should be doing differently, and how you should be doing it.

Often one has to be sensitive to the *denotation* and *connotation* associ-ated with a particular word or image. The denotation is the literal and precise definition of an object or process. The connotation is the context in which a word is used together with its associated meanings and the emotional reactions that it evokes. For example, the young lad working for the gas board would not wear his reflective jacket when working on the road outside his old school in case his mates saw him and thought him a cissy.

Safety communication is a gift

Many of the preceding four problems come together in the way we think about why people are either very good or very bad at communicating about safety.

Some of the typical things that are said are:

'You've either got it or you haven't.'

The implication, therefore, is that it can't be improved, that there is no point in practising, and therefore you might as well stop worrying about it and accept your present communication style as fixed.

'He is a born communicator.'

By implication, therefore, their skills can't be taught or learnt by others.

'Safety communication is an art.'

The unspoken implications here are perhaps the most profound of all. Art carries the implication that questioning the process is dangerous. The image of the artist who questions how he is able to be creative is closely associated with the image of that artist losing his creative ability because he was foolish enough not simply to accept and be satisfied with his creative gift.

Safety communication is not a secret art: it is a highly precise science. The way that we communicate can only be changed by careful planning. Consultants may offer us instant solutions to our problems by handing us the magic spell ... a formulaic prescription which will transform our safety communication. Safety communication is only improved by the application of general principles in an appropriate way in the specific context of the safety manager's workplace.

These beliefs create real barriers to changing the way we communicate, and to improving our personal effectiveness as safety managers.

Case study 9.3

West Midland Industries Ltd employed Dr X to sort out its safety problems. Dr X was employed on a three year contract. He is a positive, articulate and enthusiastic sort of person and in three years had improved the accident record of WMI significantly and saved the firm several hundred thousand pounds. He was referred to by management as an excellent communicator but the workforce referred to him as being 'a flash ***' but a good 'safety man'.

If the way that common sense leads us to think about safety communication can be a barrier to improvement, is there an alternative? There is, and that is a view of safety communication which sees it as a craft rather than as an art, and as a skill that has to be learnt, rather than a gift that we are given.

How has this alternative view come about?

Because, although we accept that you need natural ability and certain personal characteristics to be an effective safety manager, we also accept that ability needs to be directed, and tuned, and built upon. In other words, that skills are involved which have to be learnt, and which aren't inborn or natural. This is particularly true of subordinates whose main responsibility may not be safety communication.

What are safety communication skills? How can an analysis of these skills be of help to us? An illustration of motor skills involved in this process is given in Figure 9.1.

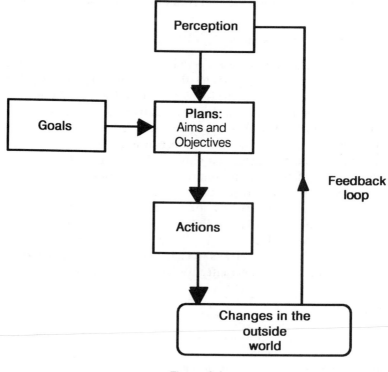

Figure 9.1

Model of motor skills

The following are some examples of safety communication skills:

1. Planning a campaign

That planning a campaign is a skill can be seen in the way that people get faster with practice, that they make fewer mistakes as they become more practised, and that the end product improves. The essence of the skill is in knowing the essential elements of a campaign, and the order in which they can best be assembled.

2. Devising a poster

Examples here are numerous, and again the element of skill can be seen in the way that good performance is dependent on practice. Devising a poster also introduces the idea of timing. That is, posters are about images and message, and to some extent style. It is not enough simply to have the right messages, but they have to be in the right sequence, and positioned, relative to one another, quite precisely in a visual field at the right time.

3. Being an effective safety communicator

The skill of 'getting the message across' illustrates two important characteristics of skills. One of them is that, whilst early in the learning process, the skill of personal communication is one which demands our total attention, and which we deal with with our conscious problem-solving abilities (remember making your first presentation, and the very self-conscious way that you introduced the topic), with practice, even very skilled performances become a background activity operating at a very low level of conscious attention. It also illustrates the way in which the unit of skill becomes larger as the level of skill increases. We no longer worry about the problems of changing an OHP slide, this is done semi-automatically, but we do worry about our audience, about whether they understand us or not. There are two further points that making a safety presentation illustrates. The first is the important role that goals play in skilled behaviour. We do not normally make a presentation unless we have a particular objective, for example reducing hand injuries. In order to achieve this we will make a decision about the best means of communication to employ. Part of the skill is in selecting the best means to reach the goal. The second point is that although the goal may stay constant, we may change our original plans about how best to achieve this. For instance, if we are doing a leaflet campaign and we find from statistics that there has been an increase in the number of accidents, we may decide to use a training video instead.

Our communication behaviour, and our plans, are being updated in the light of feedback, and the ability to identify relevant feedback, and to respond to it appropriately are important aspects of skilled safety communication.

4. Devising a safety communications system

This example illustrates the importance of the repertoire of possible behaviours available to the skilled manager. The 'weak' manager tends to have one or two preferred means of communication. The good 'manager' is strong all round. The good safety manager is likely to be a strong all-round communicator at least in part because they have practised their weaker skills, and have forced themselves to use certain other methods, for instance a poster campaign, when their 'natural inclination' was to resort to their favourite methods of personal briefings.

Safety communication also illustrates the importance of assessing your environment. This is not only the physical environment of safety risks, but also your audience. You will weigh up their strengths and weaknesses, and by and large, you will try to compensate for their weaknesses, and avoid wasting resources consolidating their strengths. In other words, you will formulate tactics as a way of achieving your goal of being an effective safety communicator.

Psychologists have now developed a good understanding of such skills, and have developed explanatory models which describe what is involved in being skilled.

Consider the following example:

- Perception – looking at the number of fire points on a plan before visiting an industrial complex.
- Goals – deciding that you need to install more equipment.
- Plans – deciding to install smoke detectors at every 100 metres.
- Actions – ordering and installation of equipment.
- Feedback – reports from supervisors and further site inspections show equipment has been installed correctly.

Safety communication is like each of these, and it is also like none of them. It is like each of them because it includes them; it is like none of them because it is a combination of all of them, and as such is more complex and more complicated.

It involves:

- Assembling component elements: words and phrases, topics and themes.
- Sequencing actions, and pacing the performance.
- Setting goals and choosing the appropriate means.
- Noting feedback, and modifying plans and actions accordingly.
- Choosing actions from a repertoire.
- Adjusting to the opposition, and taking into account the resources available on your own side.

We can represent some of the essential elements in this view of communication in a 'communication skill model' given in Figure 9.2.

There are a number of very important implications which follow from this view of 'communication as a skill'. Unlike the common sense view of communication, if we assume that communication is a skill, it follows that it can be described, analysed, and evaluated. It can also be changed and improved. Design principles involved are illustrated in Figure 9.3.

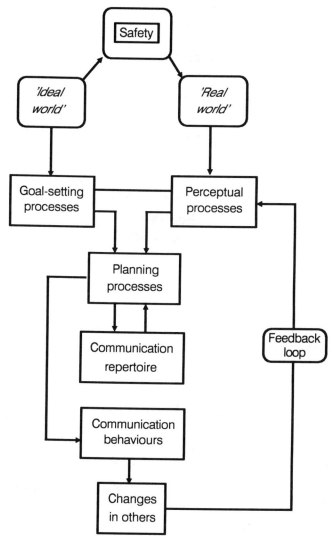

Figure 9.2

A model of communication skill for safety managers

Some implications for
communications system design

It can be specified
It can be analysed
It can be described
It can be tested
It can be evaluated
It can be improved

Figure 9.3
Communications system design principles

I. Description

We can describe communication by dealing with it in small but meaningful units, we can describe how these are interrelated, and the way in which smaller units combine to form larger units of behaviour.

2. Analysis

We can explain why the units are important, and why they fit together in the way they do.

3. Evaluation

We can identify the good and the not so good performances. For instance, we can identify people we like talking to, and identify what it is that they do that other people don't.

4. Change and improvement

If we can identify what it is that characterises good performances, we ourselves can learn to add them to our own behaviour. Similarly, we can identify the things that are characteristic of poor performances and try to eliminate them from our own behaviour and that of others.

One of the advantages that the model gives us is that it tells us what kind of things to look for in order to improve our performance. That is, we can improve by improving each of the components of the model. Implications of this are summarised in Figure 9.4.

```
┌─────────────────────────────┐
│ Improvements are possible   │
│ in communication systems    │
│         by developing       │
│                             │
│  1. Appropriate goals       │
│                             │
│  2. Defined aims            │
│                             │
│  3. Specified objectives    │
│                             │
│  4. Valid strategies        │
│                             │
│  5. Valid tactics           │
│                             │
│  6. Effective behaviours    │
│                             │
│  7. Improved perception     │
│                             │
│  8. Feedback loops          │
└─────────────────────────────┘
```

Figure 9.4

Implications of the communication skill model

1. Develop better goals

Every organisation has a mission be it explicitly stated or implicit. It may be as basic as trading at the maximum profitability or it may be unstated, but nevertheless incorporates the need for safe working practices and respect for the environment. Derived from this mission statement and your defined role as safety manager you will be able to determine certain goals such as improving safety and reducing accidents, loss of life, injury and accident costs. Laudable as these goals are (they are likely not to change), they are impossible to achieve without specifying particular aims and objectives. These have to be capable of measurement within a particular timescale.

2. Develop better strategies and tactics

If we decide that we want to persuade someone to do something, there are a variety of strategies and tactics that we can use. Using strategies that work is obviously better than using those which don't. The problem is that common sense often encourages us to use strategies which don't work very well. An example from the field of negotiation is our tendency to try to persuade the other person of the reasonableness of our position (which may make us feel self-righteous, but which rarely affects the outcome of the negotiation), rather than concentrating on what it is that we can offer them in trade. Successful negotiations are based on offering them something that they want in exchange for something that we want.

3. Develop better behaviours

In this context not only does one want to improve existing skills, one also wants to extend the repertoire of skills available to the safety manager, for example the use of incentive schemes, publicity strategies, public relations campaigns, developing a knowledge of media production skills.

4. Develop better perception and feedback

A characteristic of good safety communicators is that they are good observers (they notice when someone is looking worried, or is looking pleased), and that they are able to make sense of the things they observe. They are also keen to get feedback on the effects their behaviour is having on others, and they act on this feedback when they do get it. It is possible to teach people to be better observers, by teaching them what to look for and how to make sense of it when it does happen, how to ensure that adequate feedback mechanisms exist.

Whilst most of the implications of seeing safety communication as a skill are liberating, there are also some negative implications, at least at first sight. If we no longer see safety communication as an art, then we can no longer rely upon the company, or the safety manager waving a magic wand, and as a result see our safety communication transformed instantly and completely.

Because safety communication is a skill, change will only occur as shown in Figure 9.5.

Some characteristics of
communication systems
implementation

It is impossible to:
1. Improve instantaneously
2. Improve without making an effort
3. Improve without practising
4. Improve without making mistakes
5. Improve without occasional relapses
6. Improve without future modifications
7. Improve without adjusting to change
8. Improve without clear goals
9. Improve without apt feedback loops

Figure 9.5

Problems of the communication skill model

1. Gradually, not instantaneously

Like any other skill, it takes time for new behaviour and ways of thinking to be developed, and for old habits to be replaced. You don't become an excellent driver overnight. It takes several months, and certainly does not end when you stop taking driving lessons.

2. Through effort

Changing our behaviour takes considerable effort. There is always the temptation to go back to the old way of doing something, particularly when the going gets tough. It is particularly difficult because, early on, the new way of doing something often means that we do things less well than the old way. It takes effort to persevere, hanging on until our performance improves, initially back to its old level, and then beyond that to a higher level of performance. Anyone who has had sports coaching and been told to 'change their grip' or 'change your stroke' will recognise the difficulties involved.

3. Through practice

Initially, we are very self-conscious of new behaviours. We produce them stiffly, with difficulty, and fearing that people will not accept new ways. We will be very nervous. The only way to get over this barrier is to practise, so that the behaviour becomes habit, and we are confident that we can do it, and do it well.

4. Allowing ourselves to innovate and thus make occasional mistakes

5. Recognising that we will occasionally relapse

A process model of learning is summarised in Figure 9.6.

Changing the way that we communicate about safety is a gradual process, and every now and again we will make a mistake, and every now and again we will forget and slip back into our old ways of doing things. This does not mean that the new way is wrong, or that we will never master the new way of doing things. It simply means that we are human, and that nobody gets it right 100% of the time.

Although the Churchillian promise of 'blood, sweat and tears' may be rather alarming, there is a safeguard embodied within it. Individuals will change their safety communication behaviour only to the extent that they want to, and to the extent and in ways that they are prepared to work at creating.

We have concentrated on the example of safety communication as a way of introducing the idea of a skill, and the way that applying this idea can change an apparently 'unmanageable' problem into one which can be worked on and where improvements can be made. They will not necessarily be spectacular, but they will be worthwhile and dependable, and they will be cumulative. In the first part of this chapter we have concentrated on the general principles applying to safety communication. There are, however, a number of particular skills that need to be developed in the effective safety manager. Foremost amongst these are the interpersonal skills of communication including the skills of listening and information processing.

Identifying the characteristics of good listeners

- Listening is our primary communication ability. According to various studies, we spend about 70–80% of the time we are awake in some

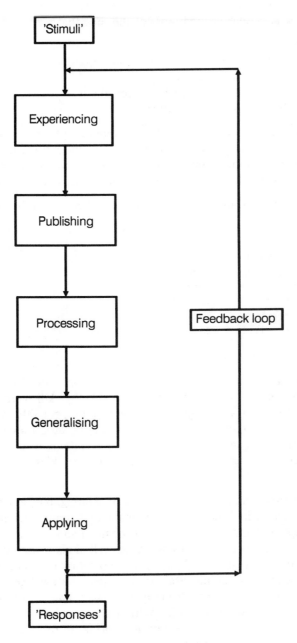

Figure 9.6

A process of learning

kind of communication activity. Typically, for people in middle-class, white-collar occupations, of the time that we spend communicating, about:

— 9% of it is spent writing;
— 16% of it is spent reading;
— 30% of it is spent speaking; but about
— 45% of it is spent listening.

● Although, in terms of time spent, listening appears to be the most important of our communication abilities, and writing the least, it is interesting to look at our educational system to see the priority that is given to the learning of the different communication skills.

These proportions are illustrated in the pie-charts given in figures 9.7A and B.

Skill	Amount of training	Order of learning
Writing	most	4th and last
Reading	next most	3rd
Speaking	next least	2nd
Listening	least	1st

This table also shows that, in the typical person's life, listening is the skill we learn first, whereas writing is typically the skill learnt last. The amount of formal training given to these skills probably reflects this ordering, with the skills we are least aware of, because they were learnt earliest, receiving the least attention. A rational training would be planned on a different basis, giving greatest priority to the skills that were most important.

● Our listening habits are not the result of training, but rather the result of the lack of it. Because listening is the first communication skill we develop, and the least taught, we could assume that it is a well-practised skill which is normally done well. This is not borne out by the evidence available. Tests have shown that immediately after listening to a 10-minute oral presentation, the average listener has heard, understood and properly evaluated and retained approximately *half* of what was said. Within 48 hours that has dropped to half again, giving a final retention of no more than 25%.
● The value of good listening, and the problems created by poor listening are now well known. Recent surveys of safety managers have shown that listening, and listening related skills, are cited as the most critical managerial skill, and the one in which training is most needed.

The safety manager's workload

Communication is the central task

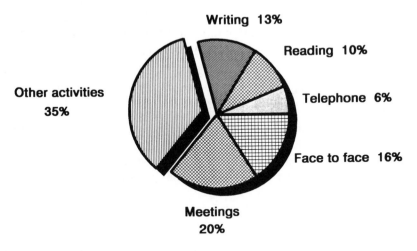

Writing 13%

Reading 10%

Telephone 6%

Face to face 16%

Meetings
20%

Other activities
35%

Figure 9.7A

The safety manager's communications

Taxonomy of communication activity

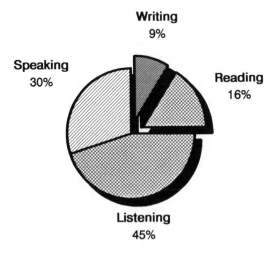

Writing
9%

Speaking
30%

Reading
16%

Listening
45%

Figure 9.7B

For instance, Borman and his colleagues report that 'the most essential attribute of a good manager was the ability to listen'. In a study by Robert Likert (Harvard Business Review 1959) it was found that '95% of foremen believed that they understood their subordinates' problems whereas only 34% of their subordinates thought that their foremen understood them.'

- We know how important good listening is from our own experience of life. The problem is to identify the skills and techniques of good listeners.

There are three major reasons why good listening is valued in this way:

1. From the point of view of the listener, it is the source of information which is vital to both the successful completion of the task and the maintenance of the relationship;
2. From the point of view of the speaker, it demonstrates that they are valued by the other person. Bad listening devalues the other person; and
3. The recognition of the importance of listening recognises the two-way nature of communication.

This last point is quite subtle, but is worth illustrating. The conventional model of communication is the *packet* model. This is shown in Figure 9.8.

The packet model of communication (e.g. that developed by Shannon and Weaver) proposes that there is:

A sender who has some information or an idea which is packaged in the form of words and/or images, and via a medium (e.g. speech, writing, video, slide-shows, etc.) it is transmitted to another person. The receiver unpacks the message in order to recover the information or idea that it contains so that they now have a replica of the original information or idea. Noise, which distorts the message, can occur at any stage in this process.

An alternative model, which represents real communication rather better, is the 'group' or 'organisational' model of communication. This sees communication as a much more communal enterprise. It recognises that the sender may, at the time they begin talking, be rather unclear about what it is that they want to say. They may not know what information they have, or what information is relevant. They may have a rather unclear idea which they find difficult to put into words, and which has not yet been thought through in all its details. The information and ideas which are then communicated during a conversation are as much a result of the efforts of the listener as they are of the speaker. The good listener may simply be a sounding board. They are more likely to be actively involved, asking questions, seeking more detail, encouraging the speaker to go on, keeping quiet when they are having difficulty finding a way of expressing themselves, actually contributing ideas and alternatives at some points, etc. It is a common experience for people to come away from a good conversation with a new idea, but with none of them knowing exactly whose idea it was. The answer is that it was the idea of all of them. There was no receiver of an idea dispatched by some sender; all participants were both senders and receivers.

Description of a listening model, together with Bales' categories of communication, is illustrated in figures 9.9, 9.9A and 9.10.

The 'packet' model of communication
after Shannon and Weaver

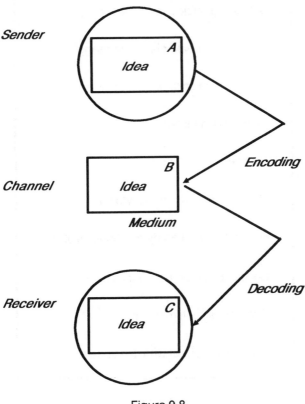

Figure 9.8
A model of communication

Barriers to listening

It is possible to identify a number of barriers to good listening.

1. Safety manager does not pay attention to the speaker;
2. Safety manager fakes paying attention to the speaker;
3. Safety manager assumes that the subject is uninteresting;
4. Safety manager assumes that the speaker is uninteresting;
5. Safety manager focuses on the speaker's style or mannerisms;

Barriers to good listening

A. Not paying attention

B. Faking attention

C. Assuming subject is uninteresting

D. Assuming speaker is uninteresting

E. Focusing on style or mannerisms

F. Allowing distractions

G. Concentrating on details

H. Trying to remember everything

I. Reaction dominated by emotional triggers

J. Concentrating on partial message

K. Avoiding difficult material

L. Not thinking about what the speaker is saying

Figure 9.9
Some problems in personal communication

6. Safety manager allows themselves to be distracted;
7. Safety manager concentrates on details;
8. Safety manager tries to remember everything;
9. Safety manager's reaction is dominated by isolated emotion-laden words or phrases;
10. Safety manager concentrates on only one of the things said;
11. Safety manager avoids difficult material; and
12. Safety manager does not think about what is said.

Skills of good listening

A. Pay attention to the speaker

B. Keep your mind open

C. Judge the message content

D. Reduce distractions

E. Support the speaker

F. Search for the main ideas

G. Organise the material

H. Record the material

I. Follow up

J. Do not interrupt

K. Do not anticipate

L. Defer judgment

M. Think about what the speaker is
   saying

Figure 9.9A
Principles of effective personal communication

Bales' categories of communication

A. Socio-emotional category: Positive reactions	1. *Shows solidarity* e.g. raises others' status, gives help, rewards. 2. *Shows tension release* e.g. jokes laughs, shows satisfaction 3. *Agrees* e.g. shows passive acceptance, understands, concurs, complies
B. Task category: Attempted answers	4. *Gives suggestion* e.g. direction, implying autonomy for others 5. *Gives opinion* e.g. evaluation, analysis, expresses feeling, wishes 6. *Gives orientation* e.g. information repeats, clarifies, confirms
C. Task category: Questions	7. *Asks for orientation* e.g. information, repetition, confirmation 8. *Asks for opinion* e.g. evaluation, analysis, expression of feeling 9. *Asks for suggestion* e.g. direction, possible ways of action
D. Socio-emotional category: Negative reactions	10. *Disagrees* e.g. shows passive rejection, formality, withholds help 11. *Shows tension* e.g. asks for help withdraws out of field 12. *Shows antagonism* e.g. deflates others' status, defends or asserts self

Figure 9.10

A taxonomy of communication activities

I. Safety manager does not pay attention to the speaker

We know that not paying attention to the speaker is very damaging to good communication. Not only does it mean that we cannot listen, it also destroys the ability of the speaker to talk. It is seen as rude, and is socially unacceptable. Note that we sometimes use it as:

● A way of punishing people.
● A means of controlling people, for example somebody being abusive about a safety procedure.
● A way of trying to mark our status relative to someone else.

2. Safety manager fakes paying attention to the speaker

Because blatantly not paying attention to someone else is socially unaccept-able, we learn to fake attention. We give off signals which are meant to fool the other person into thinking we really are paying attention. (Sometimes, this attempt to fake attention is not meant to fool the other person, but seems intended merely to prevent them from protesting that 'you're not listening' by allowing us the response 'Oh but I am, can't you see...' Such exchanges are common in deteriorating relationships.)

The problem with faking attention is that the listener is able to fool not only the speaker, but they can also fool themselves. This might be referred to as the 'busy safety manager syndrome'. It is a common complaint of workers that safety managers do not really listen to what they are saying, but are in fact dealing with a previous problem, or are preparing for the next meeting, or are actually writing out a notification of dangerous occur-rence before they have heard what the worker has to say. The 'busy safety manager syndrome' is a caricature, and many safety managers are very good listeners. However, the safety professional does provide us with a good case study of the consequences of bad listening.

A number of studies have shown that safety managers are not very good at obtaining information from workers, and that they need the extra information that good listening would provide. It is estimated that some 40–60% of the first accident analysis diagnoses made by safety managers are incorrect, and that this often arises because they fail to obtain the information they need, and that the worker can provide.

3. Safety manager assumes that the subject is uninteresting

Oscar Wilde wondered 'if one does not judge by appearances, what can one judge by?'. The good safety manager would reply that you should judge by the impression of the message as a whole. In particular, initial prej-udices that because the message is about a particular subject it is bound to be boring, difficult, or simply a waste of time, prevent the safety manager from even beginning to understand what is being said. There are topics, and which ones they are will vary from person to person, which lead to an almost instantaneous switching off; for example, the attitudes of militant trade union officials toward safety laws or COSHH definitions. We all have such prejudices. The problem is that we may be rejecting useful information as we protect our prejudices.

4. Safety manager assumes that the speaker is unimportant

Good ideas, or important information can be ignored because we have already passed judgment on the speaker before we have heard what they have to say. A dramatic instance of this is given by a study conducted by psychologists researching the efficiency of American Air Force bomber crews. The three-man crews were given difficult problems to solve, and at intervals clues were given to help them. The researchers found that if they gave the clues to the pilot, the time taken to reach the solution was greatly reduced. If the clues were given to the engineer the time taken was reduced, but by not quite as much. If the clues were given to the tail-gunner it made little or no difference to the time taken. In many teams, the tail-gunner could be given the solution and it still did not appear to help the team. The reasons appear to lie in the status of the people in the team, and the willingness of people to listen to them. The pilot has the greatest status, and the team will therefore listen to him. The tail-gunner had little or no status, and therefore, even if what he had to say was of great importance, the team did not listen to what he had to say.

5. Safety manager focuses on the speaker's style or mannerisms

The United Kingdom is fortunate in many ways because of the rich variety of its regional speech styles; its dialects and accents – they give colour and interest to our language. This is unfortunate in other ways. One problem they raise is that many people have strong opinions about the correct and the incorrect way to pronounce particular words. George Bernard Shaw wrote, in the preface to *Pygmalion*, that 'it is impossible for an Englishman to open his mouth without being despised by some other Englishman'. The problem with such reactions is that we ignore *what* is being said because of our strong reactions to *how* it is being said. Studies have shown that exactly the same thing, said in an RP (received pronunciation) accent (RP is the accent of the BBC Radio 4 newsreader) is thought to be more intelligent and better informed than exactly the same thing said in a Birmingham or Manchester or other regional accent. Put most generally, our speech triggers stereotypes in the minds of our listeners, and their reactions are reactions to what they think we will say, not to what we are saying. This is particularly so for major civil engineering sites where workers are recruited from all over the country.

6. Safety manager allows himself to be distracted

It is difficult to concentrate when we are distracted. Good listening demands high levels of concentration. As listeners we therefore need to reduce distractions to a minimum. The problem is that many of the things that distract us, such as the telephone, the noise of radios and televisions, of traffic, etc, are treated as uncontrollable. Perhaps the best example of this is the telephone. The ringing of a telephone during a conversation is very distracting, to both speaker and safety manager, and the majority of people seem unable to resist the demand to answer the caller even if in mid-conversation with someone else. It is perfectly possible to control the telephone. Calls can be diverted, the telephone can be unplugged, it can even be left off the hook. This is rarely done. The same helplessness in the face of our environment occurs in response to many other distractions.

We can also allow ourselves to be distracted by the internal environment. Our own thoughts and emotions, worries about other problems and concern with other issues mean that we do not concentrate on what the other person is saying.

7. Safety manager concentrates on details

A simple-minded approach to the notion of good listening runs the danger of equating good listening with being able to remember a large number of facts. This is not the case. The problem with facts is that they do not usually have any meaning unless the point has been understood. The argument that they form part of is the most important thing to grasp. The argument tells you which facts are worth remembering, and which can be simply forgotten. It also allows you to organise the facts so that they are more easily remembered. If you concentrate on the details you will not understand the broad picture.

In many conversations it is more important that you appreciate and respond to the emotions and mood of the speaker than that you remember all of the details of the account that they are giving you. Similarly, it is often more important that you understand the action that needs to be taken rather than any of the details associated with it.

There is an irony in this. It is that details, the facts of the matter, are actually rather easily remembered by using the simple device of writing them down, either by taking notes or by asking the speaker to 'put it in writing.' Expending great effort to remember them is simply a waste of precious energy.

8. Safety manager tries to remember everything

The extension of this problem is to try to remember everything. This is neither possible nor worthwhile. A general characteristic of human perceptual systems (our eyes, our ears, etc) is that they are highly selective. It might be argued that they are devices for rejecting information rather than for gathering it. It is the selective nature of our senses that means that we are not continually distracted by the background hum of machinery, and that the scene we see before our eyes usually looks rather better than the photograph we take of it. Good listening should follow the same principles. The good safety manager concentrates on trying to understand what is being said in order that they only need to remember a small proportion of what is said. What they do remember, however, is that which is most important.

9. Safety manager's reaction is dominated by isolated emotion-laden words or phrases

Whilst the good safety manager concentrates on extracting the highlights from what is said, this is based on looking for the overall pattern of what is being said, and it is based on looking for the recurrent themes. The poor safety manager tends to be attracted by the isolated item. This is typically a word or phrase which for them carries considerable emotional weight. Different people will have different trigger words or phrases; here is a selection which seem to be current:

'You'll have to use the computer'

'This will involve a bit of mathematics'

'Well your predecessor, Mr Johnson, always...'

'I don't know how many times I've had to tell you'

The point is that the emotional reaction to the isolated phrase dominates and distorts the ability to process the rest of the message. It is not that we should react unemotionally to messages, it is that we should not allow single items to dominate our response to a much larger message.

10. Safety manager concentrates on only one of the things said

Over-reacting to the isolated word or phrase which for us carries particular emotional weight is a particular form of a more general problem. That is, the problem of focusing on only one aspect of the message. The message may contain an item of bad news, and this can absorb all of our attention so that the good news which follows it is not heard (or vice versa). An example of this is again given by studies of safety communication. Research which has examined what it is that workers can remember of what their safety manager has told them repeatedly report 'not much'. Typically, workers can remember only some 10% of what they have been told by their safety manager during a formal interview. What they can remember is usually the disciplinary consequence, and this is usually not the most important or useful thing to remember. The disciplinary consequence is remembered because this is usually what the safety manager tells the worker first, and understanding and absorbing the implications of this information often means that the remainder of the information that the safety manager provides, about how the problem should be treated, what the outcome is, and so on, is simply not listened to. Safety managers who understand about the problems of listening will change the order in which they give information to their workers, telling them first of all about the outcome and then about the actions which should be taken to improve matters. They will leave telling the worker the disciplinary consequences until the very end.

11. Safety manager avoids difficult material

The converse of concentrating on only one of the things said is that other things are ignored. Often, that is a primary motive. What counts as difficult material will vary from person to person. For some it will be emotional topics, for instance someone telling you of their feelings about another person. For others it will be particular topics, for instance those involving computers or technology. And for others it will be particular classes of information, such as bad news.

12. Safety manager does not think about what is said

Underlying all of these barriers is the issue of how we process the information we receive during a conversation. Good listening is in fact good thinking. Central to the skill of good listening is the ability to see the whole picture, to identify patterns, to notice recurring themes, to work out how different pieces of information relate to each other … in other words, to understand what the communication means. This is, admittedly, hard work. However, the listener does have some advantages. The primary one is that we are able to think faster than we can talk. The listener is able to process what is heard faster than the normal person can speak. It is possible to considerably accelerate speech (by a factor of almost 2 to 1) and for people still to have little or no difficulty in processing it. The problem is that in normal conversation this ability is wasted. It is wasted for a number of reasons. One of them is simply that we are inclined to let our attention wander. Precisely because we only need a fraction of our attention to appear to listen, we only devote a fraction of our attention to the task of listening. If we do devote the whole of our attention to the conversation it is usually because we are planning what we are going to say next, rather than listening to what the other person is currently saying.

The skills of effective listening

It is possible to identify a number of skills which lead to more effective listening.

1. Pay attention to the speaker;
2. Keep your mind open;

3. Judge the message (primarily) by its content;
4. Reduce distractions;
5. Support the speaker;
6. Listen for the main ideas;
7. Actively organise the material;
8. Continually record the material;
9. Follow up: question, check, summarise;
10. Don't interrupt;
11. Don't anticipate;
12. Defer judgment;
13. Think about what the speaker is saying.

1. Pay attention to the speaker

The key to more effective listening is to pay attention to the speaker and what the speaker is saying. Attention should not be paid to what the listener is going to say next. For one thing, it may well change as a result of what is learnt by listening. For another, it does not really matter if there is a short pause while a decision is made about what to say next; the other person is likely to interpret this as a sign that the listener is thinking seriously about what they have said, and will see this reflectiveness as a positive characteristic of the listener.

2. Keep your mind open

It is not possible to eliminate our prejudices and stereotypes. They are a characteristic of the way that people think about their world. It is possible, however, to be aware of our own particular prejudices, and to be aware that such pre-judgments can prevent us from listening properly to new information and ideas. One way of thinking about this is to ask ourselves what it is that we are afraid of losing? The answer is often nothing, our inattention being simply habit. If we are afraid of losing something, it is generally because we know that these are simple prejudices, and we value the comfort they give us. Keeping an open mind can be an exciting enterprise!

3. Judge the message (primarily) by its content

It is important to separate the presentation of the message from its content. It is not the case that the presentation is not important, it is. However, it is important primarily because of what it tells us about the presentation. The person's delivery can tell you whether they are nervous or confident, whether they come from Scotland or Somerset, and whether they buy their clothes from Jaeger or Marks and Spencer. It does not directly tell you anything about the content. This is a very important principle that much recent writing on the importance of non-verbal behaviour has tended to obscure. When judging the content of a message it is important that presentational factors are given their proper weight.

4. Reduce distractions

If the conversation is affected by distractions, and it is possible to do something about them, do so. Moving to a quieter place, or putting paperwork on one side, or diverting the telephone to another extension are all simple but effective ways of reducing distractions. The difficulty is often in realising that they are distractions, and in realising that it is possible to do something about them. There is an added benefit. The speaker will see the effort made to reduce distractions as a very favourable characteristic of you as a listener, and will be more positively disposed as a result.

5. Support the speaker

A speaker needs to be supported. Support can be given in a variety of ways, from smiling and head nods to 'mmmms' and 'yeahs' and on to simple prompts such as 'that's interesting; can you tell me more?'. In a normal conversation such support is often not noticed until it is withdrawn. When it is absent it is quickly noticed, and the speaker is likely to come quickly to a halt. The importance of the listener's support of the speaker illustrates the fact that conversation is a joint production, with the listener's role being as important as that of the speaker.

6. Listen for the main ideas

Effective listening is essentially a cognitive skill. That is, it is about the sense that is made of the message. In order to make sense of a mass of information and ideas it is important to have a framework in which to organise them. This framework should consist of the major ideas that underlie the message. It is this framework that will allow all of the other information to be organised and assimilated.

Planning to process the information given to us by another person is rather like the process of planning a journey. Consider for instance the planning of a publicity campaign to reduce injuries. It is quite clear that the planning should start at the level of the 'main ideas', such as the particular injuries to be reduced, what budget is available and when the campaign should run. Decisions can then be made as to, say, which media to use. It is only in the very last stages of planning that a particular set of posters would be considered.

7. Actively organise the material

Effective listening is an active process. The listener should be continually trying to make sense of the information they are being given by fitting it into the framework they are developing. This process provides confirmation and gives confidence if the information can be fitted into the framework, and it quickly provides warnings if the information does not fit. This should signal the need to explore alternative organising frameworks.

Perhaps the best analogy here is of the accident investigator seeking clues in order to determine the cause of a chemical explosion. The solution emerges in the way that the clues fit together, not in the meaning of any one clue. What is important is that it is the pattern (the contributory factors) that is provided by the earlier clues which guides the accident investigator to seek further information, and to recognise its significance when found. If the accident investigator simply sat around waiting for all the forensic information to accumulate it is unlikely that any clues would be found at all.

8. Continually record the material

One of the problems with effective listening is that it quickly demonstrates that there is much more information available than we can remember. A simple rule is to take notes. It is far less obtrusive than people normally imagine, and to the extent that it is noticed it is usually approved of; it is, after all, a sign that the other person is interested in what is being said, and thinks it is important enough to make a note.

9. Follow up: question, check, summarise

The two previous activities, of organising and recording information, will normally reveal the need for further information. The listener becomes aware that they do not understand a particular point, so will ask for clarification. The listener will become aware that the information is incomplete, so will ask for elaboration. The listener may become aware that the information does not make sense in some way, and will therefore ask for an explanation. The listener is now becoming an important partner in the creation and communication of information and ideas, because they may be asking for clarifications, elaborations and explanations that the speaker did not, until asked, realise were necessary.

10. Don't interrupt

One of the best ways of getting another person to talk is to be silent. The problem with silence is that it is often seen as a problem, and people rush to fill it. Rather than being a problem, it may simply indicate that the other person is thinking. A good listener will allow the speaker the time, and therefore perhaps the silence, to do this thinking.

II. Don't anticipate

In all conversations the listener is to some extent anticipating what the speaker is about to say. It is in fact a measure of the extent to which the listener understands the speaker that they are able to do this. If the first half of the sentence has been understood, then it is often possible to finish the second half before the speaker does. (It is in fact a nice demonstration of the fact that we can process the information we hear much faster than it can be spoken that this does so often happen.) In normal social conversations it is common for this anticipation to be vocalised aloud, and for it to be, if anything, seen as a positive sign of the listener's interest, involvement and understanding. The problem is that at crucial points it can interfere. It can interfere simply because the speaker is irritated and annoyed by it. It can interfere because the speaker was in fact going to say something else, but stops when the listener's preferences are (apparently) made clear. It can interfere because it is seen as a challenge to what was going to be said, and a confrontation is created where one did not, or should not, have existed.

Both good and bad listeners will anticipate. The difference between them is that the good listeners will keep their anticipations to themselves.

There is a further problem to anticipating which should be guarded against. The listener may be so confident that they are able to anticipate the way that the conversation will end that they do not bother to listen. They may even cut the conversation short. By doing so they may have failed to listen to the most informative (precisely because it was the least predictable) part of the conversation.

12. Defer judgment

It is important to keep an open mind not only at the beginning, but throughout the conversation. Judgment about the value of the information and ideas being communicated should be deferred until all of the information is available, and often until after a period of reflection. This is an extension of the two previous points. It is possible to interrupt and to anticipate without saying anything to the speaker. The listener simply 'switches off'. If they do, then there is the danger that important information will be lost.

13. Think about what the speaker is saying

All of the above can be summarised in the proposition that effective listening is effective thinking, and the requirement that the good listener should think about what the speaker is saying.

Questioning skills

'I keep six honest serving men
(They taught me all I knew)
Their names are What and Why and When
And How and Where and Who!'

Rudyard Kipling (1865–1936)

In the previous section the emphasis was placed on listening as a cognitive skill: effective listening is effective thinking. An important additional part of the skill of being a good listener is the availability of behavioural skills, particularly the skills that are needed to support the speaker. In this section the skills of questioning and encouraging (reinforcing) the speaker will be examined.

This section examines the nature of questions. The next section looks in more detail at different types of questions, and their use when conducting an accident investigation. The final section examines the role of reinforcement in supporting the speaker.

Asking good questions is difficult. It is difficult because there are many different types of questions, and each of them has a different effect or consequence. A characteristic of the skilled safety manager is that they use particular types of question appropriately. To do this, it is necessary to be able to recognise the different types of questions and to understand their differing. It is all too easy to know that there are different kinds of questions, but then to use them inappropriately. A summary of why we ask questions is shown in Figure 9.11.

Perhaps the first question that needs to be posed is 'why do we ask questions?'.

1. To obtain information;

but also:

2. To focus attention on a particular topic;
3. To arouse interest in a topic;
4. To express an interest in the other person:
   (a) to initiate and maintain interaction,
   (b) to encourage another person's participation;
5. To inform ('creating enlightenment');
6. To persuade;

7. To assess the other person:
   (a) to assess ability,
   (b) to assess attitudes,
   (c) to assess information;
8. To make a request;
9. To issue an invitation; and
10. To divert attention from another issue.

The point about this list is that whilst 'obtaining information' is one of the reasons why questions are asked, it is by no means the only, or even

Why do we ask questions?

1. For information

2. To focus attention

3. To arouse interest

4. To express interest

5. To inform

6. To persuade

7. To assess

8. To request

9. To invite

10. To divert attention

Figure 9.11

Purposes of personal communication

the most common reason. However, to the safety manager it is important, and much of the early discussion of questions will focus on this aspect of questioning. It is common practice to distinguish two types of question: the open and the closed question (see Figure 9.12).

The closed question is commonly defined as: 'a question which discourages the other person from talking.' It often takes the form of a 'yes/no' question, that is, a question which only allows the answer to be either 'yes' or 'no'.

Closed question:

A question which discourages
a person from talking.

Often takes the form of
a 'Yes/No' question.

Open question:

A question which encourages
a person to talk.

Often takes the form of
a 'Wh -' question.

Figure 9.12

Types of question

A typical closed question might take the form: 'Did you follow the proper procedures?'

Closed questions are usually constructed by inverting the order of the verb in a statement. For example, 'You were late arriving here!' becomes 'Were you late arriving here?'.

An open question is commonly defined as: 'A question which encourages the other person to talk.' It often takes the form of a 'wh-' question, i.e a question which begins with one of the 'wh-' words, such as what, when, why, etc.

A typical open question might take the form: 'What did you think of the safety procedures at this factory?'

A major difference which is said to differentiate open and closed questions is that people will say more in response to an open question than in reply to a closed question. Replies to closed questions are shorter, replies to open questions are longer.

It is usually implied that using open questions is better than asking closed questions. It is also usually accepted that asking open questions is more difficult than asking closed questions, and that most people use closed questions more often than they use open questions. The principal difference between different kinds of questions is the amount of control they give to the respondent versus the amount of control that is retained by the questioner. They differ in the amount of freedom that the respondent is given over the way that they will talk about the topic, and about the way the topic is specified (see Figure 9.13).

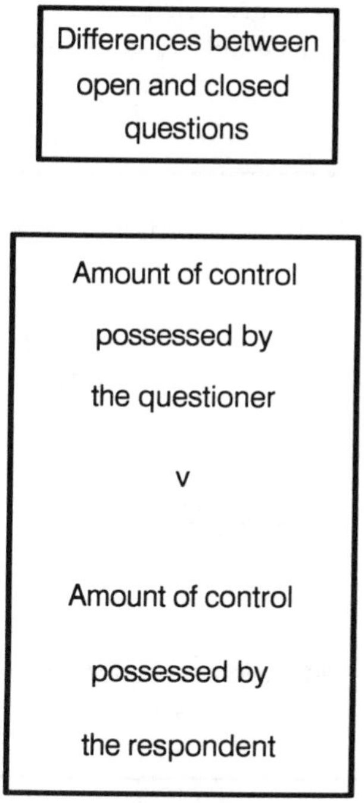

Differences between

open and closed

questions

Amount of control

possessed by

the questioner

v

Amount of control

possessed by

the respondent

Figure 9.13

Comparison of types of question

Closed questions

Closed questions require a specific answer. They narrow the range of possible answers and focus on a particular point.

They can take the form of:

- Yes/no questions:

    — 'Did you disobey the safety instructions?'

- Selection questions:

    — 'Did you or did you not disobey the safety instructions?'

- Identification questions:

    — 'During the last week, on which days did you disobey the safety instructions?'

Relationships are summarised in Figure 9.14.

Closed questions are important for extracting facts and information quickly. They are only effective when the questioner already has considerable knowledge and understanding of the topic being discussed. They are worded so as to limit the topic discussed and the kind of information that can be offered. Because of this ability to control the conversation, they are

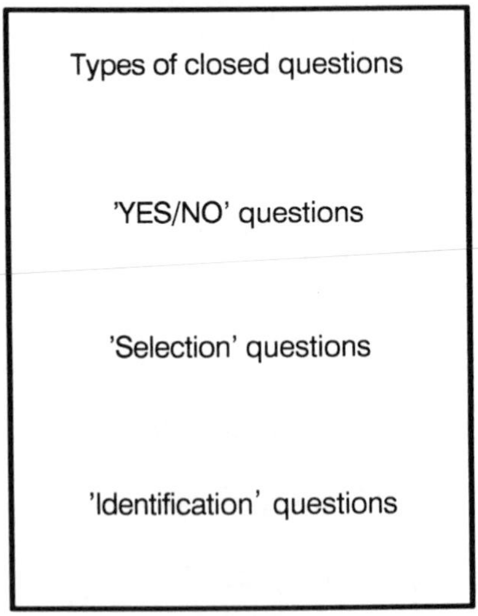

```
Types of closed questions


'YES/NO' questions


'Selection' questions


'Identification' questions
```

Figure 9.14

Examples of types of question

useful for:

- Gathering specific information.
- Guiding the discussion to a particular topic (or returning it to that topic).
- Eliminating misunderstandings about the answer required.

Closed questions can be irritating and confusing, especially when they are asked quickly and repetitively without reaction. They can be seen as threatening, and they can therefore cause the respondent to close down. They can simply miss the point and the information given in response is irrelevant or meaningless.

On the other hand, they can be used to put respondents at ease by limiting their uncertainty about what is required of them, by giving them questions which they are able to answer easily and well, and by creating the impression of a useful and productive interchange.

Open questions

Open questions are those questions which do not require a reply of a specific form in answer to the query made.

They can use 'wh-' words, but that is not absolutely necessary.

Examples of open questions are:

- 'Could you tell me what happened?'
- 'What do you feel are the underlying causes?'
- 'How do you see this situation?'
- 'Why do you think that?'
- 'Please tell me what happened.'

Open questions are primarily intended to encourage respondents to answer as they wish. They give the interviewee more control of the conversation. They allow respondents to express personal viewpoints in idiosyncratic ways. (These ways may be very brief and brusque; not all respondents will choose to use the freedom given by an open question to give lengthy replies.) They allow unanticipated information to be given, and they leave room for the conversation to move to other topics and in directions not anticipated by the questioner. Because they focus attention on, and give control to, the respondent, they allow the questioner to refrain from revealing their own opinions or information that they have. Open questions also tend to be seen, because they are less controlling, as less threatening.

Open questions also have disadvantages. They reduce the questioner's control, and therefore make it more difficult to manage the conversation. For instance, it is more difficult to stick to the point and it is more difficult to manage the use of time. The proportion of irrelevance is also increased.

If open questions are used, their use must be sincere, and time for a considered response must be given. They are too often asked as a ritual and are then answered by the questioner: 'How are you? All right? That's good' (see Figure 9.15).

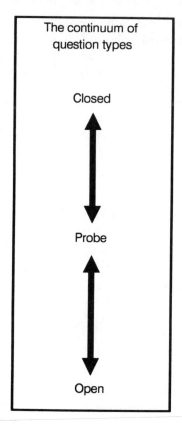

Figure 9.15

Relationship of types of question

The distinction between open and closed questions is in fact an artificially absolute one. Open and closed are not categories, but rather are opposite ends of a continuum. The continuum consists not only of open and closed questions, but it also includes a range of probe questions.

Closed ⬌ Probe ⬌ Open

A probe question is one that asks for more information or a more complete explanation of what has just been said.

Examples of probe questions are:

- 'I'm not sure I understand your thinking on this; could you tell me a bit more...?'
- 'You say it always happens; do you mean every time..or...?'
- 'I think I understand your point; could you give me a couple of examples?'

Probe questions are used to enhance the questioner's understanding; they may also be used to promote the respondent's understanding by asking them to think more carefully about what they have just said. They seek to clarify points which have just been made and to check that what has been said has been correctly understood. They also function to show that the questioner is listening and is interested in what is being said.

Different probe questions can focus on different aspects of what has just been said. Probe questions can ask for:

- Clarification.
- Precision (accuracy).
- Justification.
- Relevance.
- Exemplification.
- Extension.

This classification of probe questions is not definitive. In many cases, the categories overlap, or may be impossible to fill, or may not fit some possible examples. However, the classification does allow you to show that different probes will turn the speaker's attention to different aspects of what has been said, and can act as a way of steering the conversation in a particular direction. One way of thinking about probe questions is that they act as a torch beam used to illuminate different aspects of the topic being discussed. This analogy not only emphasises the power of the probe question to reveal further information, but also suggests that, because the questioner chooses to shine the torch beam in a particular direction, this necessarily means that other aspects of what has been said still remain unilluminated. A series of different probe questions may need to be used to reveal all of the required information. The concept of differing probe questions can be illustrated by taking the following example (see Figure 9.16):

Imagine a conversation in which a person has just said:

'Of course, if we are going to make significant progress with the use of auto cut-out systems, then the company is going to have to support safety on a massive scale.'

The listener can follow this up by asking a number of different probe

Types of probe question

```
┌─────────────────────────┐
│      'Clarification'     │
│                         │
│       'Precision'        │
│                         │
│      'Justification'     │
│                         │
│       'Relevance'        │
│                         │
│     'Exemplification'    │
│                         │
│       'Extension'        │
└─────────────────────────┘
```

Figure 9.16

Alternative types of probe question

questions, as follows:

- Clarification:
    - 'What do you mean by 'auto cut-out systems'?'
- Precision (accuracy):
    - 'Can you be more specific about what you would count as the kind of *significant progress* we might expect in this field over, say, the next five years?'
- Justification:
    - 'Why do you think it has to be the company?'
- Relevance:
    - 'Why do you think auto cut-out systems is a particularly pertinent solution?'

- Exemplification:
  - — 'Can you give me a specific example of the kind of support you'd like from the company?'
- Extension:
  - — 'Do you think that this is the only area of safety where company support is crucial?'

Having seen that there are in fact a range of questions, each of which has advantages and disadvantages, the problem is to know when to use a particular kind of question. One way of organising the sequencing of questions is to use the 'funnel model'.

The funnel model suggests that a conversation can be thought of as a series of topics. As each topic is introduced, the questioner should use open questions in order that the respondent, not the questioner, can define the nature of the topic and how it will be talked about. As the questioner gets a better idea of what is being said, probe questions can be used to follow up information and ideas introduced by the respondent. As the conversation on this topic progresses, closed questions can be used to increase the questioner's control over the form and content of the information being given.

When the conversation then switches to another topic, the questioner should revert to the use of open questions again. For each topic, the process of progressively 'focusing in' is followed (see Figure 9.17).

If the 'funnel model' is used, it is often useful for the questioner to 'signpost' the structure of the conversation. That is, the questioner will announce that they want to talk about subject X as a way of introducing the topic, and when that part of the conversation has come to an end, they will explicitly say so, and point to the next topic of conversation (see Figure 9.18).

Not all questions are good questions. There are a number of common kinds of problematic questions:

1. Leading questions;
2. Loaded (or accusatory) questions;
3. Point-scoring questions;
4. Rhetorical questions;
5. Multiple questions;
6. Ambiguous questions; and
7. Jargon questions.

1. Leading questions

These dictate the answer that the respondent should give. They are phrased to get a response the questioner wants rather than a response the respon-

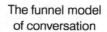

The funnel model
of conversation

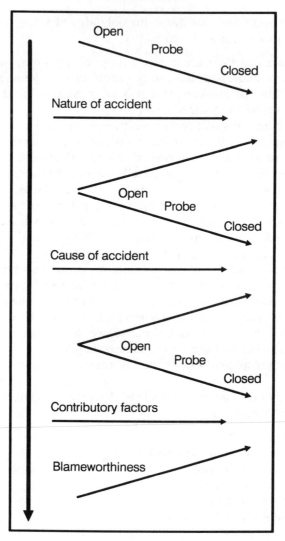

Figure 9.17

Use of questions in an accident investigation

dent might like to give. They can do this either by limiting the kinds of answers that can be given, or by indicating what the preferred answer would be:

- Was that the first time you'd been on a safety course?
- Isn't it a good idea?
- I'm sure you agree with our present policies, don't you?
- Surely you wouldn't want to ignore the regulations?
- As a law-abiding worker, wouldn't you agree that we should dismiss other workers who disobey the rules?
- How small was the explosion? (compare with: How large was the explosion?)
- Did you see the bare wires? (compare with: Did you see any bare wires?)

Types of
problematic
question

'Leading'

'Loaded'

'Point scoring'

'Rhetorical'

'Multiple'

'Ambiguous'

'Jargon'

Figure 9.18

Questions to be avoided by the safety manager

2. Loaded or accusatory questions

These evaluate, either explicitly or implicitly, the possible answers that the respondent can give. As such, there is an overlap with leading questions, but loaded questions have a much clearer emotional or attitudinal content.

- Why did you try to do that without asking me first?
- Why didn't you tell me the rules were being ignored?

3. Point-scoring questions

These are an extension of loaded questions. It is clear that they are not really requesting information, or at least, not information the questioner does know. They are designed to show the questioner in a good light, and the respondent in a bad light:

- I don't expect you to know the answer, but what are the provisions of the COSHH regulations?
- How long did you say it took you to find the information?

4. Rhetorical questions

These are an extension of loaded questions. It is clear that they are not really questions at all, either not calling for any response, or only allowing one possible response, and demanding that you agree with the questioner:

- Well, I ask you, who wouldn't be angry in a situation like that?
- What will happen if you don't obey the safety rules? I'll tell you what will happen.

The effect of all four kinds of problematic question is to block the transfer of information from respondent to questioner. They do this because the focus of these questions is actually on the questioner, not on the respondent.

5. Multiple questions

These are often the result of nervousness on the part of the questioner, and are often the result of the questioner's desire to help the respondent. The initial question is asked, but the reply does not come quickly enough. The questioner attempts to help by asking another, easier question. The respondent is now confused as to which of the two questions they should answer, and so hesitates. The questioner tries to help by asking an even simpler question:

- Have you talked to the men yet?
- Are they responsive?

- What about the rule books?
- And the new plastic covers?

In the end, the questioner will often find that they have to answer the questions themselves, because the respondent is paralysed by the bombardment they have been subjected to. Again, the effect is to block the transfer of information from the respondent to the questioner (see Figure 9.19).

6. Ambiguous questions

These use terms or structures where more than one interpretation is possible:

- Are you coming down soon?
- Where's that thingy?

Statements
which are
questions

Safe system?
He did?
Yes?

Questions
which are
statements

Isn't it a good system?
Why did you do that?
Can you do any better?

Figure 9.19

When is a question **NOT** a question?

7. Jargon questions

These use terms which are understood by the questioner, but are not necessarily understood by the respondent.

- How many Section 12 incidents were notified last weekend?
- (Answer: It depends on when you think the weekend starts and finishes. If you think it starts at 5 pm on Friday and finishes at 9 am on Monday you are likely to have had more incidents than if your weekend starts at 9 am on Saturday and finishes at midnight on Sunday.)
- Did you sort out the PDF for HASAWA?

```
┌─────────────────┐
│   Supporting    │
│   the speaker   │
└─────────────────┘
```

```
┌─────────────────┐
│     'Nods'      │
│                 │
│    'Smiles'     │
│                 │
│     'Gaze'      │
├─────────────────┤
│  'Semi - words' │
│                 │
│    'Prompts'    │
│                 │
│    'Silence'    │
└─────────────────┘
```

Figure 9.20
Ways of controlling the interview process

Ambiguous and jargon questions do not block the flow of information, they simply devalue the information that is transferred. A major problem with such questions is that it may not be realised that there is a problem. It is only later, when the problem has become concrete that it is realised that an ambiguous or jargon question has been used. The questioner is in fact fortunate if the respondent says at the time of asking that they do not know what is meant, or realises that there is ambiguity. In many cases the respondent either does not realise that they are using the term differently, or is unwilling to admit that they do not understand the term (see Figure 9.20).

Further reading

Bergin, F (1981) *Practical Communication* (Pitman Publishing)

Hamilton, S C (1987) *A Communication Audit Handbook* (Pitman Publishing)

Jackson, P C (1987) *Corporate Communication for Managers* (Pitman Publishing)

10

Safety education

Introduction

Safety education can be distinguished from safety training in that education is seen as the proactive development of knowledge, attitudes, behaviour and skills whilst safety training will usually concentrate on these issues in a reactive way. By its very nature, safety education tends to be used for the long-term development of knowledge in the hope that good safe attitudes, behaviour and skills evolve, thus contributing to the overall accident reduction programmes. It is common for organisations such as the Royal Society for the Prevention of Accidents (RoSPA), the Department of Trade and Industry, the Home Office and local authorities to provide for safety education via schools and colleges. This does not necessarily absolve other organisations from providing an input into the local school curriculum but advice from one of these main agencies should be sought before attempting to provide school based safety education.

More short-term based safety education may be required to educate the general public or the workforce itself regarding some potential or actual hazard. In order to discuss safety education in more detail it is necessary to consider some aspects of the psychology of learning. This has been discussed by educationalists for many years and it is generally accepted that five stages need to be considered:

1. The learning process;
2. The readiness of learners;
3. The cognitive or thinking process;
4. The trial or testing period; and
5. The feedback phase.

An outline of the five stages is given in Figure 10.1.

Long-term safety education which may form part of the National

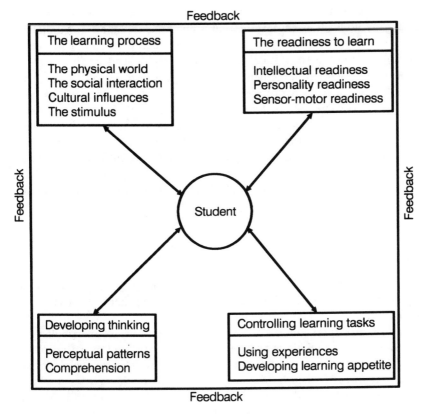

Figure 10.1

A model for the development of learning

Curriculum in mathematics, science and English is an integral part of the safety education process and is discussed below. From this it is possible to consider those issues which fall within the perimeter of adult safety education as a factor within the safety mix.

The learning process

It should be remembered that all students, regardless of socio-economic level or ethnic background bring with them a variety of social experiences to the learning situation. Also, the learning environment provides many other experiences and stimuli which are strong factors in the way that the student learns. On occasions, these situational influences may overpower the instructor's desire to influence the learning process. In such cases, it might be impossible to attempt the stimulation of the learning situation by normal methods. It is important that something is done immediately to deal with any factors which surround the learner which can inhibit learning. The instructor's success will ultimately depend upon this.

The social interaction element is the most easily observed factor in the learning process. A visitor to a school will notice students in various kinds of groups and some sort of teaching skills would involve setting up such groups. Further observation would highlight the teacher measuring social interaction and using the principles of group dynamics in managing the social interactions of the learning environment. A skilled teacher would also be aware of parental and sibling influences and those from other persons who may affect the learner. Relationships with important people can:

- encourage.
- motivate.
- frighten.

The aim of the skilled teacher is to foster social growth which includes role development, leadership, group goal setting and effective social interaction.

Cultural pressures on occasions come to the surface particularly in schools with mixed religions or when concern is expressed over the content of such subjects as sex education or peace studies. The calculated impact of cultural forces is seen by the large amount of work spent in designing appropriate curricula. This is particularly important where the workforce (students) is of mixed ethnic backgrounds. Curricula planning is worthy of detailed study time since the safety educator should be in a position to locate any unit or lesson on a scope and sequence chart (see Figure 10.2). These will provide an overview of exactly what is to be taught.

The point of contact between the social, physical and cultural factors in the learning environment and the readiness to learn is referred to as the *stimulus*. The figure shown in Figure 10.3 illustrates the stimulus element within the operational context of the learning process. The skilled instructor will consider aspects of the social world, cultural background and select appropriate topics accordingly. These are then brought together to form a focus of learning by the use of effective teaching stimuli.

Little learning takes place without giving attention to and contact with a relevant stimulus. Some object or action must become a focal point for a learner if benefit from the teacher is to be derived. Able instructors use a variety of ways for *showing* and *telling* with the purpose of gaining attention. The use of the stimulus does depend on the content of the learning environment as well as upon the learner. A competent instructor will ensure that the students are hearing and seeing clearly, that the training is well paced and that appropriate needs are being clarified as the lesson proceeds.

Scope	Sequence
The need to wear safety clothing	
Accident data (in-house)	
Different types of safety clothing	
Company policy	
The law	
Accident data (national)	
Circumstances where safety clothing is worn/not worn	
Weather conditions	
What happens if there is an accident and safety clothing is not worn?	
Responsibility for looking after safety clothing	
Rules governing external operations	
Company discipline procedures	
Feedback and evaluation	
Safety clothing exchange procedures	
Special features	
Company accident prevention policy	

Safety educators may wish to sequence these topics to suit their own working situations.

Figure 10.2
A basic scope and sequence chart

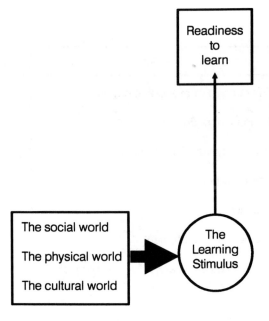

Figure 10.3

The learning stimulus

At the same time, long-term observation will reveal the degree of novelty exhibited by the instructor whose aim is to enrich the student's opportunity for learning by providing a variety of educational programmes whilst making use of appropriate media. Teachers cultivate interest at two levels:

1. At the elementary level which includes a sincere effort to provide a variety of novel activities; and
2. At an upper level in that the instructor enjoys providing a variety of current relevant examples.

Once that consideration has been given to the factors that are important to improve social, cultural and physical aspects, the teacher communicates with the learner by presenting a lesson or activity as a stimulus.

Readiness to learn

Many educationalists recommend an instructor to assess *readiness* as a first step in the promotion of learning. This means that they want to know the readiness level of the student before any other considerations are made. It is accepted that sooner or later the sensory-motor readiness, the intellectual capacity and the self-concept of each learner must be assessed in order to determine the appropriate materials and activities. The instructor will avoid materials and activities that are too simple and fail to engage the student's interest or those that are too difficult for the learner's aptitude level.

Visual and auditory defects do not in themselves represent handicaps but sensory or motor deficit may show up dramatically. Subtle health problems require constant attention and motor co-ordination is the basis for many learning experiences. Such practices as setting up needed rest periods and occasional alterations to activity give a student a higher interest level.

The traditional IQ concept which yielded a numeral to describe an aptitude, such as the Wechsler or Binet tests, is regarded by educationalists to be out-dated, and alternative multi-factor theories of intelligence are common and referred to when necessary. This means that intelligence is probably not unitary. A person does not have a certain amount of single intellectual ability. Rather, each person would possess many kinds of intellectual talents which could be capitalised on by a teacher. An individual who possesses a small amount of one sort of intellectual ability could have more talent in another area. Experience will allow the instructor to approach students in different ways according to the intellectual readiness of their trainees and not assume that all intelligence is the same.

It is important for the teacher to have some idea of the way in which intellectual abilities or aptitudes develop. Often an instructor will make estimates of aptitude based on performance rather than referring to standard aptitude achievement tests. Some instructors make the opposite mistake in that they rely solely on such tests as the basis of aptitude assessment. Since no ideal method exists for determining aptitude, both approaches should be used to a degree. Make use of all sources of information even that concerning a student's hobbies or leisure interests. However, the aim of the instructor in this skill area is:

- To adapt teaching materials to the intellectual level of students.
- To assist students to develop a variety of intellectual talents.

A trainee's values and aptitudes are at the centre of their behaviour. As self-concepts develop so aspiration levels increase in that a student will value their abilities in relation to what they want to accomplish. Much effort is focused on the development of trust and respect from students as an aid to their maturity. It has been found that students who like and believe in themselves and trust their teachers are happier citizens and learn more quickly and with greater ease. It is important to develop a little understanding of personality functioning, without becoming a psychologist, to become familiar with ways of communicating with students. This will help the learning situation develop more efficiently.

Once a learning situation has been created it is important to consider the readiness of the students to learn the material. A note should be made of each student's physical and intellectual readiness to learn and there should be sufficient flexibility to match each student to useful but challenging material.

Developing the ability to think

Instructors everywhere have a prime objective to get their students to *think* and in safety terms this is usually *think before you act*. Researchers reveal a wide range of theories on how perceptual and cognitive processes interact. As a student observes perceptual regularity it becomes convenient to label such precepts with' babytalk. Later comes more complicated language until eventually learning to manipulate mental representations of the perceptual phenomena in highly skilled ways. The most fundamental behaviour comes from the Gestalt psychology which is referred to as *patterning*. For example, we try to see shapes in clouds or an open fire, or a pattern in a series of dots. Here, the learner structures primitive form and motion meaning from various events. The instructor's aim shortly becomes that of assistant thus helping learners perceive essential parts and difference between shapes, structures and relationships. Help is more refined by giving guidance, issuing terms of reference or providing assembly plans or giving formulae. Modern researchers refer to this as *cultivating auditory and visual literacy*. Although basic perceptions of detail and patterns relate to instant awareness, cognition refers to making such precepts more permanent and understandable by naming recurrent regularities that possess common identifiable attributes. These names (or labels) are referred to as *concepts* and become the vocabulary of the learner. The forming of such concepts becomes an important part of the teaching role through illustration and the provision of examples so that the definition is clear. The more clearly a concept is defined, the more chance it has of being understood. At higher cognitive levels, the process of inference and comprehension develops as the learner comes to terms with language as a talker, listener and reader.

The testing phase

Following the creation of a learning environment, and the readiness of the student to learn and give consideration to the thinking process, it is important to bring these together. As materials have been prepared it is important to ensure that learning trials or response activities are well planned and as efficient as possible. All learning needs activity and a trial refers either to mental or physical activity on the part of the student. In a trial, the learner is required to give a response to a previous stimulus.

The effectiveness of the trial will depend on how much previous experience is remembered and on the effectiveness of the mode of work. Throughout the trial, both remembering and action affect each other until the task is complete.

Learning which is new depends on memory, whether muscle, feeling or idea memory. Motor memory is recognised as the ability to ride a bicycle, whilst feeling memory is seen as the recall of nasty and nice experiences. Idea memory is seen as the recall of facts and figures. When present behaviour reflects past experience, either as a basis upon which to learn new material more easily, or in creating problems which interfere with present activities, then *transfer* or *inhibition* is taking place. There are two kinds of transfer:

1. That which occurs by identity; and
2. That which occurs by generalisation.

When aiming for transfer, it is important to provide sufficient rote repetition of such things as numbers, safety procedures and the like, so that they are identified and remembered. Also, it is necessary to provide enough variety of examples and opportunities to use principles so that they too will become firmly established and be used in a variety of new situations. There are more complex principles such as those used in formulae (e.g. those used in chemistry) or learning to drive a motor car where the student is provided with the opportunity to practise on a wide variety of instances; so that each part of the principle is clear and that the learner is provided with enough time to see its application in a variety of situations. This goes way beyond the power of learning by rote because a given principle can be generalised to an infinite number of instances.

A teacher must help students to work effectively and will be constantly planning present and new activity. A practical way of enhancing the effectiveness of a learner's activity is by carefully describing the task and the behavioural sequences involved. Task analysis and the writing of behavioural objectives clarifies both what is wanted and what is expected. Two other considerations are also required:

1. To decide whether the learning is best done inductively, deductively or in a variety of combinations. In using an inductive approach, the student is presented with a set of open-ended questions or activities which are configured to lead to a desired principle. With deductive methods, information about rules is given along with a demonstration. The student is then given time to use what has been given; and
2. To decide how to maintain learning momentum.

Classroom management requires careful planning if a smooth transition of information is to be achieved. A checksheet is often used by student or instructor to indicate the task elements completed to date (see Figure 10.4).

| Name of teacher | | Reference | |

| Name of student | | Department | |

| Subject | |

Stage	Topic	Completed date	Remarks

Figure 10.4   A simple checksheet

Also, the instructor will need to consider the sort of practice scheduling, prompting and work monitoring time to use with each student.

Getting feedback

The learning cycle is completed by the provision of feedback which is designed to help maintain the student's interest and enthusiasm and to supply information that will allow improvements to be made. A student's attribution of success or failure whether on the basis of internal or external factors which may be perceived as rewards or punishments will influence learning. However, effective feedback, although essential for learning, is in itself insufficient. Such feedback must be supplemented by information concerning the correctness of the trial which will support direction to subsequent effort. In the case of affective feedback, the student is asking 'what is in it for me?' whereas in the case of information type feedback the student is saying 'am I right?'. Although these kinds of feedback often occur together, they do meet different learner needs and are therefore identified as separate aspects of the learning process. In the final stage, the aim of the instructor is to encourage creativity within the problem-solving processes which can be based upon self-rewarding/correcting decision making.

Encouragement is regarded as the simplest form of affective feedback. Specific praise should be used wherever possible because general praise loses its effectiveness over a period of time. This implies, therefore, that praiseworthy comments should be directed towards some special activity achieved by an individual. Psychologists who have been interested in the modification of behaviour have developed several principles which refer to stimuli that can elicit specific behaviours and use factors that do not allow for rewarding students for non-productive or destructive behaviours. Positive reinforcement systems stress 'seeing the worker taking safety precautions' and then rewarding that behaviour.

One method of obtaining feedback is by correcting tests, promoting motor-movements and suggesting alternative solutions. Another method, although more difficult to implement, is the sort of feedback activities which occur when an instructor studies a test in order to detect any group error patterns or when a student is guided through a step by step process in order to identify problems or mistakes. It is important not to correct student errors immediately. In a working situation, it may be appropriate to allow the student to get a *feel* for a dangerous situation before getting him/her out of it.

When assessing a student about their level and quality of performance it is necessary to highlight areas for further study. Also, this analysis provides for a teacher to plan review lessons and to alter emphasis. This is usually more relevant following accident studies. It is important that the instructor provides the student with sufficient evaluative information to ensure that the effort has been worthwhile.

The purpose of self-directed feedback is to assist the learner to achieve self-direction both in terms of self-reward and self-correction and evaluation. This provides a natural progression to the study of *discovery* and it helps students to learn more effectively using their own initiative and to arrive at their own conclusions. This is achieved by creating plans, materials and special designs and to use the most appropriate research methods.

It has only been possible here to cover very briefly the five points of the learning process. There is a good selection of reading materials available that will cover these issues in much greater depth. As far as the safety manager is concerned he is required to educate his workforce in various matters from time to time particularly when new legislation places

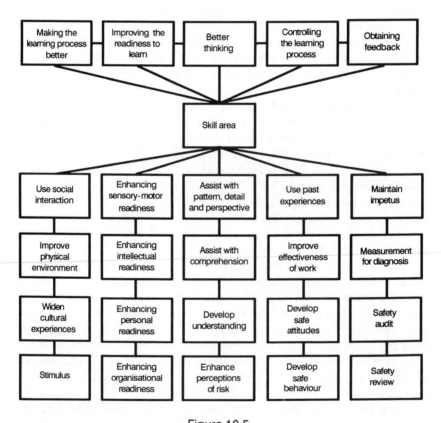

Figure 10.5

A summary of the learning process

additional requirements upon an organisation. Although the safety manager might not be directly concerned with the teaching process it is necessary to have a working knowledge of some of the principles involved. An example of this would be the planning of a lesson. This is discussed below. A diagram summarising those points discussed above is shown in Figure 10.5.

Planning a lesson

The safety manager will need to consider the planning of lessons and in particular the time involved in the teaching process. If an organisation is to bring certain parts of its workforce from a productive environment for a period of time it can be regarded as an expensive activity. It is important, therefore, that lessons are planned efficiently and effectively. When planning a lesson, there are a number of factors which must be considered. The first aspect is to define what the aim(s) and objective(s) of the lesson are and these must be clearly understood by everyone. From this it will be necessary to:

- Locate a suitable classroom: this must be large enough for a fixed number of students to be comfortable and be well ventilated and have sufficient light. It should have a clock, preferably at the back of the room so that it can be easily seen by the teacher.
- Know details of the students, their socio-economic grouping, ages, academic background, achievements, interests, intellectual level and disabilities. This will assist in pitching the lesson at the right level and in presentation and style.
- Decide the method of delivery. This will include the types of visual aids to be used and equipment necessary to use them.
- Set the start and finish times.

Materials to be used for a lesson can be obtained from a variety of sources. These could include:

- In-house accident data.
- National accident data.
- HSE publications.
- Legislative documents.
- RoSPA publications.
- Books.
- Journals.
- Experience.

Having gathered material it is important to select those items which are relevant and discard the rest. From this it is possible to divide up the information into logical and orderly sequences. Ensure that your sequences list is readily to hand and that your visual aids are in the right order and can be easily 'got at.'

The lesson should be divided into roughly four stages. These are:

1. *An introduction:* this should not be more than one-fifth of the total lesson time. It is important to state clearly the aim of the lesson and to list the objectives to be achieved. It is important to stress the relevance of the lesson and to link it to known examples or experiences existing within the group. Explain what is to happen during the lesson and what is expected of students. If the lesson is not the first in a series it will be necessary to recap on what was learned in the last lesson. Use humour wisely!;
2. *The elucidation:* this should concern the main thrust of the lesson and occupy some three-fifths of the lesson time. This phase will include appropriate repetition to aid reinforcement of certain points and to emphasise key areas. Make use of questions and answers and ensure that everyone is involved in the learning process;
3. *Summary:* this should recap on the main points covered paying attention to key areas. Approximately one-tenth of the total time should be spent seeking appropriate answers as a test to see if points have been understood; and
4. *The continuation:* the remainder of the time should be spent linking this lesson with that of the next and administering any assignments or additional work to be undertaken.

This is illustrated in Figure 10.6.

Gathering the information on what to say during a lesson is helped considerably by referring to the external agencies such as the HSE, RoSPA or Centre for Safety Studies (CSS) but having obtained the information, sorted it and sequenced it, it is largely up to the expertise of the teacher to get the information across to the students. There are some tools to help do this. The use of appropriate visual aids and some points on speaking in public are briefly discussed below.

Visual aids

The need for effective presentation of lesson material requires more than an individual's knowledge of the subject or even the ability of the instructor to communicate with others. Various means are utilised to bridge the senses so that the learning situation involves more than just the sense of hearing. It must be remembered that visual aids do not teach but are seen as an aid to teaching. The brain obtains information through the senses and with most people it does this best via the eye. When using static

BLOGGS & BLOGGS Plc

Department of Safety Education

Lesson Plan No [   ]

Name of Teacher	
Subject	
Course	
Year	Age Range
Ability level	
Length of lesson	

Aim of the Lesson

Time	Salient Points	Method	Visual Aids

Visual Aid Summary:

References:

Figure 10.6 A Typical Lesson Plan

aids, the student can absorb information at his/her own pace, whilst moving aids assist the transfer from item to item smoothly. There are several types of visual aid in common use and these are:

- Models and samples.
- The chalkboard.
- Feltboard, flannelgraph or plastigraph.
- Magnetic boards.
- Charts and diagrams.
- Overhead projectors (OHP).
- Strips and slides.
- Episcopes/diascopes/epidiascopes.
- Loop-cassette projectors.
- Movie-projectors.
- Screens.
- Video.
- Interactive video.
- Computer screens.

Models and samples

These can be manufactured to suit the exact requirements of the instructor and are realistic. Although they are more valuable if produced by the students themselves the disadvantages of using this approach are:

- They need time and effort to produce.
- They can be expensive.
- They suffer from wear and tear.
- They need space to store.

Some operations are more suited to this type of visual aid than others. For example, if students are required to visualise a whole conceptual arrangement then a model might be the best means of illustrating this in a contextual sense. A bomb disposal trainee, for instance, would derive great benefit from seeing a model of something which later had to be tackled in a real-life situation!

The chalkboard

There are several types available, some of which use an easel whilst others are of the pull-down type. The chalkboard is not as popular as it was and is considered by some as messy but there are still many to be found in schools, colleges and in classrooms within the workplace. Some points to bear in mind when using this as an aid are:

- Clean it properly.

- Use colour with discrimination.
- Write clearly using print.
- Use good quality chalk.
- Prepare involved work.
- Watch spelling!
- Do not talk to the board.

Feltboards, flannelgraphs and plastigraphs

There are many types and makes available. They consist of felt objects adhering by friction to a rough surface. They have many advantages:

- They are extremely portable.
- Excellent for young students.
- Quiet.
- Worthwhile for repeat/reinforcing lessons.
- One can be made quickly and cheaply from an old blanket.
- They have a high retention rate.

However, they do need time to prepare and bits and pieces can easily get lost.

Magnetic boards

These are flat metal boards made of iron or steel and can be used with magnetic models. This allows:

- Movement from semi-static position and for build-up.
- Magnetic rubber strip and symbols to be used which are readily available.
- Chalk, string, and non-permanent felt-tip pens to be used.

On the minus side, they do need to be kept clean and protected from denting and other damage, and the models can easily become broken or lost.

Charts and diagrams

These include the turn-over pad and the flip-chart and allow for notes to be made as the lesson proceeds. They are useful for close inspection both during and after the lesson. The pre-printed teaching charts are bold and clear but not too detailed. Flash cards are smaller and more suited to younger children. However, they soon become shabby and can be expensive to buy. They are best stored by suspending from clothes pegs or similar device.

Overhead projector (OHP)

This can usually replace the chalkboard for most purposes. It requires no blackout facilities and can take rollers or individual slides. Using an overlay method a build-up can be created. It is light and portable, but do not move it when the lamp is hot. 3D models can be projected if they are transparent – for example, if they are made in perspex. The disadvantages are:

- The screen needs to be angled to avoid distortion of the image.
- Long periods with this can make the operator thirsty.
- Do not leave the slide on the screen when talking about something else.

Strips and slides

The instructor can use these with his/her own voice at their own speed. The most popular size is 35mm and most modern cameras allow the instructor to create their own slide set quickly and cheaply. Slides can also be made using a scratch pen and they last longer than strips. They can be stored easily and care should be taken to see that slides are in the right order and the right way round.

Strips are still available and being used widely. If they are of the half-frame type then they need to be partly covered as the lesson develops. It is advisable to use a short throw lens in order to get the projector near to the teaching position.

Episcope/diascope/epidiascope

An episcope projects pictures including pages from books, journals and magazines whilst the diascope projects slides. The epidiascope does both. The machines are rather heavy and require complete blackout. There are still a few of these machines around but most have been made redundant with the advent of the OHP and modern photocopying technology.

Loop-cassette projector

These projectors still exist and are usually of the 8mm or Super 8mm variety. There are projectors around that take both sizes but come in different types. They are either silent or sound so it is important to check beforehand which type you have. There is no film threading required and they are simple to use and usually come with built-in or normal screens. They can take approximately 10 minutes of film before going around again. They are useful for showing repeat skills. If you still possess an 8mm camera then you can take your own films.

Movie-projector

Most educational films are 16mm in size, in colour with sound. Some projectors allow for stills to be shown and have a reverse facility. It is important that the teacher is competent to operate and handle a projector properly. Ideal for large audiences.

Screens

There are a variety of surfaces on conventional screens and each has some effect upon picture quality and definition from various viewing angles. Daylight screens have special surface characteristics to enable their use in high ambient light situations but there are problems about their siting and viewing angles. Back projection screens are made of translucent plastic material and the projector is positioned behind the screen. By using back projection, the screen image is 10 times brighter by transmitted light than by reflected light (conventional screen). Straight through back projection requires the slides to be placed in the carrier the wrong way round unless reversal is affected optically by:

- A mirror which is set at 45 degrees to the screen.
- A prism.

Back projection units are still used by some organisations but are being gradually replaced by the video.

Video

This is the most commonly used visual aid and one which is ideally suited to the small group. Video film is much cheaper to buy than the 16 mm variety and can be stopped, reversed and fast forwarded without damage. It is not susceptible to sprocket hole damage like the 16 mm film. With advances in technology most organisations now have easy access to video cameras and this provides for local films to be made relatively cheaply and quickly. They are easy to store and keep clean. The disadvantage is that they are not effective for large audiences.

Interactive video

These are now becoming more popular and involve the linking of a computer to a video which uses video disks. They are expensive and at present not many training aids are available but as technology advances, the price should come down to a level more acceptable to safety training budgets.

The computer

These can be used to show slides but like the video they are only suitable for small groups of students. They are, of course, extremely useful for preparing OHP slides and for the preparation of teaching notes and handouts which accompany a lesson.

Slide-type synchronising

This method of combining sound with visual material has a valuable contribution to make to the effectiveness of the lesson. Make use of music and other relevant sounds as they add to the quality and effectiveness of the presentation.

Oral presentation of the lesson

You should prepare the lesson as described above on page 423 and illustrated in Figure 10.6. It should be remembered that adults have a listening ability of up to 35 minutes. After this time concentration lapses. The following are some suggestions which might help a teacher/lecturer when delivering a lesson or talking to a group of people.

However good or sensible safety may seem it must be carefully thought out into logical sequences and the teacher must talk with, rather than at, the audience. The speaker must not be seen to be on a crusade or being righteous and above the need for safety. Reference to the instructor's own mistakes or vulnerability will counter this.

Manner and style of presentation is important to an audience listening to safety related matters. Sit on a desk rather than behind it and avoid high positions. This should prevent the instructor being seen as a lofty, distant voice sitting in judgment on the assembled class. To the younger audience, researchers have found that appeals for common sense have been found to be irrelevant. They are short on experience and common sense is dull and boring. Young people often like speed, risk and excitement and life is cheap to some of them. Loss of life or limb is beyond comprehension and any use of threat is wasted. An elderly Second World War winner of the Victoria Cross was recently being interviewed about his award which was won against tremendous odds. When this medal was won, the gentleman was only 23 years old. The interviewer asked 'what qualities do you think you possessed to carry out such a brave task under such terrible conditions?'. The war hero replied 'inexperience'.

It is never good policy to make one of the group the target of fun or laughter although there is usually always one 'character' in every class. Laugh at oneself if necessary. Deal with self-elected leaders tactfully but firmly. Do not be afraid to use humour on occasions throughout the class period as this helps to maintain attention.

The success of a safety lecture comes from the positive involvement in the group to help each other prevent accidents from happening.

Methods of teaching

There are several methods of presenting the safety programme to a group of people. This can be done by:

- The lecture.
- Individual/group projects.
- Assignments.
- Discussion groups.
- Tutorials.
- Role play.

These are discussed in more detail below.

The lecture

The most common method for the safety educator is the lecture. It is cost-effective in that larger groups can be dealt with at one time. If 200 people have to be familiarised with the implications of the COSHH regulations quickly, then the lecture becomes an attractive proposition. However, it is rather a formal and can sometimes be regarded as an impersonal method of teaching. As a result, there can be difficulty in testing whether everyone has understood and grasped the aim of the talk. Wherever possible, this method would benefit from recapping previous work and needs to be linked with the topic in hand. If it is a stand-alone lecture on a specific topic then relevance is an important factor to get across in the introduction.

There is little or no opportunity to become involved as lectures tend to be static presentations. If there are to be handouts given as part of the lecture then it is best to give these out at the end otherwise the audience will start reading them rather than listening to the speaker.

Individual/group projects

Individual/group projects can be a very cost-effective method of teaching but care should be taken when choosing it as an option. The project method takes time to prepare and complete and individuals must be selected on their capability to undertake and complete such an activity as students will need to work without supervision on occasions. However, it is important that the individual or group is/are clear on what is expected from the project and that they are aware of where help can be obtained if needed. This method is recognised as an effective means of education and can be controlled more easily. Periodic testing is made much simpler thus allowing for the effectiveness of the teaching and learning processes to be monitored. Problems can arise if motivation and interest is not maintained and completion time must be regularly monitored (see page 418).

Assignments

Assignments are small tasks usually issued to individuals over a period of time designed to make the student develop discovery techniques within the learning process. They are effective in helping to maintain motivation in that assignment tasks are normally small and varied. In order to test the effectiveness of this method of learning several small tasks need to form part of the safety education programme. The use of assignments can be cost-effective in the more technical environments but the safety manager should not rule out this method even if his area of responsibility is not regarded as technical.

Although the use of assignments is time consuming and more expensive than some alternative methods, this method is more effective than the lecture method (but less efficient). Careful and regular monitoring is also required to ensure that motivation and interest is maintained.

Discussion groups

When leading a discussion group, the functional theory of leadership applies in two areas:

1. Diagnosing how effective the group is; and
2. Intervening in appropriate ways to increase its effectiveness.

A instructor needs to be able to diagnose which behaviours are needed in the group in order for it to accomplish its task and maintain itself over a period of time. This will involve such things as identifying which functions are being met and those which are not, which norms are present or absent in the group and what is the current learning climate of the group. In order to make such a diagnosis, the instructor needs to know how to obtain valid and reliable information from the group on its functioning. In diagnosing the ongoing process of a discussion group a person needs to have some criteria against which to evaluate the present level of functioning and some idea of the behaviours needed to fulfil the task and maintain the functions of the group.

A few criteria for judging the effectiveness of a discussion group are:

- The prevalence of a warm, accepting, non-threatening group climate that makes it safe for students to risk exposing their ignorance and to ask questions.

● A co-operative approach to learning in which students give mutual aid in developing understanding of the material under discussion.
● Participation and leadership behaviours distributed across the group with the responsibility for the group's successful operation being shared by all members.
● The successful learning of the safety material/subject being covered.

The main types of behaviour needed in order for a discussion group to function are:

● Initiating and contributing ideas.
● Giving and asking for information.
● Giving and asking for opinions and reactions.
● Clarifying, synthesising, summarising and giving examples.
● Evaluating the effectiveness of the group and diagnosing difficulties in group functioning.
● Encouraging and supporting participation of all group members.

After a diagnosis of the group's functioning is made, the instructor should possess the skills necessary to intervene effectively in the ongoing process of the group. Intervention skills depend primarily upon self-awareness and flexibility of behaviour. Through an awareness of how the student is behaving and how the behaviour is perceived by members of the group, the instructor should establish control over this behaviour. For example, when a teacher wishes to give support to a particular group member who is having difficulties in participating in a discussion, the instructor should be aware of the cues used to communicate support and how this is perceived by the others.

A person's behaviour is often misinterpreted. For example, a simple supportive comment such as 'thankyou for your support John' can be construed to be sarcastic and punishing. As a result, behaviour should be modified to communicate the intent more clearly. An awareness of the control over the teacher's own behaviour enables him/her to behave flexibly according to the demands of the situation and the characteristics of the group members.

A teacher who is locked on to one style of behaviour in groups, such as the democratic/authoritarian style, will not be able to function effectively under a variety of conditions. At times, a group may need a strong, directive leader and at other times it may need a moderator who only initiates a discussion topic and then sits back and allows the group members to do the rest.

Both the instructor and the students are responsible for behaving in ways that will help the group accomplish its task and maintain itself in good working order. There are, however, two major roles that the instructor will perform that are difficult for students to assume:

1. The instructor in most instances will know what materials, information and readings are most relevant and helpful for the group; and
2. A group performance role of teaching the students the group skills that they need to function effectively in a discussion group. This may involve skill sessions whereby the students are given practice in fulfilling different roles in the group and/or periodic evaluation of the functions present in the group and these are needed to improve the quality of the group's functioning.

In a discussion group, the members should clearly understand what is expected of them. The instructor's expectations and the procedure that the group is going to follow should be as clear as possible. Goal-directed behaviour cannot be achieved in the absence of perceived goals. If the goals are not clear even the most highly motivated student will have difficulty in being effective because he would have no conceptual model or clear understanding of the kind of behaviour that would contribute to building a good group.

This does not mean that the teacher should impose a clear structure upon the students but that the teacher and the students need to develop a clear understanding of what the objectives of the group are, of what the criteria are against which the performance of the group can be evaluated and of what behaviours are needed in order to ensure an effective learning group.

The use of the discussion group can therefore be an extremely effective but time consuming method of teaching. Safety officers should consider this method with courses aimed at senior managers.

Tutorials

When considering the tutorial system it is important to consider whether professional assistance is available or where the use of team teaching makes it possible for one or more of the team to provide tutorial services. The person acting as tutor will work with one or more students but not necessarily at the same time. This is particularly effective when students have a particular problem, and specialised or concentrated help is required.

Tutorials rely upon a mixture of oral/aural skills and can be used to control individual projects and/or assignments. They provide an opportunity for instructor and student to get together periodically to discuss those tasks which have been assigned to the student. The teacher or supervisor must be available to give time to the student and it may not be possible for tutorials to take place in work time. It is usual for these to be held after working hours so that more time can be allocated to the review process. Where actual case studies are used it is important that the student is in possession of all the relevant facts and has authority and support to obtain additional material if it is required. Students should be given objectives to meet between each tutorial and guidance as to how information/assignments are to be presented.

The provision of tutorials can be extremely beneficial to particular students but they are expensive and often difficult to provide on a large scale. Thus the question arises as to which student(s) are entitled to such specialised help. Many safety managers would reject the use of tutorials because of this.

Role play

This method of teaching allows the student to enact a particular part or role. The student can play out a simulated life-like situation which thus gives an insight into how other people might live, react, behave, or perceive things. Because of the total student involvement in this process, interest and motivation is maintained throughout as both theory and practice are permitted to come together. The student is allowed to make decisions of their own and is free to express and to form opinions. For example, in a safety management situation, students might take it in turns to be the safety manager whilst others might be the director of finance or production manager or trades union representative or the HSE inspector and so on. Each student will play their role within a general framework. Safety problems are simulated which the students, playing their various roles, will have to solve. The teacher must have first hand experience of the problem and how to solve it so that appropriate guidance can be given to students as the play proceeds. He must also act as referee in cases where the debate might get too heated and also be able to provide additional information which may be requested from the role playing group. Careful planning is needed to prepare the simulation and to get it started. From this the role play will develop its own characteristics and intergroup personalties.

This teaching method is an extremely enjoyable one and is very effective although it can be rather time consuming and costly. Safety managers, however, should consider this method as it provides an opportunity for all grades of worker to enact each others' roles, albeit in a simulated set of circumstances.

Summary

Safety education forms an important part of the safety mix and it has only been necessary here to cover some of the basic issues concerning the learning process and methods of teaching. It must be remembered that for safety education to be effective it has to be continuous. Safety education should form part of the National Curriculum so that good attitudes towards safety are formed at an early age. There are opportunities for this under the broad headings of mathematics, science and English. For example, accident statistics will meet criteria in the new curriculum under mathematics and information technology, whilst heat, combustion, balance, gravity, friction, centrifugal force, etc, will form part of the science syllabus as will the impact of pollution on the environment. Statistics show that more men are involved in accidents than women. Why this might be so could form the part of a language development programme under the English heading. All this will, in the long term, make the job of the safety manager a much easier task.

For the more discerning safety practitioner a further reading list is provided below.

Further reading

Bligh, D A (1972) *What's the Use of Lectures?* (Penguin Books)

Russell, G J (1972) *Teaching in Further Education* (Pitman Educational Library)

Stone, D R and Neilsen, E C D (1982) *Educational Psychology: The Development of Teaching Skills* (Harper and Row)

Safety training and safety management development

Introduction

Safety training is a very broad term which includes any activity that is to improve an individual's performance, increase his contribution to organisational effectiveness and to reduce or prevent accidents from happening. There are many approaches to safety training within organisations that vary from the systematic approach to vague ideas about things people ought to know about in order to do their job safely. Safety management development is an area often singled out from the general area of training in order to identify the process of improving safety practitioners' knowledge, understanding and abilities in order to improve the competence of the safety management team. Safety management development programmes are often more individually tailored than, for example, training programmes for shop floor workers. Whilst there may be differences in the type of learning objectives and in the time scale involved, it is felt that the same principles apply throughout the general area of safety training and safety management development. The management of the safety training function is a fourfold process:

1. Assessing the need — determining the safety training requirements for *all* types of staff, deciding priorities and defining standards;
2. Programming — plans and procedures aimed at fulfilling the needs in terms of the policy on internal or external courses; individual development plans; deciding upon the best techniques appropriate to each type of safety training;
3. Organising — how best to use the staff, finance and resources available for safety training purposes; and
4. Evaluation — how well the results meet the original needs; budgetary control of resources.

A major problem concerning safety training is that often it is carried out with unclear objectives and a failure to diagnose real training needs which may lead to the whole value of safety training being questioned. In this chapter, the following shall be discussed:

- Objectives of safety training.
- Approaches to safety training.
- Safety training methods.
- Evaluation of safety training.

General aspects to consider when using safety training as remedial strategy are also discussed later in the chapter.

Objectives of safety training

The objective of safety training can be stated quite simply as an activity designed to improve organisational effectiveness and safety. However, this overall general objective needs to be broken down into more specific goals. The area of safety training can be divided into two major activities:

1. Safety training; and
2. Safety development.

This division is based on the objectives which are to be achieved. If the activity is specific, factual, short-term and including only a narrow range of material (e.g. new safety regulations such as COSHH) then it can be defined as training. If the activity is concerned with developing abilities, skills and changing attitudes in the broad safety management sense then it is often termed safety development. The division between training and development is very unclear and many organisations carry out safety management training which could well be described as safety development and vice versa.

A typical safety training objective might be to increase a worker's knowledge and understanding of a particular subject such as the HASAWA, COSHH regulations or internal fire alarm procedures. Or, to develop skills both physical and mental, safe use of equipment, problem solving, etc. Attitudes may be changed regarding safety procedures, policies and practice, and rewards can be made to individuals for good safe work. A safety training objective might be to maintain the labour force in good safe condition. Although these objectives are extremely general it is important that if training is to be effective the objectives need to be thoroughly considered and related to the objectives of the organisation. Safety training for safety training's sake frequently occurs because safety objectives have not been drawn up in any meaningful way. Safety training requires objectives to be:

- Specific.
- Realistic.
- Measurable.

Approaches to safety training

There are several ways in which an organisation may approach the activity of safety training, varying from ways which develop training policies to those which operate on an ad hoc and unsystematic basis. In order to understand more clearly the question of approaches to safety training there are four approaches to safety training activity:

1. The administrative approach;
2. The individual approach;
3. The organisational development approach; and
4. The systematic approach.

These four categories are now discussed.

The administrative approach

Here, safety training is approached with an administrative bias as the name would suggest. Courses are organised and people are fed into them by their departments or by the safety manager. The disadvantage is that the diagnosis of their safety training needs is very weak and whole groups of jobs, such as all supervisors, are sent on courses whether or not they are appropriate. The evaluation of this approach tends to be weak as success is often seen as numbers trained and the amount of grants received or levies not paid. Whether or not the training has improved either the individual's safety performance or the organisation's safety effectiveness seems of secondary importance.

The individual approach

As the name suggests, safety training is given based upon the needs of the individual. It is normally instigated by an individual requesting a training course and for the organisation to support this request. The safety training requested may well meet the needs of the individual but these may not be linked to the organisational needs. Often the safety training is carried out on an external basis by consultants or safety organisations and the courses may attract people from different industries and backgrounds, with the safety training consequently lacking direct relevance. This technique tends to be weak in terms of evaluation as it is based on the subjective assessment of the individual who attended the safety course, seminar, conference, etc. This approach is prevalent in many organisations and it is difficult to justify when considering those safety training objectives discussed above on page 438.

The organisational development approach

This approach lays great emphasis on the diagnosis stage of the safety training process. The specialist and relevant managers spend considerable time attempting to define the real problem and what real safety training requirements should be and whether it is a safety training issue at all. The primary concern of this approach to safety training is to concentrate on improving health and safety processes that operate within the organisation. This approach is also concerned very much with organisational change and diagnosing needs in this area rather than concentrating on the traditional areas of safety training for a particular industry.

Internal and self-managed safety training is stressed to a great extent in this approach. Management should be involved in planning and carrying out their own safety training by using and learning from their own experiences. Much of the safety training under this category is concerned with groups of workers on vertical, diagonal or horizontal slices through the organisation. Safety training should be developed at a group level if major changes are to be made in the organisation particularly if safety performance is to be improved.

The systematic approach

This follows a rigorous approach to all aspects of the total safety training process. For convenience it can be divided into four important steps:

1. The diagnosis of safety training needs;
2. The objective setting phase;
3. The design of the safety training programme; and
4. Evaluation of the safety training programme.

This approach to safety training is time consuming and because of this is often neglected by organisations.

Diagnosis of the safety training needs

To define specific training needs, it is necessary to begin at the macro-level and then come downwards towards the individual safety training needs at the micro-level. In order to start at the macro-level, it is important to know the organisation's objectives so that any shortcomings in safety performance may be identified. Areas such as accident rates or dangerous occurrences should be examined to see if there is any deterioration in performance. It should be remembered that detailed accident analysis is required if contributory factors are to be identified. These factors may well have little to do with training (e.g. the 0.25 enforcement sector within the safety mix may need to be increased), but assuming that a safety training need has been identified it is necessary to consider at what occupational level safety training is required and in particular, what individual safety training needs exist.

There are a number of questions that need to be answered at this stage:

- For which occupations is safety training required to cater for current weaknesses or for future accident reduction needs?
- How many people will need training?
- What are the critical areas?
- Where can the best return on the investment be made?
- What resources and constraints will affect these questions?

Having answered these questions it is then necessary to examine the job or occupations selected as the priority area and decide whether the present system could be changed or reorganised to obviate the need for safety training. Assuming that it is accepted that a safety requirement exists, as is quite often the case, the individual job needs to be analysed in terms of its objectives, activities, component parts, skills, knowledge necessary to carry out the job safely and effectively. The next step is the final one before considering the objective setting sequence. As a detailed analysis of the skills and knowledge required to perform the task has been drawn up it is necessary next to detail the skills and knowledge already possessed by the target population. The difference between the skills and knowledge already possessed and those required to do the job effectively and safely is known as the *safety training gap*.

Objective setting

This part of the systematic safety training process is really attempting to answer the question: 'What are we wanting the trainee to be able to do when training is complete?'

This means that criteria should be developed which are both quantifiable and measurable. This can be a difficult process as often safety training programmes are attempting to achieve vague and indefinable changes such as an improvement in attitude or behaviour. However, wherever possible it is worthwhile to attempt to develop criteria which can be assessed as this clarifies the process of programme design as well as the evaluation process.

Objective setting tends to be easier where straight knowledge and physical skills are involved but becomes more difficult when concerned with safety management training which goes further than straight knowledge inputs.

Designing the safety training programme

This stage contains two steps:

1. To decide the content of the training activity; and
2. To plan the method and sequence of the programme.

The content of the safety programme should stem from the training gap identified earlier and will obviously link closely with the objectives that are defined. The second step is probably more difficult as it involves making decisions about the sequence of learning, where it will take place, who will carry it out and what resources are available, etc. The answers to these questions will depend on many factors such as the level of motivation of the trainees, the degree of complexity of the material and the safety manager's (or his trainer's) beliefs concerning learning theories and so on. The planning of the safety training programme can only be carried out within the context of a particular situation and therefore the many factors that need to be considered cannot be detailed here as they need to be referred to specific cases in point. A further important point concerns the teaching methods to be employed. There are many methods available and these will be discussed later in this chapter.

Evaluation

This part of the process is usually ignored by many safety practitioners yet if properly organised can answer important questions such as:

- Has the training achieved its objective?
- Has it satisfied the training need?
- Do the benefits justify the costs?

This aspect is discussed later on page 444.

Safety training methods

There are several methods available for transferring safety information to others. At the basic level, safety training methods can be divided into on-the-job and off-the-job, and again the decision as to which is most appropriate will depend upon the situation in question. These two types of safety training are now discussed.

On-the-job safety training

There are five major methods of on-the-job training to consider:

1. Sitting with Nellie;

2. Project work;
3. Job rotation;
4. Cook's Tour; and
5. Coaching.

Sitting with Nellie

This is a very common method and is used for simple tasks where the risk factors are very low. As the name implies, this method involves a new worker sitting with an experienced operator and learning the job by observation and by trial and error. This can be an inexpensive method of learning provided that the operator is familiar with safety procedures and has a good safe work record. Because this method relies heavily upon the attitude and abilities of the skilled operative it has gained a bad reputation in terms of effectiveness.

Project work

This is often used where employees are required to have reached a certain academic and intellectual level such as graduate trainees who are allocated specific problems to work on, understand problems and develop solutions. This can be an effective safety training method as long as the projects are chosen with the trainees' needs in mind and encouragement and feedback are given on a systematic basis. All too often, projects are allocated on the basis of giving the trainee something to do and little interest is taken in the trainee or the results of their work.

Job rotation and Cook's Tour

These methods can be considered together as they are based on the same principle of moving a trainee around either between departments or between various specific jobs. Job rotation can be useful where the operator is to be promoted to a supervisory position and a knowledge of safety procedures of the various jobs under their supervision is necessary, particularly if they are to be effective managers. The Cook's Tour is often used as part of a graduate trainee programme and involves movement between departments for varying lengths of time. The idea is to familiarise the trainee with the various functions within the organisation and to grasp the overall safety requirements of the organisation. This is a useful method of learning but often suffers from the trainee becoming disenchanted unless a sense of achievement is reached by the trainee as they move about.

Coaching

This is an extremely useful method of safety training which develops from the manager/subordinate relationship. Regrettably, many managers do not see the safety training of subordinates as part of their specific role but it is an area of great potential benefit to both manager and subordinate trainee. The philosophy behind coaching is that the manager and subordinate develop a relationship whereby time is spent in a teacher/student situation where job problems and risks are discussed and they are used to improve the subordinate's safety performance.

Off-the job safety training

There are many methods of safety training which are available and the reader will have experience of many of them. The methods need not be discussed in great detail but are merely listed, as advantages and disadvantages of each type can be drawn from readers' experience. The more common safety training methods are:

- Lectures.
- Seminars.
- Closed circuit television.
- Interactive video.
- Programmed learning.
- Films.
- Cases.
- Role play.
- Business games.
- Experimental learning techniques.
- Conferences.

Evaluation of safety training

The evaluation of safety training, particularly at management level, is an extremely difficult process and it is for this reason that many organisations balk at the thought of attempting to carry it out. However, if the training provided is to be improved, some evaluation is necessary to determine where the shortcomings lie. There are four levels of evaluation which can be considered:

1. Reaction level;
2. Immediate outcome level;
3. Intermediate level; and
4. Ultimate level.

These are now discussed in more detail.

Reaction level

Here, the safety training is evaluated on a subjective basis by the trainee immediately after the safety training has been completed. This is a very superficial evaluation but can contribute to the overall evaluation process. The sort of questions that might be asked would concern:

- The presentation of the information.
- The presentation of material.
- The relevance to the trainee.
- The usefulness of the training.

Immediate outcome level

This level of evaluation involves some objective testing of the trainee in terms of skills learnt or safety knowledge acquired. The trainee can be tested before the training takes place and again after it has been completed and the difference can be quantified.

Intermediate level

Here the evaluation is made some time after the safety training and focuses on changes that have taken place in the trainee's actual job performance. This kind of evaluation is particularly concerned with the transfer of safety training to the job. This is a critical area as often the trainee may be happy with the training provided but be unable to put it into practice. The problem at this level, is that there are many factors which might have affected the trainee's job performance other than the training itself. To relate any improvement in job performance to the training (to the exclusion of all other factors) is a difficult process.

Ultimate level

The objective of safety training should be to improve overall organisation effectiveness which will include its safety record. It can be argued that true evaluation of safety training only takes place where the safety training is linked to some improvement in organisational performance. If safety training is to be worthwhile, the attempt must be made to ensure that it does lead to an improvement in organisational effectiveness otherwise it will become difficult to justify.

Safety training should be an important activity in any organisation and it does not necessarily always need to be course based. Safety training forms a part of the overall safety mix and should not therefore be used in isolation but should be linked to some other aspect of the mix. Managers should understand the importance of developing their subordinates' safety awareness, and thus realise that safety training, in either a formal or informal sense, is an important part of their role and cannot be totally delegated to a training department or ignored altogether.

The value of induction training

This training is usually carried out by an organisation in order to help recruits to overcome their sense of strangeness, secure their acceptance by existing employees and develop in them a sense of belonging. A large amount of labour turnover occurs during the early weeks of employment usually because no effort has been made to enable the newcomers to feel welcome. From this he becomes unhappy and will leave to find alternative employment. This sort of training is an opportunity to introduce the new employee to the organisation's purpose and to discuss its safety policies, procedures, practices and programmes thus seeking to establish the correct link between each individual, his work and activities external to the organisation. In addition there is an opportunity to:

- Explain the new employee's place in the company.
- Explain the relationship between the employee's work and the finished product.
- Explain the relationship between the employee's company, industry and community.
- Explain the company's positive attitude to health and safety.
- Explain how the new employee can put ideas and points of view to management.

In smaller firms, the induction course is an informal affair and carried out normally by the recruit's immediate superior. A typical agenda for an induction course in a larger organisation is shown in Figure 11.1.

Such a programme should be conducted as often as the number of new recruits warrants and should be organised by the personnel department. It is important that senior executives are involved as this gives a good impression to the recruit and also adds prestige to the occasion. The safety manager might be responsible for conducting a tour of the workplace in order to explain:

- How each job fits safely into the flow of production.
- Departmental rules, procedures, practices, discipline, etc.
- Accident prevention procedures.
- Protective clothing policy.
- Action in an emergency.
- Hygiene rules and regulations.

- General safety and health policy.
- How to contribute to the well being of others, trade union membership and knowledge of members of the safety committee.
- Safety training policy.

If these points are to be covered in written form it is important that the information is well presented, readable and kept up to date. Occasionally tenth generation photocopies are used for this purpose and it is important to ensure that sufficient copies of the original are available for recruits. It

Bloggs & Bloggs plc

- *Welcome by Director*

- *Film 'Bloggs on the move'*

- *Talk by the Production Manager*

- *Talk by Public Relations Manager*

- *Talk by Safety Manager*

- *Tour of the works*

- *Coffee break*

- *Talk about social and welfare matters*

- *Summary*

**Course assembles in Training Room No 1 at 0900 hours
Monday 10th February**

Figure 11.1
A sample induction course programme

is worth holding a follow up meeting at a later stage for these recruits in order to evaluate the induction process.

Further reading

Cuming, M (1977) *The Theory and Practice of Personnel Management* (Heinemann)

Gane, C (1972) *Managing the Training Function* (Allen and Unwin)

Humble, J (1973) *Improving the Performance of the Experienced Manager* (McGraw-Hill)

King, D (1968) *Training Within the Organisation* (Tavistock)

Livy, B (1988) *Corporate Personnel Management* (Pitman Publishing)

Safety publicity management

Introduction

Safety publicity forms an important part of the education process within the safety mix. It is not necessarily confined to campaigns specifically and can include public relations and low key educational programmes designed specifically to inform rather than to persuade or change behaviour. Safety publicity can be an ideal way of promoting the company safety image whilst at the same time being an effective tool against accidents. It can be expensive and does require careful planning if it is to be used. Researchers have found, however, that safety publicity is not very cost-effective used in isolation and therefore it should be considered as part of an overall safety related programme. At the early planning stages it is important to identify the key areas of the safety mix which are to be employed and if safety publicity is to form part of this it is essential that its role is clearly defined. Many organisations have, in the past, been over-enthusiastic about publicity strategies because they advertise what is being done when in fact little or nothing may be being achieved at all. These exercises tend to be public relations exercises rather than carefully planned campaigns designed specifically to contribute to the accident reduction efforts of an organisation.

From the analysis of accident data areas for remedial action will be identified. Assuming that an effective strategy will be the use of a safety publicity campaign and sufficient financial resources are available then the following will need to be considered:

- Has a similar exercise been conducted in the past either internally or externally? Conduct a search of relevant literature to find out.
- What form is the campaign to take? Creative ideas need to be discussed and tentative plans drawn up.

- Who is the target audience? Set campaign objectives.
- Consider the communications brief.
- Consider the involvement of external and other agencies.
- Consider non-media countermeasures.
- Focus on the implementation strategy.
- Refine the plan.
- Implement the campaign.
- Monitor.
- Conduct the campaign review.

A model illustrating this process is given in Figure 12.1. Although external campaign agencies can be employed to conduct safety publicity campaigns it falls to the safety manager to liaise between agency and company. It is important, therefore, to understand the processes involved in this aspect of the safety mix.

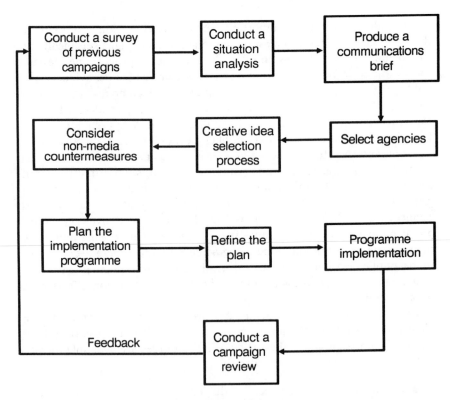

Figure 12.1

A basic safety publicity plan

Conduct the literature search

The past is a powerful indicator that will enable the safety manager to decide whether a campaign is appropriate to the problem and whether others have used a similar strategy in the recent past. It is the experience of others that will prevent us from reinventing the wheel. If a particular campaign has been successful in the past then it is possible to learn from the experience. Conversely, a failure is as important as a successful campaign and will allow the safety manager to put his ideas into perspective. Selling safety is different from selling specific products therefore literature searches should confine themselves to past safety campaigns and should not include product campaigns. Previous campaigns concerned with any aspect of social advocacy would be appropriate and might include litter campaigns, health, conservation, etc. Learning from the past is important because:

- Current research shows that social advocacy campaigns including safety campaigns are more likely be unsuccessful.
- Campaigns are extremely expensive and must compete with all other forms of advertising.
- Campaigns are high profile exercises and are sometimes used for other reasons than accident reduction.
- Learning from the mistakes (and successes) of others is good practice.

The importance of conducting a thorough *historical* survey prior to the planning stage cannot be stressed too strongly and all too often safety managers omit this important process.

Safety v other products

It is important to stress that advertising safety is somewhat different from advertising a specific product in the following ways:

- Selling the message is not always clear and the recipient may not identify with the message or feel it relevant. It may even be regarded as non-beneficial.
- Product marketing is usually aimed at small specific target audiences but safety and other social advocacy programmes are usually aimed at anyone who will listen!
- The philosophy behind product advertising is to build upon existing beliefs about a product and accept small changes from other products to the one being advertised.
- The behavioural objectives of product advertisers differ from those of

the safety advertiser in that the changes required are very small, do not concern negative issues and the status and ego are usually not threatened.

- The planning for safety campaigns needs far more care because the message must be impeccable with no room for error. It cannot show any undesirable behaviours thus providing an opportunity to ignore the message.
- Product advertising can be ongoing over longer periods of time whereas safety campaigns should be short and to the point.

People are not always rational and information alone is not sufficient to make them change. It is for this reason that the safety mix is required. The target group is rarely interested in the message unless it can be made relevant to them, and if it can be made sophisticated enough, then the target group may extract the intended meaning from the advertising.

When considering a safety campaign, it is important to think about what can and what cannot be achieved. From research carried out and the discussion so far it would seem that little can be achieved. It truth little can be achieved in safety terms if advertising is used in isolation. Safety campaigns used as an overall part of the safety mix can be successful particularly if there are specific tasks to accomplish. For these purposes, behaviour change would not be a realistic task but the following areas could be regarded as positive contributions:

- Campaigns can increase the awareness of a safety problem or a behaviour.
- Help reinforce or confirm beliefs.
- Raise the safety problem profile.
- Raise the interest level in a particular area.
- Assist in the education of a specific target group.

If the campaign is intended to change a behaviour or an attitude then it is unlikely to succeed but it can be used to show the need to change in the light of new legislation or the introduction of some change in company policy, procedure or practice.

Who do we design our campaign for?

When considering an overall change in behaviour as part of the safety mix it might be more appropriate to avoid directing the actual target group themselves, and instead to involve others. For example, a campaign aimed at miners who drink too much might consider those miners who do not. Such a theme might say 'would you work on the coal face if your mate had been drinking?'. In cases where the target audience have very rigid attitudes, say towards drinking, then a campaign aimed specifically at that group will probably not succeed. Most indirect approaches are more successful. Sometimes a campaign might be aimed at the workforce in general and can be justified on the grounds of developing salience to a particular safety issue. For example, an organisation wishes to introduce a revised working procedure and therefore might wish to communicate the point that more accidents occur in daylight, during clear fine weather than at any other time. A good point to remember is that people are influenced by what others think, particularly where workers operate in groups. An understanding of group norms is essential. Public opinion matters too and can act as a strong influencing factor on the beliefs and behaviour of individuals. Psychologists have long known that people's opinions and behaviour are influenced by what others say and do. Some refer to this as the 'sitting on the fence' theory. Individuals observe which opinions are gaining in popularity (or otherwise) and they will opt for whichever one they think is likely to prevail in the community. Safety campaigns can therefore play a useful role in suggesting to the public things to think about. Some publicists refer to this as *setting the agenda*. It is important to understand that advertising campaigns on safety education are able to tell people about what to think rather than how to think. What this implies is that safety campaigns can assist in forming public opinion to a certain degree by suggesting items that should be considered at both work and individual levels. The agenda setting process is a legitimate function of the advertising process but will not directly affect behaviour on its own.

On completion of the campaign, it has usually been found from research that little will have been achieved. This also applies to product advertising and safety and health campaigns. There is further evidence to suggest that advertising must form part of the safety mix if it is to be successful. People resist change and they do so by constructing a system of beliefs and attitudes which are designed to provide stability. Some say that people build a wall around themselves for this purpose. If this is so then for any campaign to be effective it must be able to attack each individual wall! What experience has taught us is that trying to change the wall is very difficult. Success is greatest when it is able to reinforce existing beliefs and builds upon existing needs to change. The thickness of the wall is built up over time as a result of experience. Familiarity with a particular process can breed a certain amount of contempt thus allowing accidents to happen. From this our experience leads us to a belief system which justifies our behaviour. To break through the wall requires new experiences thus allowing an opportunity to undergo a change of mind or attitude. Changes in legislation, procedure or internal codes of practice can allow for new experiences which may allow attitudes to be changed. An illustration showing the relationship between attitude and behaviour is given in Figure 12.2.

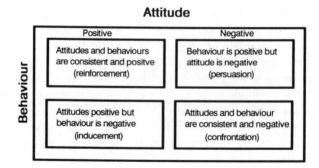

Figure 12.2

The relationship between behaviour and attitude

Planning a campaign

Areas for any form of remedial action should only be obtained from the analysis of appropriate accident data as described in earlier chapters of this book. It is recognised that some problems are in need of continuous remedial effort whilst others might only require the workforce to be reminded on certain occasions. When planning the budget it is always important to know if your intended programme can key in to any other similar campaign organised by the HSE or RoSPA. This may help to keep costs down. If this is not possible, then a local budget will have to be set aside. There is no simple formula to calculate this. If a preliminary budget is required then it will be necessary to:

- Assess the amount of funds which will be available for such an exercise. Consideration will need to be given to the production of leaflets, posters, public relations exercises and other promotional material.
- Isolate those areas which need to be addressed in the short term against those which require periodic treatment.
- Allocate available funds accordingly.
- Consider extending the potential of the budget by sponsorship or other means.
- Not to forget to allocate funds to the evaluation process at the end.

Some campaigns are judged on their creative content but whilst this is an important ingredient it must not be at the expense of the strategy. Exercising a controlled approach to the use of creativity is more effective (see Chapter 9). Within any organisation, reaction to the suggestion of a campaign can be varied. Some see this idea as a good means to be seen to be doing *something* positive whilst others need convincing that costs are justified. Only careful planning supported by evidence will convince the sceptics of the effectiveness of a well planned creative exercise. Conducting a situational analysis is how to determine the role that communications will play. Whilst being aware of the limitations of advertising campaigns, ultimate behavioural goals will be expected of the exercise since the safety campaign will try to influence voluntary discretionary behaviour such as wearing reflective jackets or protective headgear when unsupervised. For some the campaign would merely serve as a reinforcing exercise whilst for others it would involve confronting established behaviour and attitudes head on. It is important to:

- Ask if the campaign seeks a change in attitude, behaviour or both and how big a change is expected.
- Assess the barriers to change and list the rewards which may be associated with change.
- Assess whether compliance requires the acquisition of new skills.
- Ascertain if the most at risk groups have any specific media exposure patterns which might help with cost-effective targeting.

In developing our understanding of the target audience, a number of misconceptions exist, particularly the following:

- Arousing strong emotions changes behaviour.
- Using shock/horror tactics works.
- Equating self-reported behaviour with actual behaviour.
- Accepting the view that people know best what is good for them.

As a result of the situation analysis exercise it should now be possible to:

- Isolate the target audience.
- Target the behaviours.
- Target the theme(s).

Whatever the campaign objectives chosen as a result of considering these areas it is likely that they will involve one or more of the following:

- Increase demand for a range of countermeasures.
- Increase public awareness.
- Increase specific knowledge.
- Reinforce existing beliefs and behaviours.
- Modify attitudes or beliefs about specific countermeasures.
- Create a positive image.

Provided that the main aim of the advertising campaign is to be in a supportive role to other countermeasures then all of these communication objectives above are potentially achievable.

Communications

Following the literature search and the situation analysis programme it should be possible to prepare the communications brief. This document will contain the aims and objectives of the campaign and should provide some rationale behind the exercise. The main difference between the situation analysis document and the communication document is that the former is an internal brief and the latter is for external consumption. It is a more precise document and will be used to see the campaign through to its eventual evaluation. There are several methods of laying out the contents of a communications brief and the following is a suggestion taken from one of the many. It should contain:

- An outline of the problem.
- The aims and objectives.
- A specification of the strategies to be used.
- Identification of the role of the campaign within the context of the safety mix.
- Specification of the other factors within the safety mix.
- Specification of the change objectives expected.
- Specification of the target audience.
- Methods to motivate the target audience.
- Campaign message specifications.
- Budgetary details.
- Campaign timing and duration.
- Evaluation criteria.
- Constraints.
- Contractual arrangement details if appropriate.
- Other information such as technical data or research literature.

Such documents form an important part of the research phase for future campaign plans and should be properly filed together with the evaluation report for future reference.

The communications brief should be flexible enough to allow for creative freedom as opposed to artistic licence but should only be altered under exceptional circumstances, particularly where development research suggests changes. Altering or moving away from communications briefs is all too common and restraint should be exercised except for those instances mentioned above. One common justifiable reason usually given for changing the brief is cost. If cost or timing is presented as a reason for changing the brief will illustrate poor initial research.

The implementation phase

There are things that can go wrong with the start of the campaign and the reasons may be due to one or more of the following:

- The relevance of the campaign may not have been emphasised strongly enough.

- The quality of the campaign theme or its execution.
- The cost.
- Timing due to unforeseen circumstances (e.g. printing delays).
- Ethics.

The most common problem is operating within the time constraints particularly if the campaign is aimed at specific times of the year. Given that the time of the campaign is immovable then it is vital to control the timing of the campaign development. If time is not managed effectively then two possible outcomes are possible:

1. Creative messages and executions are cut down to fit because time will not allow for other options to be considered; and
2. Timing and costs go hand in hand together. If posters and leaflets, for example, do not arrive in time then this influences effective distribution and can increase costs.

If exhibitions are to be a feature of the campaign then timing is equally important so that displays are located where they should be in accordance with instruction in the communications brief.

The evaluation phase

Very few organisations evaluate their publicity campaigns and in today's economic climate the need to be cost effective is essential. Learning from experience is the best teacher and learning from failure is very productive. Without an evaluation phase within the communications brief, there are likely to be missed opportunities and a consequent waste of valuable resources. Evaluation provides us with an opportunity to discover what works and what does not – what can be achieved and what cannot. Evaluation is not, therefore, just a study of the past, since it provides information for the future. However, the results of evaluation are not always welcomed. If aims and objectives can be shown not to be achieved they can be seen as a failure of the organisation to get things right. No senior manager likes bad news therefore evaluation is seen as an unnecessary and troublesome exercise by some. This is further consolidated by the fact that most evidence shows the probability of receiving such bad news is quite high. It is therefore important that the results of the evaluative process are seen as a positive contribution to the safety publicity process for the future.

Safety practitioners are acutely aware of the high cost of carrying out controlled experiments yet it is only by using such methodology that it is possible to demonstrate effectiveness. The use of outside agencies and consultants is a more efficient way of doing this but even thorough scientific research experiments can show inconclusive results. There are few examples of campaign evaluation reports which can demonstrate measurable effects which may largely be due to this but those that have been conducted have used the following research tools in a variety of stages:

- Examining the opportunities and barriers (formative research).
- Assessing the creative message strategies (process research).
- Examining the strengths and weaknesses of a particular implementation strategy (pre-testing).
- Examining campaign effectiveness (outcome research).

Evaluation from the point of view of safety decision makers and researchers usually involves providing answers to the question 'did it work?'. This and the following questions should be answered:

- How could the campaign have been improved?
- What lessons and techniques are worth keeping for next time?
- What pitfalls must be avoided?

The choice is not an easy one − whether to maximise the likelihood of success or to prove success. If funds are available then it would be desirable to undertake both studies but if not then it might only be possible to conduct these on a campaign by campaign basis.

The safety programme audit

It is important that the evaluation phase of the campaign effects is not the only form of evaluation undertaken. If lessons are to be learned from the exercise then it is necessary to examine the key elements of the campaign as a whole and carry out an evaluation of any external agencies involved. A complete safety audit of these elements is necessary as an aid to future planning. The safety audit should include the following key areas:

- The situation analysis.
- The communications brief.
- The campaign development processes.
- The campaign implementation strategy.
- The media mix.
- Budgetary provision.
- Agency selection process.
- Agency performance.
- Client organisation.

It is important that safety practitioners try to share their experiences of using safety campaigns so that each may learn from the other. Although this may be difficult for individual companies, it is usual for organisations such as RoSPA and the CSS to act in this capacity.

Public relations

This is an important part of the safety management function but differs from campaign management in that behavioural or attitude change are not the prime motives for the exercise. On the contrary, public relations in safety management terms is an exercise in keeping the safety message in a prominent position within the organisation or externally. For example, a petroleum company may wish to employ tanker drivers of a particularly high standard. This standard becomes known and accepted and, properly publicised, can become reassuring to the general public. Public relations or PR lies somewhere between marketing and advertising but is neither one nor the other. It is not an ad hoc exercise. Like the advertising campaign strategy discussed above effective PR must have:

- An aim.
- An audience.
- A message.
- A method of getting the message over.
- A means of checking results (evaluation).

Looking at these areas in more detail we need to clarify why a PR exercise is necessary in the first place. All too often these exercises are carried out because it seemed like a good idea at the time or because they have always been held at a particular time. Some typical aims for the safety manager might be to:

- Increase/regain confidence from either the workforce or public or both.
- Establish an identity.
- Get things changed.
- Establish a community presence.

It is possible that more than one aim is intended such as to reassure the public (not forgetting shareholders), recruit school leavers, attract customers and build up confidence within the workforce. Knowing why a particular exercise is being undertaken is essential. Having a purpose will improve effectiveness. Holding publicity stunts for no clearly defined purpose is not productive.

Having decided the aim of the exercise then a decision must be made as to who are to be the recipients of the exercise. Also, it is possible that the exercise may be seen by more people than expected depending on the newsworthiness of the plan. This could also lead to distraction from the real purpose. For example, barracking the chairman of the planning and highways committee because of proposals which would be detrimental to your organisation might be a good way of attracting public sympathy but will not advance your cause with the authorities, particularly at the public enquiry stage. It is also possible that certain actions can reverse the intended purpose of the publicity. Publicity stunts, therefore, should be avoided. Here are some audiences which might be approached:

- Potential customers.
- Existing customers.
- Creditors and shareholders.
- Government and authorities.
- Schools.
- Opinion formers.
- Employees.

There are other audiences and many reasons for wanting to reach them but one important factor in communication is knowing the target audience. A safety manager working in the education department of a local authority would not approach Radio 4, for example, to get a message to young students. The local 'pop' radio might be more fruitful.

Having planned the aim of the exercise and consideration having been given to the target audience, the next step is to consider the message. Whatever medium used it is advisable to keep the message short and to the point. The gist of the message might be:

- We are safer now than last year.
- We do not allow explosions to ruin the community any more.
- We no longer pollute our rivers.
- Our ferries do not sink or catch fire any more.

Although these short statements summarise what is to be the gist of the message it might be that a 100 to 500-word press release can say this thus avoiding a half-hour speech in which to try to get the same message over verbally. The point in any message is to maintain one core message and just a small number of salient points. Remember that audiences can only absorb a limited amount of information at any one time. Any more than six points and by the time point number six has been arrived at point number one will usually have been forgotten.

PR should be used to promote the truth about an organisation. It would not be appropriate to use PR to cover up defects in an organisation or to tell untruths on its behalf. They get found out! There is of course a process called defensive PR which allows for difficult things to be said in times of difficulty. For example, at the time of the Zeebrugge ferry disaster (or any other disaster for that matter) the news media will require a quote from someone within the organisation. 'A company spokesman said' approach is bad news whereas the defensive PR approach is to come up front and admit to being upset and to reassure the public that something constructive is being undertaken and that a full investigation is to be held. Until this has occurred only opinion can be issued. This should not be given.

In a recent lecture to PR students at Bournemouth Polytechnic the lecturer stated:

'Keep words to a minimum and avoid jargon or government gobbledegook. Simple, short statements have impact. For example, the Lord's Prayer contains under 70 words, the Ten Commandments have 197, the American Declaration of Independence has 300 and the EEC Directive on the importing of caramel contains 26,911 and requires a linguist to translate.'

He also went on to say:

'Two million adults in Britain cannot read, only 40% of the country understand what is meant by the word *vulnerable*, only 17% know what a *decade* is, only 13% understand what *chronological* means, even less (4%) know what *autonomous* means and less than 1% have any idea what *empirical* means.'

Whilst it is not known which survey this information actually came from the point is illustrated that small simple words will be understood by a much wider audience.

Getting the message over is therefore important and to do this it is necessary to examine the channels of communication. There are two types:

1. Informal channels; and
2. Formal channels.

Informal. These are usually conducted on a one-to-one basis and a typical informal channel of communication would be at a safety conference talking to delegates over lunch about your organisation and how you may have tackled a particular problem. The process is complete when these delegates may mention this to other colleagues later, and so on. Also included in this category are speeches and lobbying of officials.

Formal. These channels cover the main media channels of the press, radio and TV but the point here is that there are many different types of audience for the different types of press and programmes. There are many journals dealing with safety issues for example, several local newspapers, radio stations and radio/TV programmes, etc.

Formal channels can be created by generating interest in some aspect of the safety process. This can be achieved by issuing a press notice, making a telephone call, holding a press conference or even by taking the local news reporter to lunch. Whatever method is decided upon it should be remembered that the press cannot be bought. They will report, in most cases, what they understand from:

- The press release.
- Their questions.
- Their investigations from other sources (contentious items).

Having put out the message, the final stage is to check whether the selected target group have received and understood the content of it. Very few people actually carry out this important exercise but there seems little point in spending valuable resources undertaking various PR activities if no check is made to see whether the right or wrong interpretation has been made or whether the message has reached the right group of people. There are ways of finding this information out. As discussed above on page 457 there are ways of evaluating programmes. It might be that a survey (questionnaire) needs to be circulated. It does not have to include everyone provided that a good representative sample is obtained. If the organisation is small then the exercise can be a low key affair conducted on a one-to-one basis when talking to them in the normal course of events. For example, when the manager responsible for safety next talks to his (sub-contractors) face to face or on the telephone (even by letter), about a particular exercise he might say:

'By the way did you see our press coverage last week? what did you think of it?'

The point to make is that the evaluation exercise does not necessarily have to be elaborate and can involve other staff in the organisation not normally responsible for PR matters. What is more important is that a file is maintained showing all press coverage of these safety/PR exercises as this will build up a picture of the extent of the coverage received. This can also be used for comparison purposes, such as answering the question: 'Was our PR exercise better this year than last year?'

It is also useful to observe what others do and consider whether that particular idea can be used or modified slightly. Advice can also be obtained from a PR consultant and there are several about who can offer advice with ideas, contacts and services (e.g. writing press releases). If using a PR consultant for the first time it might be appropriate to speak to at least three and ask them how they would tackle a particular problem and ascertain the cost. Find out something about previous clients and whether they have been satisfied with the service provided. If the PR consultant is new (everyone must have a first contract at some point in their career) try him out on a few small jobs first or provide a short-term contract.

Presentations and demonstrations

These must not be confused with lessons or indeed lectures, and the person giving the presentation cannot be regarded as a teacher or lecturer. Although someone making a presentation might use the same techniques as the teacher and lecturer the main difference lies in the audience:

- In school, the audience are there because the law requires them to.

- In a lecture hall the audience have a desire or interest in what the person has to say in a particular subject.
- In the case of the presenter or demonstrator the audience may be present because they have to be there.

In addition, lecturers and teachers are usually required to follow some sort of syllabus whereas a presentation or demonstration can often be a stand-alone exercise and can involve either senior management or shop floor workers. For example, it might be required that a first-aid or fire extinguisher demonstration or presentation is to be held.

Like all previous exercises it is important in the planning stages to have a clear and precise aim and a set of objectives for either a presentation (no audience participation) or a demonstration (with audience participation). Having decided which method of delivery to use to match set aims and objectives, it is then possible to identify the audience and to learn something about them. It is also necessary to think about:

- The message to be conveyed.
- Who the message is to be conveyed to.
- What they know already.
- Their general interest level (are they attending because they have to?).
- Recent relevant experiences.
- Whether there is any resistance.

Knowing something of the audience will help the planning of the programme to be completed. The process, like that described in Chapter 10 under lesson planning, allows for the presentation to have three parts, namely a beginning, a middle and an end. The introduction is the most important part of the exercise. It is used to set the scene and the pace, used to create interest and to confirm relevance. Here the demonstration scores over the presentation type method because of the practicalities involved in taking part. This creates interest and confirms relevance. There are four parts to the demonstration. These are:

1. *The explanation:* this includes the introduction features and puts the exercise into perspective. The explanation should include a summary of the aims and objectives for the group or audience and an outline of what is expected of them.
2. *The demonstration:* here the presenter demonstrates to the audience what they have to do and what is expected from the group when they have to do it.
3. *Imitation:* if sufficient equipment is available, get the group to imitate the presenter going through the step by step sequences. For example, in the first aid or fire example mentioned above the audience may work in groups copying the mouth to mouth resuscitation technique or particular emergency fire fighting technique; and

4. *Practice:* get the group to practise the staged techniques on their own until an acceptable standard is achieved or time period ends. The audience may wish to practise certain techniques in their own time later.

Presentations usually only require a classroom, lecture theatre or other similar room with facilities for using appropriate visual aids. The demonstration, however, may require a mixture of both. If, for example, a PR exercise was to be carried out to demonstrate some particular product or service then apart from a lecture theatre a demonstration area would also be required. The usual rules of safety must apply and should not be overlooked particularly when the exercise is safety related!

Some useful tips when making presentations or giving a demonstration are:

● Avoid unscripted presentations.
● Do not read from a paper.
● Use visual aids wisely (not for the sake of using them).
● Keep to the time limits.
● Use simple language (avoid using abstract nouns).
● Plan the facts.
● Use plenty of examples.
● Aim for the majority in terms of experience and knowledge.
● Use clear speech (the audience must be able to hear at the back).
● Watch for those unfortunate mannerisms and other distractions.

When the demonstration or presentation plan has been completed and is ready for delivery it is useful to hold a dress rehearsal. This allows for the timing of the exercise to be checked. It is also advisable to get someone who you can trust to listen to it and make constructive suggestions for improvement.

As in all aspects of safety publicity, it is always good safety management practice to carry out an appraisal or evaluation of the exercise. This provides valuable management information so that improvements can be made in the future. Each safety practitioner should audit his work regularly to improve the efficiency and effectiveness of organisational effort.

Further reading

Bland, M (1982) *Be Your Own PR Man* (Kogan Page)
Evans, R (1988) *Production and Creativity in Advertising* (Pitman Publishing)
Jay, A (1984) *Effective Presentation* (British Institute of Management)
Jenkins, F (1985) *Advertising* (Pitman Publishing)
Jenkins, F (1988) *Public Relations* (Pitman Publishing)

Appendix I
Duties of employers (Section 2)

Summary of main provisions of Health and Safety at Work etc Act (1974)

1. It shall be the duty of every employer to ensure, so far as it is reasonably practicable, the health, safety and welfare at work of all his employees.

2. **The employer will provide:**

   (a) the plant, maintenance thereof and systems or work that are, so far as it is reasonably practicable, safe and without risk to health. (2(2)(a))

   (b) arrangements for ensuring, so far as it is reasonably practicable, safe and healthy handling, storage and transport of articles and substances (2(2)(b))

   (c) information, instruction, training and supervision as is necessary to ensure, so far as it is reasonably practicable, the health and safety of all of his employees (2(2)(c))

   (d) safe access and egress to and from working area (within premises) (2(2)(d))

   (e) adequate facilities and arrangements for their welfare at work. (2(2)(e))

3. **Policy statement:** It shall be the duty of every employer to prepare, and as often as may be appropriate revise, a written statement of his policy with respect to the health and safety at work of his employees and the organisation and arrangements for carrying out that policy and bring the policy to the notice of all of his employees. (2(3))

4. **Appointment of safety representatives:** Shall make provision for appointment by recognised trade unions of safety representatives, and those persons shall represent the employees in consultation with employers. (2(4))

5. **Duty to consult with safety representatives:** It shall be the duty of every employer to consult any such representative with a view to making arrangements which will enable him and his employees to co-operate effectively in promoting health and safety at work. (2(6))

6. **Establishment of safety committees:** It shall be the duty of every employer to establish, if requested by the safety representative, a safety committee having the function of keeping under review the measures taken to ensure health and safety at work.

Duties of employers to persons other than their employees (Section 3)

7. It shall be the duty of every employer to conduct his business in such a way as to ensure so far as it is reasonably practicable, that persons not in his employment, who may be affected thereby, are not exposed to risks to their health and safety, and in prescribed cases, provide information about aspects of the way he conducts his undertaking as might affect their health and safety.

Duties of persons concerned with premises to persons other than their employees (Section 4)

8. This section has effect for imposing on persons duties in relation to those who:

(a) are not their employees but
(b) use non domestic premises made available to them as a place of work or as a place where they may use plant or substance provided for their use there and applies to premises used in connection with them. (4(1))

9. It shall be the duty of each person who has, to any extent, control of premises to which this section applies or of the means of access thereto or egress therefrom or of any plant or substance in such premises to take such measures as it is reasonable for a person in his position to take to ensure, so far as it is reasonably practicable, that the premises, all means of access thereto or egress therefrom available for use by persons using the premises, and any plant or substance in the premises, or, as the case may be, provided for use there, is or are safe and without risks to health. (4(2))

10. Where a person has, by virtue of any contract of tenancy, an obligation of any extent in relation to:

   (a) the maintenance or repair of any premises to which this section applies or any means of access thereto, or egress therefrom or

   (b) the safety of or absence of risks to health arising from plant or substances in any such premises that person shall be treated, for the purpose of paragraph 9 above, as being a person who has control of the matters to which his obligation extends. (4(3))

Duties of manufacturers and suppliers (Section 6)

11. (a) It shall be the duty of any person who designs, manufactures, imports or supplies any article for use at work to:

   (i)   ensure, so far as it is reasonably practicable, that it is designed and constructed to be safe and without risks to health

   (ii) carry out or arrange for the carrying out of tests and examinations to ensure safety of article

   (iii) provide with article adequate information as to the use for which it has been designed and tested.

   (b) Duty of any person who erects/installs any article for use at work to ensure that nothing about the way in which it is erected or installed makes it unsafe or a risk when used.

General duties of employees at work (Section 7)

12. It shall be the duty of every employee whilst at work:

   (a) To take reasonable care for the health and safety of himself and of other persons who may be affected by his acts or omissions at work; and

   (b) As regards any duties or requirements imposed on his employer or any other person by or under any of the relevant statutory provisions, to co-operate with this so far as is necessary to enable that duty or requirement to be complied with.

Duty not to interfere with or misuse things provided (Section 8)

13. No person shall intentionally or recklessly interfere with or misuse anything provided in the interests of health and safety or welfare.

Duty not to charge (Section 9)

14. No employer shall charge any employee in respect of anything done or provided in pursuance of any specific requirement of the relevant statutory provisions.

Offences (Section 33)

15. It is an offence for a person:

    (a) To fail to discharge a duty to which he is subject by virtue of Sections 2 to 7
    (b) To contravene Sections 8 or 9
    (c) To contravene any health and safety regulations or any requirement or prohibition imposed under any such regulations (including any requirement or prohibition to which he is subject by virtue of the terms of any condition or restriction attached to any licence, approval, exemption or other authority issued, given or granted under the regulations).

Offences due to the fault of another person (Section 36)

16. Where the commission by any person of an offence under any of the relevant statutory provisions is due to the act or default of some other person, that other person shall be guilty of the offence, and a person may be charged with and convicted of the offence by virtue of this section of the Act whether or not proceedings are taken against the first mentioned person.

Offences by the body corporate (Section 37)

17. Where an offence under any of the relevant statutory provisions committed by a body corporate is proved to have been committed with the consent or connivance of, or to have been attributable to any neglect on the part of, any director, manager, secretary or other similar officer of the body corporate or a person who was purporting to act in any such capacity, he as well as the body corporate shall be guilty of that offence and shall be liable to be proceeded against and punished accordingly.

Appendix 2

Statistical analysis for safety managers

In this appendix, the principal formulae for use in connection with the variety of safety activities are presented. As there is no accepted convention regarding the use of symbols but sampling theorists tend not to use Greek letters for population parameters the symbols used here are those which are used most commonly in the field of safety management.

Simple random sampling

Estimating a population mean:

Best estimate of population mean:

$$\hat{\mu} = m$$

Best estimate of standard error of m:

$$\hat{\sigma}_m = \frac{\sigma}{\sqrt{n}} \sqrt{\frac{N-n}{N-1}}$$

The finite population correction factor (fpc), $\sqrt{\frac{N-n}{N-1}}$

may be ignored if $n < 5\%$ of N i.e., if $\frac{n}{N} < \frac{1}{20}$

95% confidence limits for μ:

$$m \pm 2\hat{\sigma}_m$$

Sample size required to estimate μ with a precision of B:

$$n = \frac{4\hat{\sigma}^2 N}{(N-1)B^2 + 4\hat{\sigma}^2}$$

$$n = \frac{4\hat{\sigma}^2}{B^2}$$

when N is very large.

Estimating a population percentage

Best estimate of a population percentage:

$$\hat{\pi} = p$$

Best estimate of standard error of p:

$$\hat{\sigma}_p = \sqrt{\frac{p(100 - p)}{n - 1}} \sqrt{\frac{N - n}{N}}$$

The fpc, $\sqrt{\dfrac{N - n}{N}}$ may be ignored if $\dfrac{n}{N} < \dfrac{1}{20}$

95% confidence limits for π: $p \pm 2\hat{\sigma}_p$

Note that the formulae for estimating the population percentage involve the use of the normal distribution as an approximation of the binomial and give satisfactory results provided that π is not near 0 or 100. For values of π less than about 10 or greater than 90, values of n need to be very large for these formulae to be valid.

Sample size required to estimate π with a precision of $\pm B$:

$$n = \frac{4p(100 - p)N}{(N - 1)B^2 + 4p(100 - p)}$$

$$n = \frac{4p(100 - p)}{B^2} \qquad \text{when } N \text{ is very large}$$

Systematic sampling

Estimating a population mean:

Best estimate of a population mean:

$$\hat{\mu} = m$$

Best estimate of standard error of m:

$$\hat{\sigma}_m = \frac{\hat{\sigma}}{\sqrt{n}} \sqrt{\frac{N - n}{N - 1}}$$

NB The standard error depends on whether the population listing is:

- random

- ordered
- periodic

If it is random, then all formulae are the same as for random samples. If ordered, an unbiased estimate of σ_m cannot be obtained from one sample but since σ_m using a systematic sample under these circumstances is less than σ_m for a random sample, a conservative estimate is obtained using the equation for the best estimate of standard error of m given above.

95% confidence limits for μ:

$$m \pm 2\sigma_m$$

Sample size required to estimate μ with a precision $\pm B$:

$$n = \frac{4\hat{\sigma}^2 N}{(N-1)B^2 + 4\hat{\sigma}^2}$$

$$n = \frac{4\hat{\sigma}^2}{B^2} \text{ when } N \text{ is very large.}$$

Estimating a population percentage

Best estimate of population percentage:

$$\hat{\pi} = p$$

Best estimate of standard error of p: $\hat{\sigma}_p \sqrt{\frac{p(100-p)}{n-1}} \sqrt{\frac{N-n}{N}}$

NB The remarks given under the best estimate of standard error m given above apply here.

95% confidence limits for π:

$$p \pm 2\hat{\sigma}_p$$

Sample size required to estimate π with a precision of B:

$$n = \frac{4p(100-p)N}{(N-1)B^2 + 4p(100-p)}$$

$$n = \frac{4p(100-p)}{B^2} \text{ when } N \text{ is very large.}$$

Stratified random sampling

The notation used refers to a sample involving L strata, N_i being the population size and n_i the sample size of the ith stratum.

Estimating the population mean

Best estimate of population mean:

$$\hat{\mu} = \frac{1}{N} \sum_{i=1}^{L} N_i m_i$$

Best estimate of standard error of $\hat{\mu}$:

$$\hat{\sigma}_{\hat{\mu}} = \frac{1}{N} \sqrt{\sum_{i=1}^{L} N_i^2 \left(\frac{N_i - n_i}{N_i} \right) \frac{\hat{\sigma}_i^2}{n_i}}$$

95% confidence limits for μ:

$$\hat{\mu} \pm 2\hat{\sigma}_{\hat{\mu}}$$

Sample size calculations are complicated by the question of how the total sample size is allocated between the L strata. There are three common types of allocation. These are:

- proportional allocation $n_i = \dfrac{N_i}{N} \times n$

- optimum allocation $n_i = \dfrac{N_i \hat{\sigma}_i / \sqrt{c}}{\Sigma (N_i \hat{\sigma}_i / \sqrt{c_i})} \times n$

- Neyman allocation $n_i = \dfrac{N_i \hat{\sigma}_i}{\Sigma (N_i \hat{\sigma}_i)} \times n$

The type of sample allocation among strata determines the standard error σ_u and for each allocation an expression for σ_μ can be obtained by substituting for n_i in the equation for the best estimate of standard error of $\hat{\mu}$ given above.

- proportional $\sigma_{\hat{\mu}} = \sqrt{\dfrac{1}{N^2} \sum \dfrac{N_i \hat{\sigma}_i^2}{n} - \dfrac{1}{N^2} \sum N_i \hat{\sigma}_i^2}$

- optimum $\sigma_{\hat{\mu}} = \sqrt{\dfrac{1}{N^2} \dfrac{1}{n} \left(\sum N_i \hat{\sigma} \sqrt{c_i} \right) \left(\sum \dfrac{N_i \hat{\sigma}_i}{\sqrt{c_i}} \right) - \dfrac{1}{N^2} \sum N_i \hat{\sigma}_i^2}$

- Neyman $\sigma_{\hat{\mu}} = \sqrt{\dfrac{1}{N_2} \dfrac{1}{n} \left(\sum N_i \hat{\sigma} \right)^2 - \dfrac{1}{N^2} \sum N_i \hat{\sigma}_i^2}$

In turn, each of these expressions can be set equal to $B/2$, where B is the precision required for 95% confidence limits, and the expression solved in n. This gives the required sample size for each type of allocation.

- proportional $n = \dfrac{N \sum N_i \hat{\sigma}_i^2}{N^2 \dfrac{B^2}{4} + \sum N_i \hat{\sigma}_i^2}$

- optimum $\quad n = \dfrac{\left(\sum N_i\hat{\sigma}_i\sqrt{c_i}\right)\left(\sum N_i\hat{\sigma}_i/\sqrt{c_i}\right)}{N^2 \dfrac{B^2}{4} + \sum N_i\hat{\sigma}_i^2}$

- Neyman $\quad n = \dfrac{\left(\sum N_i\hat{\sigma}_i\right)^2}{N^2 \dfrac{B^2}{4} + \sum N_i\hat{\sigma}_i^2}$

Estimating a population percentage

Best estimate of population percentage:

$$\hat{\pi} = \frac{1}{N} \sum_{i=1}^{L} N_i p_i$$

Best estimate of standard error of $\hat{\pi}$:

$$\hat{\sigma}_{\hat{\pi}} = \frac{1}{N} \sqrt{\sum N_i^2 \left(\frac{N_i - n_i}{N_i}\right) \frac{p_i(100 - p_i)}{n_i - 1}}$$

95% confidence limits for:

$$\hat{\pi} \pm 2\hat{\sigma}_p$$

Sample size allocations depend on the mode of allocating the sample among strata. Dealing with the three main types of allocation, we have the following results for sampling allocation.

- proportional $\quad n_i = \dfrac{N_i}{N} \cdot n$

- optimum $\quad n_i = \dfrac{N_i\sqrt{p_i(100 - p_i)}/\sqrt{c_i}}{\sum N_i\sqrt{p_i(100 - p)}/\sqrt{c_i}} \cdot n$

- Neyman $\quad n_i = \dfrac{N_i\sqrt{p_i(100 - p_i)}}{\sum N_i\sqrt{p_i(100 - p_i)}} \cdot n$

Total sample size required for 95% confidence limits on π to have a precision of $\pm B$ are as follows:

- proportional $\quad n = \dfrac{N \sum N_i p_i(100 - p_i)}{N^2 \dfrac{B^2}{4} + \sum N_i p_i(100 - p_i)}$

- optimum
$$n = \frac{\left(\sum N_i\sqrt{p_i(100 - p_i)/\sqrt{c_i}} \right)\left(\sum N_i\sqrt{p_i(100 - p_i)}/\sqrt{c_i} \right)}{N^2 \dfrac{B^2}{4} + \sum N_i p_i(100 - p_i)}$$

- Neyman
$$n = \frac{\left(\sum N_i\sqrt{p_i(100 - p_i)} \right)^2}{N^2 \dfrac{B^2}{4} + \sum N_i p_i(100 - p_i)}$$

Cluster sampling

It is necessary to use a substantially different notation to cope with the analysis of cluster sampling. The following is used most commonly.

N = number of clusters in the population
n = number of clusters selected in a simple random sample
m_i = number of elements in the ith cluster

$$\bar{m} = \frac{1}{n}\sum_{i=1}^{n} m_i = \text{average cluster size for the sample}$$

$$M = \sum_{i=1}^{N} m_i = \text{number of elements in the population}$$

$$\bar{M} = M/N = \text{average cluster size for the population}$$

$$y_i = \text{total of all observations in the } i\text{th cluster}$$

Estimating a population mean

Best estimate of a population mean:

$$\hat{\mu} = \bar{y} = \sum_{i=1}^{n} y_i \bigg/ \sum_{i=1}^{n} m_i$$

Best estimate of standard error of $\bar{y}$:

$$\hat{\sigma}_{\bar{y}} = \sqrt{\frac{N - n}{N_n \bar{m}^2}} \sqrt{\frac{\sum_{i=1}^{n} (y_i - \bar{y}m_i)^2}{n - 1}}$$

NB $\bar{M}$ is often not known. In such cases, it can be estimated using $\bar{m}$. Note also that this estimator is biased and is good only if n is large, say $n > 20$. There is no bias if the cluster sizes are equal.

95% confidence limits for μ:

$$\bar{y} \pm 2\hat{\sigma}_{\bar{y}}$$

The sample size required to estimate μ with a precision of $\pm B$ is calculated in the following way:

The standard error,

$$\sigma_{\bar{y}} = \sqrt{\frac{N-n}{N_n \overline{M}^2}} \cdot \sigma_c$$

where σ_c is the population quantity estimated by:

$$S_c = \sqrt{\frac{\Sigma (y_i - \bar{y} m_i)^2}{n-1}}$$

since σ_c and $\overline{M}$ are normally not known, a pilot survey is necessary to make estimates of these parameters, thus,

$$n = \frac{N S_c^2}{N \dfrac{B^2 \overline{M}}{4} + S_c^2}$$

Note that n refers to the number of clusters required.

Estimating a population percentage

Best estimate of population percentage:

$$\hat{\pi} = p = \sum_{i=1}^{n} a_i \bigg/ \sum_{i=1}^{n} m_i$$

where a_i is the total number of elements in cluster i possessing the characteristic of interest.

Best estimate of standard error of p :

$$\hat{\sigma}_p^2 \sqrt{\frac{N-n}{N_n \overline{M}^2}} \sqrt{\frac{\displaystyle\sum_{i=1}^{n} (a_i - p m_i)^2}{n-1}}$$

95% confidence limits for π:

$$p \pm 2 \hat{\sigma}_p$$

Sample size required to estimate π with a precision of $\pm B$:

$$n = \frac{N S_c^2}{N \dfrac{B^2 \bar{m}^2}{4} + S_c^2}$$

where

$$S_c = \frac{\Sigma (a_i - p m_i)^2}{n-2}$$

Note that n refers to the number of clusters required.

Appendix 3

Correlation and regression

The difference between the two types of analysis are that a correlation shows the degree of the relationship between variables whilst the regression shows the form of relationship between variables.

Correlation

Such distributions consider such things as sex, accident severity, dangerous occurrences, equipment failures, time, location and so on and are known as bivariate distributions. The main interest in the bivariate distribution is:

- to investigate a possible relationship between the two variables concerned, and
- given the existence of a relationship to express it in mathematical terms.

Scattergraphs or scatterplots are used to illustrate these events with a scale for each variable so that each pair of measurements in the distribution can be represented by a point in a plane. For example, suppose the relationship between accidents and time of day might be recorded as follows:

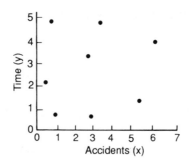

Since these data do not appear to group about a straight line then it can be assumed that no degree of linear relationship exists between the two variables. Generally, the scattergraph allows for the relationship or degrees of association between variables to be seen at a glance as illustrated below.

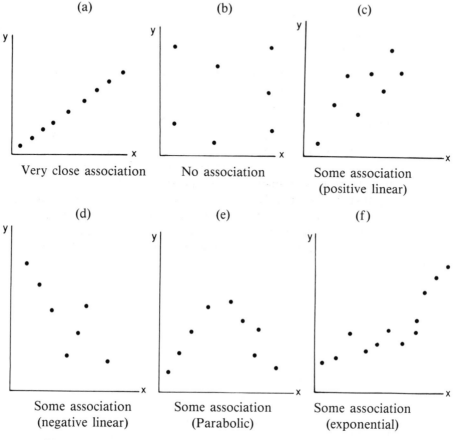

(a) Very close association

(b) No association

(c) Some association (positive linear)

(d) Some association (negative linear)

(e) Some association (Parabolic)

(f) Some association (exponential)

(a) illustrates the existence of a perfect functional relationship between the variables; such scattergraphs often result from the sample data of scientific experiments.

(b) shows a total absence of any relationship between the variables

(c) shows a positive linear trend about a line $y = a + bx$

(d) shows a negative linear trend about a line $y = a - bx$

(e) shows an association of the form $y = a + bx + cx^2$

(f) illustrates an association of the form $y = ab^x$

There are other factors which deal with linear relationships other than those illustrated above. Students wishing further statistical knowledge should read those books recommended at the end of Chapter 2.

Correlation methods are used when initial interest about how two variables are interrelated. It is usual to study the association between the variables in the hope that the relationship can be used to help in making estimates or predictions. Three basic concepts are in common use. These are:

- the straight line law
- the idea of 2 regression lines
- the idea of least squares

From these, it is then possible to calculate the regression equation. Two common approaches used by safety managers are the Multiple Regression and the Step-wise Regression. However, with the advent of the computer and the development of extremely powerful statistical analysis programmes such as the Statistical Package for the Social Sciences (SPSS) or Stat-graphics the detail of manual calculation is not too important as most statistical analysis packages come simply documented and menu driven. This makes the process of analysis so much easier and cheaper. The author has found that PC Desktop Computer analysis is the best method for the safety practitioner to use using one of the statistical packages mentioned above. Mainframe computers are all right for very large databases but screen messages such as '*job in queue*' can be not only tiresome but expensive.

Appendix 4

Safety programme – a safety review

When reviewing a safety programme it is best to use a standardised approach to gathering information so that similar data is collected on every review. This will allow for direct comparisons to be made over a period of time. In the example below it is assumed that:

The *aim* of the programme is:

To improve workforce knowledge and efficiency in the event of a fire.

The *objectives* are:

1. To carry out a publicity programme designed to educate the workforce as to what is required of them in the event of a fire.
2. To involve the Fire Service in a series of training sessions to train key staff.
3. To carry out a series of test fire alarm drills.

Whilst the planning, implementation, monitoring and evaluation of such programmes is discussed earlier, this review will concern itself only with the general review of the programme. The key question to be answered is whether the Fire Officer was satisfied that the correct procedures were carried out, the building was evacuated in an orderly and structured way and that everyone involved learned from the experience. The form on the following page is a suggestion for the review format but some safety practitioners may already have their own in general use.

Bloggs Industries Plc →

Safety Programme Review

Ref Number [   ]

Name of Safety Practitioner Conducting the review: [   ]

Title of safety programme [   ]

Location (s) of Review 1. [   ]

2. [   ]

3. [   ]

This section may be expanded to include all buildings/groups or other locations within the organisation

Date of Review [| |]   Time taken to conduct the review in m/H [|]

Status of Employees Involved in the Review:

	Number	
All		
Directors		
Senior managers		
Managers		
Supervisors		
Workforce		
Other		

Review Agreement:

	Date Approval Given
Name of Senior Manager giving approval	
Safety Committee	
Trade Union	
Other	

Review Conclusions:

Review Points for Action:

Signed [   ]   Date [| |]

Bloggs Industries Plc

Safety Programme Review

Is a current fire certificate held? `Yes` `No`

(If not ascertain reasons for this.) `[                    ]`

---

1. Are the current fire regulations: a. Known by Senior managers? `Yes` `No`

    b. Known by Supervisors? `Yes` `No`

    c. Known by the General Workforce? `Yes` `No`

2. Are the current fire regulations adequate? `Yes` `No`

3. Are the current fire regulations clearly visible and can they be clearly read by everyone? `Yes` `No`

4. Are the fire regulations discussed at staff initiaiation courses? `Yes` `No`

5. Are the fire regulations tested? `Yes` `No`

6. How often are they tested
   - Per year `[   ]`
   - Per month `[   ]`
   - Per week `[   ]`
   - Per day `[   ]`

7. Who is responsible for the publication of the fire regulations? `[                    ]`
   Name

   `[                    ]`
   Position

8. Is this person adequately trained in fire safety? `Yes` `No`

9. When did this person last receive fire safety training? Date `[   ][   ][   ]`

10. Who provided this training? `[                    ]`
    Name

    `[                    ]`
    Organisation

11. Are their sufficient fire fighting apparatus at each fire point? `Yes` `No`

12. Do es everyone know where these fire points are? `Yes` `No`

13. When were the safety appliances last examined? Date `[   ][   ][   ]`

Bloggs Industries Plc →   **Page 2**

Safety Programme Review

14. Who carried out the fire appliance inspection?   Name [   ]

[   ]
Organisation

15. How many staff are trained in fire drills? [ ]   16. How many have received training in the last 12 months? [ ]

17. How many fire drills have been held since the last Review? [ ]

18. Are assembly points known to all staff?   Yes No

19. Is there as system for identifying who would be missing?   Yes No

20. Is there a hierarchical structure of reporting at assemby points?   Yes No

21. Are Managers and Supervisors aware of their responsibilities at fire assembly points?   Yes No

22. How many building evacuation trials have been held in last 12 months? [ ]

23. Are there published guidelines of actions to be taken in the event of a fire?   Yes No

24. Are these published guideleines widely available?   Yes No

25. From the commencement of the fire alarm initially sounding, how long did it take for staff to vacate the the building and for controllers to report from their assembly points?
[ ] Minutes

26. Was the evacuation orderly?   Yes No

27. Comments from Senior Managers

Satisfied/Dissàtisfied

28. Comments from Supervisors

Satisfied/Dissatisfied

The answers to some or all of these questions may be ascertained from different groups within the organisation in a question and answer situation and several numbers of this form could be used.

Appendix 5

Accounting ratios for safety managers

In Chapter 6, matters relating to the financial structure and accounting procedures in organisations were discussed. When considering expenditure of any kind it is worth being aware of the financial situation of your organisation. To do this, a number of accounting ratios exist to help safety practitioners understand the healthy (or otherwise) nature of the organisation employing you. These are summarised here.

Rate of return on capital employed

$$\frac{\text{Net profit before tax}}{\text{Share capital} + \text{Reserves} + \text{Long-term liabilities}}$$

$$\frac{\text{Production costs}}{\text{Sales}}$$

$$\frac{\text{Selling and distribution costs}}{\text{Sales}}$$

$$\frac{\text{Administration costs}}{\text{Sales}}$$

$$\frac{\text{Sales}}{\text{Capital employed}}$$

$$\frac{\text{Sales}}{\text{Fixed assets}}$$

$$\frac{\text{Sales}}{\text{Working capital}}$$

Stockturn

$$\frac{\text{Cost of goods sold}}{\text{Average stock of finished goods}}$$

Credit policy

$$\frac{\text{Sales}}{\text{Debtors}}$$

Working capital ratio

$$\frac{\text{Current assets}}{\text{Current liabilities}}$$

Liquidity ratio

$$\frac{\text{Liquid assets}}{\text{Current liabilities}}$$

Capital gearing

$$\frac{\text{Ordinary share capital and reserves}}{\text{Fixed interest share and loan capital}}$$

Appendix 6

The measurement of safety performance

In Chapter 8, some common indices in use to aid safety performance were discussed. Below are a list of simple formulae which can be used by safety professionals in order to asess their own safety performance.

Frequency Rate

$$\frac{\text{Total number of accidents}}{\text{Total number of m/h worked}} \times 100{,}000$$

Incidence rate

$$\frac{\text{Total number of accidents}}{\text{Number of people employed}} \times 1{,}000$$

Severity rate

$$\frac{\text{Total number of days lost}}{\text{Total number of m/h worked}} \times 1{,}000$$

Mean duration rate

$$\frac{\text{Total number of days lost}}{\text{Total number of accidents}}$$

Duration rate

$$\frac{\text{Number of m/h worked}}{\text{Total number of accidents}}$$

Index

487